EXPLORING SCIENCE

for

Junior Cycle

Michael O'Callaghan
Pat Doyle
Orla Molamphy
Ger Reilly

The Educational Company of Ireland

Tháinig an páipéar a úsáideach sa leabhar seo ó fhoraoisí rialaithe i dtuaisceart na hEorpa. In aghaidh gach crann a leagtar, cuirtear crann amháin eile ar a laghad.

Published 2020
The Educational Company of Ireland
Ballymount Road
Walkinstown
Dublin 12

A member of the Smurfit Kappa Group PLC
© Michael O'Callaghan, Pat Doyle, Orla Molamphy, Ger Reilly

Editor: Life Lines Editorial Services
Design: EMC
Layout: Compuscript
Artwork: Michael Philips and Compuscript
Cover Design: EMC
ISBN: 978-1-84536-923-1

Acknowledgements

Acknowledgement is made to the following for supplying photographs and for permission to reproduce copyright photographs: Science Photo Library, iStock, Shutterstock, Alamy, Getty.

Acknowledgement is made for permission to reproduce extracts and other material to Safefood, Irish Examiner, Irish Times, Met Eireann.

Web references in this book are intended as a guide for teachers. At the time of going to press, all web addresses were active and contained information relevant to the topics in this book. However, The Educational Company of Ireland and the authors do not accept responsibility for the views or information contained on these websites. Content and addresses may change beyond our control and pupils should be supervised when investigating websites.

05M21

For the student

Welcome to Junior Cycle and your new science textbook, *Exploring Science*. Your textbook comes with a **Student Activity Book**, **complete with activities and experiments**, and a range of **digital resources**. This book will build on your learning of science from primary school by helping you to understand the world around you and the wider universe. It aims to develop your learning skills in science. You will develop these skills yourself while also learning from your teacher and your fellow students.

For the teacher

Written for the Junior Cycle Profile of Achievement (JCPA), *Exploring Science* aims to give students a sense of enjoyment and an interest in the learning of science. The book is based on the **Statements of learning** from the NCCA specification (see *juniorcycle.ie*). It develops students' knowledge of and about science through the unifying strand called the **Nature of Science**, and the four contextual strands (or units): **Biological World**, **Chemical World**, **Physical World** and **Earth and Space**.

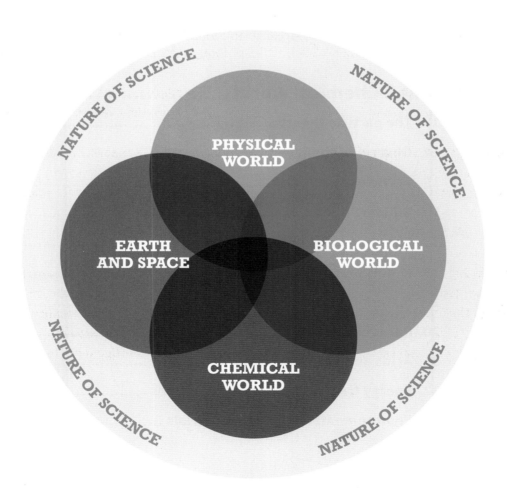

CONTENTS

Unit 4 Physical world 273

Unit 5 Earth and space 383

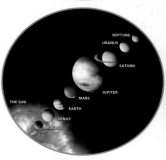

YOUR GUIDE TO EXPLORING SCIENCE FOR THE JUNIOR CYCLE

Study science in class with the *Exploring Science* textbook and complete the exercises and questions in your Activity Book

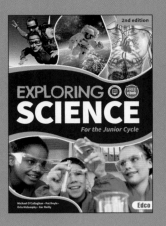
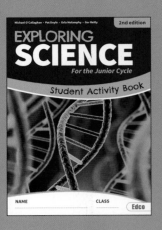

Student Book

Exploring Science comes with a whole host of interactive and digital resources to help science come to life.

Each chapter begins with Learning Intentions and Keywords and includes Did you know boxes, questions, activities and detailed diagrams.

Keywords
Important words you will need to learn to master the subjects covered in each chapter

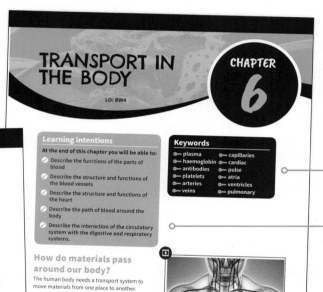

TRANSPORT IN THE BODY

LO: BW4

CHAPTER 6

Learning intentions

At the end of this chapter you will be able to:
- Describe the functions of the parts of blood
- Describe the structure and functions of the blood vessels
- Describe the structure and functions of the heart
- Describe the path of blood around the body
- Describe the interaction of the circulatory system with the digestive and respiratory systems.

Keywords
plasma	capillaries
haemoglobin	cardiac
antibodies	pulse
platelets	atria
arteries	ventricles
veins	pulmonary

How do materials pass around our body?

The human body needs a transport system to move materials from one place to another.

For example, food, oxygen and waste products have to be moved to and from all the cells in our body.

Our circulatory or transport system is made up of:
- Blood
- A system of tubes or blood vessels
- The heart, which is needed to pump blood through blood vessels.

What is in our blood?
Blood is made up of four parts, or components:
- Plasma
- Red blood cells
- White blood cells
- Platelets.

▲ Figure 6.1 *The circulatory system*

TRANSPORT IN THE BODY 55

Learning intentions
What this chapter will help you to learn on each topic

UNIT 5 EARTH AND SPACE

What is the future of space exploration?
Where do we go from here? What are the next destinations that we are looking to explore?

Mars

The planet Mars is the next big destination. Recently NASA sent probes successfully to the planet. NASA launched their Insight Mars Lander on May 5th 2018. The probe is stationary and is studying the composition of Mars.

You may wonder why Mars is the next planet scientists want to look at closely.

Apart from Earth, Mars is the other planet in the solar system that could possibly support humans living on it. It is a planet rich in the elements carbon, nitrogen, oxygen and hydrogen – all of which we need to survive.

▲ Figure 42.25 *Probes on Mars*

▲ Figure 42.26 *Mars – the next planet to explore*

▲ Figure 42.27 *A future space station on Mars*

Also Mars has one key element that makes it a good destination: it has water. Although the water is frozen as ice, the key fact for scientists is that Mars has water.

The journey to Mars takes approximately six months. Astronauts would remain on Mars for 30 days or 300 days. These might seem like odd lengths of time, but the orbit of Mars around the Sun does not exactly match that of Earth. So there would be a window of opportunity for astronauts to return to Earth at 30 days. If this was missed the astronauts would have to wait for another 270 days for Mars to have completed its orbit around the Sun and be in the correct position again to exit Mars and return to Earth.

Scientists are very aware that long stays in space badly affect our bodies. Overcoming this problem could be one of our greatest difficulties for prolonged space travel.

? Question

42.7 Discuss with a partner how a mission might remain in space for a long period of time in terms of fuel use, food and water supplies.

Explain, in your answer, how you think astronauts could access the required extra oxygen and water that they would need.

Questions within chapters
Questions that test your knowledge of the subjects covered

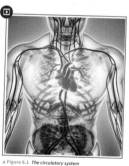

▶ 13 NASA Videos
Colourful videos on **www.edcolearning.ie** that relate to topics covered in the textbook

Questions

Each chapter of *Exploring Science* includes a full array of questions at various levels of difficulty to test and improve your science knowledge. At the end of each chapter there are Summary and Assessment questions, including exam-style questions. Additional questions are also available online.

Assessment questions
Longer questions which include exam questions from the SEC Junior Cycle Science sample paper and exam paper

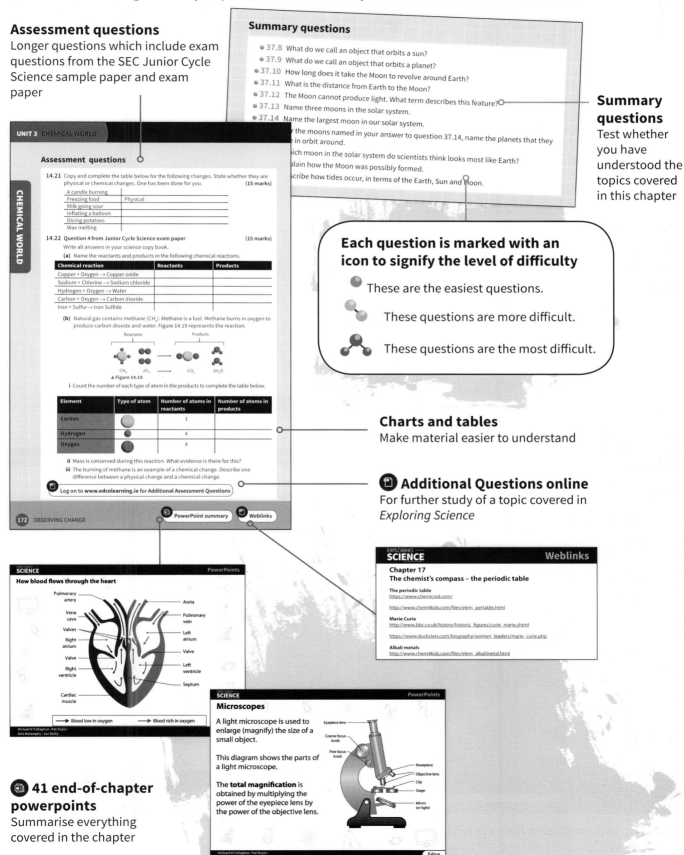

Summary questions

- 37.8 What do we call an object that orbits a sun?
- 37.9 What do we call an object that orbits a planet?
- 37.10 How long does it take the Moon to revolve around Earth?
- 37.11 What is the distance from Earth to the Moon?
- 37.12 The Moon cannot produce light. What term describes this feature?
- 37.13 Name three moons in the solar system.
- 37.14 Name the largest moon in our solar system.
- For the moons named in your answer to question 37.14, name the planets that they are in orbit around.
- Which moon in the solar system do scientists think looks most like Earth?
- Explain how the Moon was possibly formed.
- Describe how tides occur, in terms of the Earth, Sun and Moon.

Summary questions
Test whether you have understood the topics covered in this chapter

Each question is marked with an icon to signify the level of difficulty

These are the easiest questions.

These questions are more difficult.

These questions are the most difficult.

Charts and tables
Make material easier to understand

Additional Questions online
For further study of a topic covered in *Exploring Science*

41 end-of-chapter powerpoints
Summarise everything covered in the chapter

Activities

The chapters in *Exploring Science* are packed with step-by-step activities including laboratory safety advice, diagrams and illustrations. A whole host of videos online demonstrate how the activities work.

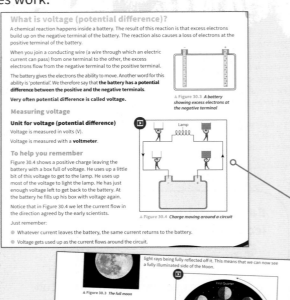

What is voltage (potential difference)?

A chemical reaction happens inside a battery. The result of this reaction is that excess electrons build up on the negative terminal of the battery. The reaction also causes a loss of electrons at the positive terminal of the battery.

When you join a conducting wire (a wire through which an electric current can pass) from one terminal to the other, the excess electrons flow from the negative terminal to the positive terminal.

The battery gives the electrons the ability to move. Another word for this ability is 'potential'. We therefore say that **the battery has a potential difference between the positive and the negative terminals.**

Very often potential difference is called voltage.

Measuring voltage

Unit for voltage (potential difference)

Voltage is measured in volts (V).

Voltage is measured with a **voltmeter**.

To help you remember

Figure 30.4 shows a positive charge leaving the battery with a box full of voltage. He uses up a little bit of this voltage to get to the lamp. He uses up most of the voltage to light the lamp. He has just enough voltage left to get back to the battery. At the battery he fills up his box with voltage again.

Notice that in Figure 30.4 we let the current flow in the direction agreed by the early scientists.

Just remember:
- Whatever current leaves the battery, the same current returns to the battery.
- Voltage gets used up as the current flows around the circuit.

▲ Figure 30.3 *A battery showing excess electrons at the negative terminal*

▲ Figure 30.4 *Charge moving around a circuit*

light rays being fully reflected off it. This means that we can now see a fully illuminated side of the Moon.

▲ Figure 38.3 *The full moon*

Phase 6: the waning gibbous
During this phase, a complete moon is no longer visible due to decreased levels of light from the Sun now striking the Moon and being reflected off it. The term *waning* means shrinking, or getting smaller.

▶ Figure 38.4 *The lunar cycle*

422 EARTH, SUN AND MOON – IT'S ALL RELATIVE

Illustrations and diagrams
Clear and detailed illustrations that help you to understand how to complete activities

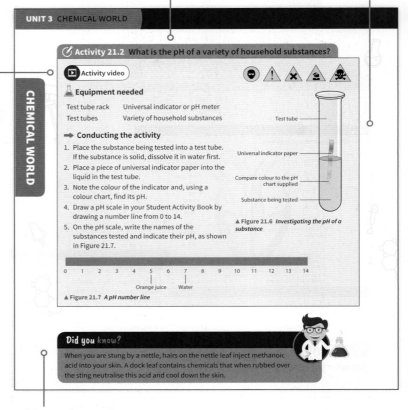

Activity 10.3 Can we investigate a factor that affects photosynthesis?

Activity video — Plants produce glucose in photosynthesis. They then convert the glucose to starch, which they store. We can use starch to indicate whether photosynthesis takes place or not.

Equipment needed
Potted plant (e.g. busy Lizzie)
Aluminium foil (tinfoil)
2 beakers
Forceps (or tweezers)
Boiling water
Alcohol (methylated spirits)
Water bath
Bunsen burner
Tripod
White tile
Iodine solution
Test tube

Conducting the activity
1. Place the plant in darkness overnight. This will remove starch from the leaves.
2. Immediately after taking the plant out of the light cover some of the leaves (front and back) with aluminium foil (tinfoil).
3. Leave the plant in bright light for several hours.
4. Take one covered and one uncovered leaf and test them for starch.

How can we test leaves for starch?
1. Put the leaf in boiling water for a few minutes to soften it.
2. Put the leaf into a test tube of alcohol.
3. Place the test tube with the leaf and alcohol into a water bath with boiling hot water. This will warm the alcohol. Warm alcohol removes chlorophyll from the leaf (but it also makes the leaf brittle).
4. Take the leaf out of the test tube with the tweezers and rinse it in warm water. This re-softens the leaf.

▲ Figure 10.12 *Plant showing some leaves covered by aluminium foil*

Leaves covered in aluminium foil
Leaves exposed to light

▲ Figure 10.13 *Softening a leaf*
Beaker
Boiling water
Leaf
Tripod
Bunsen burner

▲ Figure 10.14 *Removing chlorophyll from a leaf*
Test tube
Very hot water
Alcohol
Leaf

BIOLOGICAL WORLD

Activities

16 Activity Videos
Watch how other scientists have undertaken activities in the laboratory

4 Classroom-Based Assessment Videos
See how other Junior Cycle students have completed their CBAs

UNIT 3 CHEMICAL WORLD

Activity 21.2 What is the pH of a variety of household substances?

Activity video

Equipment needed
Test tube rack
Test tubes
Universal indicator or pH meter
Variety of household substances

Conducting the activity
1. Place the substance being tested into a test tube. If the substance is solid, dissolve it in water first.
2. Place a piece of universal indicator paper into the liquid in the test tube.
3. Note the colour of the indicator and, using a colour chart, find its pH.
4. Draw a pH scale in your Student Activity Book by drawing a number line from 0 to 14.
5. On the pH scale, write the names of the substances tested and indicate their pH, as shown in Figure 21.7.

▲ Figure 21.6 *Investigating the pH of a substance*
Test tube
Universal indicator paper
Compare colour to the pH chart supplied
Substance being tested

0 1 2 3 4 5 6 7 8 9 10 11 12 13 14
Orange juice Water

▲ Figure 21.7 *A pH number line*

CHEMICAL WORLD

Did you know?
When you are stung by a nettle, hairs on the nettle leaf inject methanoic acid into your skin. A dock leaf contains chemicals that when rubbed over the sting neutralise this acid and cool down the skin.

Did you know?
Bite-sized boxes packed with useful information that will enhance your scientific knowledge

Bringing science to life

The video icons throughout *Exploring Science* indicate that related diagram animations can be found online, and also famous scientist biography videos.

▶ 92 Diagram animations

Watch diagrams in the textbook come to life with these online animations

What impact do materials have on the environment?

Materials can have an impact on the **environment** in a range of different ways and at different times during their **life cycle**. For example, **extraction**, **transportation**, **manufacturing** and uses of **raw materials** consume energy and produce carbon dioxide (which contributes to global warming). However, when a material is recycled or re-used the wider impact on the environment is much reduced.

What is sustainable development?

Sustainable development is where demands on the environment by people can be met without harming the environment for future generations. The rules are simple:

● Leave the world better than you found it

● Take no more than you need

● Try not to harm the environment and make amends if you do.

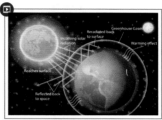

▲ Figure 23.1 *The greenhouse effect*

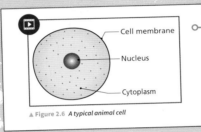

▲ Figure 2.6 *A typical animal cell*

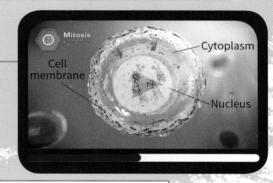

Examples of energy changes

We'll look at some examples of energy changes and consider how much energy is dissipated.

Solar water heater

The energy from the Sun is referred to as solar energy. Solar energy can be used to heat water in specially designed glass pipes. This hot water is stored in a tank and can be used for baths, showers, washing clothes, etc., so you will use less electricity or natural gas to heat your water.

● The **energy change** that occurs is from solar energy to heat energy.

● A large amount of the solar energy is dissipated. However, with improvements in design more and more of the solar energy is changed to useful heat energy.

▲ Figure 28.10 *A solar panel connected to a hot-water system*

▲ Figure 28.11 *A solar panel*

ENERGY 325

What is in the universe?

Our universe is a vast area of space within which we find all the galaxies, stars and solar systems that make up the universe as we know it.

Was there a beginning to the universe?

How did our universe begin? Where did it all start? What was there at the very beginning? These are some of the questions that humans have asked in their desire to discover the origins of the universe.

People have always had more questions than answers on this subject. The limits of our technology meant there was a complete lack of evidence for scientists to work with. These questions about the creation of the universe remained unanswered until discoveries in astronomy and physics led scientists to determine that there was a beginning to our universe.

? Questions

34.1 Find a simple explanation of a 'galaxy'. Write your answer in your copy, together with a note of the source of your answer.

34.2 Name three stars that you know of.

34.3 What is a solar system?

▶ Animated Scientist Biography

Watch an Exploring Science animation to find out more about Stephen Hawking and his theories about the beginning of the universe.

▶ Figure 34.1 *Stephen Hawking*

? Question

34.4 Find out and write a paragraph explaining what is meant by:

(a) The study of astronomy

(b) The study of physics.

▶ 8 Scientist biography videos

Find out about the lives of prominent scientists with these fun videos

LABORATORY EQUIPMENT

Beaker

Conical flask

Round-bottomed flask

Test tube

Burette

Pipette

Graduated cylinder

Tap funnel

Filter funnel

Evaporation dish

Bunsen burner

Stand

Tripod

Gauze

Spatula

Tongs

Test tube holder

Thermometer

Crucible

Test tube rack

Balance

Pipe clay triangle

Petri dish

LABORATORY SAFETY RULES FOR PUPILS

The following rules are enforced to keep you and your classmates safe while in a school laboratory.

1 Do not enter the laboratory without permission.
2 Do not use any equipment unless permitted to do so by your teacher.
3 Make sure you know exactly what you are supposed to do. If in doubt, ask your teacher.
4 Make sure you know the position of all safety equipment in the laboratory, e.g. the fire extinguishers, first aid equipment etc.
5 Always wear eye protection or gloves when instructed to do so.
6 Long hair must be tied back during practical classes.
7 Place your bag and other personal items safely out of the way.
8 Never handle any chemicals with bare hands.
9 Nothing must be eaten, tasted or drunk in the laboratory.
10 Any cut, burn or other accident must be reported at once to your teacher.
11 Always check that the label on the bottle is exactly the same as the material you require. If in doubt, ask your teacher.
12 Any chemical spilled on the skin or clothing must be washed at once with plenty of water and reported to your teacher.
13 Test tubes should never be overfilled. When heating a test tube ensure that the mouth of the test tube is pointed away from you and everyone else.
14 All equipment should be cleaned and put back in its correct place after use.
15 Always wash your hands after practical work.
16 Students should behave in a responsible manner at all times in the laboratory.

Safety labels

The following labels appear on bottles in the laboratory. They also appear on many everyday chemicals such as cleaning products and solvents. These labels indicate chemicals that could be dangerous if not used or handled properly. We use these warning symbols on activities in this book.

Toxic		Substances which can cause death if they are swallowed, breathed in or absorbed through the skin. Example: weedkiller.
Harmful or irritant		Substances which should not be eaten, breathed in or handled without gloves. Though not as dangerous as toxic substances they may cause a rash, sickness or an allergic reaction.
Oxidising		Substances which provide oxygen, allowing other materials to burn more intensely. Example: hair bleach.
Highly flammable		Substances which easily catch fire. Example: petrol.
Corrosive		Substances which attack and destroy living tissue, including skin and eyes. Example: oven cleaner.
Warning sign		This sign is used to draw attention to a warning of danger, hazards and the unexpected.
Safety glasses		Wear safety glasses to protect your eyes.

ACTIVITIES

NATURE OF SCIENCE

UNIT 1

LEARNING OUTCOMES: LO

NOS1. Students should be able to appreciate how scientists work and how scientific ideas are modified over time

NOS2. Students should be able to recognise questions that are appropriate for scientific investigation, pose testable hypotheses, and evaluate and compare strategies for investigating hypotheses

NOS3. Students should be able to design, plan and conduct investigations; explain how reliability, accuracy, precision, fairness, safety, ethics, and the selection of suitable equipment have been considered

NOS4. Students should be able to produce and select data (qualitatively/quantitatively), critically analyse data to identify patterns and relationships, identify anomalous observations, draw and justify conclusions

NOS5. Students should be able to review and reflect on the skills and thinking used in carrying out investigations, and apply their learning and skills to solving problems in unfamiliar contexts

NOS6. Students should be able to conduct research relevant to a scientific issue, evaluate different sources of information including secondary data, understanding that a source may lack detail or show bias

NOS7. Students should be able to organise and communicate their research and investigative findings in a variety of ways fit for purpose and audience, using relevant scientific terminology and representations

NOS8. Students should be able to evaluate media-based arguments concerning science and technology

NOS9. Students should be able to research and present information on the contribution that scientists make to scientific discovery and invention, and its impact on society

NOS10. Students should be able to appreciate the role of science in society; and its personal, social and global importance; and how society influences scientific research

CHAPTER 1

THE NATURE OF SCIENCE

What is science?

Science comes from the Latin word *scientia*, meaning 'knowledge'. **Science is the study and knowledge of the (physical and natural) world around us** and can be divided into different subject areas. In this book we will examine:

- **The biological world**, by investigating living things
- **The chemical world**, by investigating substances and how they react
- **The physical world**, by investigating matter and energy and how they interact
- **Earth and space**, by investigating the planet Earth and the universe.

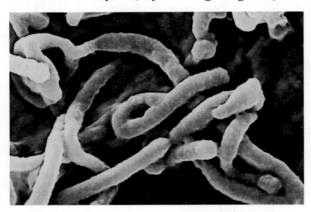

▲ Figure 1.1 *Ebola viruses bursting out of a cell*

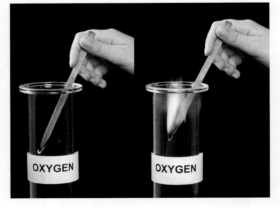

▲ Figure 1.2 *Oxygen relights a glowing splint*

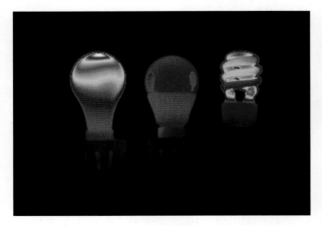

▲ Figure 1.3 *The heat given off by an old-fashioned (incandescent) bulb, a light-emitting diode (LED) and a compact fluorescent bulb*

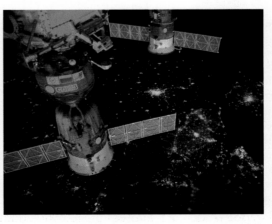

▲ Figure 1.4 *The lights of Europe from the International Space Station (London is the brightest city shown)*

The nature of science means how scientific knowledge is developed. This mainly involves understanding how science works, carrying out investigations, communicating scientific ideas and considering the role and value of science and scientists to society.

The nature of science will be outlined in this chapter. However, it is not really intended that you should learn all this material in isolation. The nature of science is included in every chapter of this book. It forms the basis of all the content and activities in each chapter. This chapter is included to allow you to understand how science works.

Keywords

- hypothesis
- prediction
- results
- investigations
- variables
- data
- safety
- correlation
- evaluation
- conclusion

Understanding about science

Curiosity and questions

Science works initially by people being curious. Asking questions and being curious is a key part of being a good scientist. Very often important knowledge has been gained because someone was curious and asked a simple question.

How science answers questions

It is very difficult to answer big questions in science. However, we can ask smaller questions. These questions may be more suited to scientific investigations or experiments and so we might be able to find answers to them.

Question

For example, we could ask the question: 'Is the boiling point of water affected by adding salt?'. In answering this question, we start by finding out as much as we can about the problem and then suggesting what we think might happen. Such a suggestion is called a **prediction**.

Prediction

We could predict that: adding salt will change the boiling point of water. **If a prediction can be tested it is called a hypothesis**.

Hypothesis

A hypothesis is a possible explanation for something we observe or notice. It is often written as an '**If ... then** ...' statement. For example: **If** *salt is added to water* **then** *the boiling point of the water will change*.

Examples of hypotheses are:

- If we study then our exam results will improve
- If drivers use a mobile phone while driving then they are more likely to crash
- If we practise sprinting then we will get faster.

Having formed a possible explanation or hypothesis, the next step is to design a way to investigate the hypothesis. This involves gathering evidence (data), and if the results from the investigation match the prediction, then the scientist can be more confident that the hypothesis is correct.

Investigating in science

Investigating a hypothesis

A hypothesis is tested by carrying out an investigation, or experiment. Normally two sets of apparatus are set up:

- One set of apparatus is the **investigation**
- The second set of apparatus is a comparison, or **control**. Both sets of apparatus should be identical, *except for one difference*.

For example, returning to our earlier hypothesis, we could boil some tap water in a beaker and use a thermometer to record the temperature at which it boils. We could then add salt to some tap water and record the temperature at which the salt water boils. When we look at the results:

- If both water samples boil at the same temperature, then our hypothesis is incorrect
- If the salt water boils at a higher temperature than the tap water, then our hypothesis is supported.

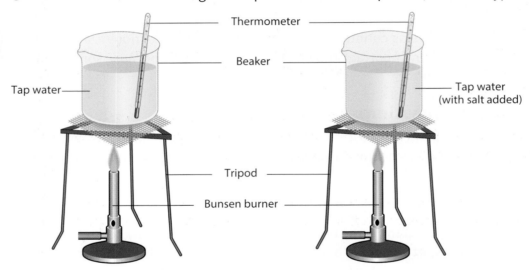

Thermometer

Beaker

Tap water

Tap water (with salt added)

Tripod

Bunsen burner

▲ Figure 1.5 *Nature of science – investigating whether adding salt to tap water will change the boiling point of the water*

The **results** of an experiment often cause us to change our hypothesis. So, if the salt water is found to boil at a higher temperature than the tap water, we would revise the original hypothesis by saying: If salt is added to water, then the boiling point of the water will increase.

Different types of investigation

Some investigations are laboratory-based. However, many investigations take place outside laboratories.

Scientists work in all sorts of exciting places, such as outdoors in forest parks and boglands, under the sea, in rainforests, close to volcanoes or near glaciers. Investigations are also used when designing spacecraft, cars, computers, phones and a broad range of new technologies.

Some scientists work alone. But many scientists work in groups. That is why it is

▲ Figure 1.6 *A team of scientists collecting animals in a forest*

important for students to be able to work to a high standard alone, but also to be able to co-operate and work as part of a team.

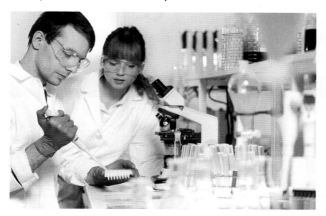

▲ Figure 1.7 *Scientists working in a laboratory*

▲ Figure 1.8 *Scientist taking lava samples near a volcano*

The results of investigations

Scientists report on how they carried out their experiments and the results they got in scientific journals. These are special types of publications that are read by science experts, e.g. journals such as *Science* or *Nature*. In this way other scientists can read them, think about them and repeat the research if necessary.

If experiments are repeated (or replicated) and the same results are obtained, then they are likely to be valid and reliable. In other words, if investigations are checked by other experts it is more likely that they are genuine and not just made up by the original author or fluke results obtained.

The idea of other scientists reading and checking on investigations is called **peer review**. This acts as a quality control system, i.e. the work and findings are reliable and can be trusted to be true.

Investigations (or experiments)

When investigating a hypothesis the experiments have to be carefully planned. This means:

● Thinking about the problem

● Deciding what methods and equipment are to be used

● Carrying out the investigation so that it is safe, fair and will give reliable results.

Variables

In investigations, scientists design an experiment so that the change in one item causes something else to change. These changing quantities are called **variables**. In an investigation you usually change one variable and measure how it affects the other variable.

There are three kinds of variable.

● **Independent variable, where one thing is changed** (for example, when salt is added in the investigation on the previous page) and the results of the one change are observed.

● **Dependent variable, which is the factor that changes as a result of our investigation.** The scientist will focus on the dependent variable (for example, the temperature at which the water boils) to see if it responds to the change (the addition of salt).

● **Controlled variable, where all other factors are the same.** For example, this might include using the same amount of tap water and the same size beaker in each case. This makes it a fair test.

Safety

When planning an investigation it is very important that it is safe. **A hazard is something that can cause harm**, such as fire, chemicals, broken glass, electricity and spillages. You must identify all hazards and come up with ways of reducing the risks. For example, when heating a liquid in a test tube with a Bunsen burner, the following precautions are taken:

Hazard	Precaution
Fire	● Always wear lab coat and safety glasses. ● Tie long hair back. ● While heating the test tube point it from yourself and others. ● Never leave the Bunsen Burner unattended when lit. ● Always use a yellow safety flame when not in use.
Chemicals	● Always wear lab coat, safety glasses and gloves. ● Long hair must be tied up. ● Use in a well ventilated room. ● Be familiar with the safety labels on containers of chemicals. ● Always report spillages to your teacher.
Broken glass	● Always wear lab coat and safety glasses. ● Always report broken glass to your teacher. ● Never handle broken glass with bare hands. ● Always clean up broken glass with a dustpan and brush.

Data

Data is the information, measurements or observations collected in an experiment. Data can be:

● **Quantitative, where the data involves the use of numbers.** For example, the temperature is 20°C, or the distance is 100 metres.

● **Qualitative, which describes something without the use of numbers.** Very often qualitative data is obtained by using our senses. For example, we say something feels soft, or an object looks green, or a gas smells terrible.

▲ Figure 1.9 *Heating a liquid in a test tube with a bunsen burner*

For example, 'We breathe out more carbon dioxide than we breathe in' is a qualitative observation. However, if we say, 'We breathe out 4% carbon dioxide but we breathe in only 0.04% carbon dioxide', this is a quantitative observation, or measurement.

Collecting data

In any experiment it is vital that our measurements and readings are as reliable, accurate and precise as possible. We should not guess or estimate the volume of water added to each beaker; we should carefully measure the same volume of water using a suitable measuring device.

The measuring equipment must be sensitive enough to accurately measure the chemicals you are using. **Resolution is the smallest change a measuring instrument can detect**; e.g. a mass balance may have a resolution of 1 g or 0.1 g.

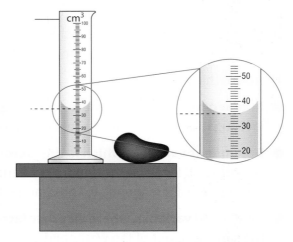
▲ Figure 1.10 *Graduated cylinder – always measure to the bottom of the meniscus*

In order for your data to be more accurate, all equipment must be calibrated. For example, the mass balance needs to be set to zero before you start weighing things.

Reliability

When carrying out an investigation, you can improve the reliability of the results by repeating the readings and calculating the mean (average). You should have at least three readings so you can calculate an average result.

▲ Figure 1.11 *Mass balance*

Precision

Precise results are ones where the data is close to the mean.

Organising data

Once the data has been collected, it can then be organised in a table.

Flask	Result 1 (cm³)	Result 2 (cm³)	Result 3 (cm³)	Mean (cm³)	Range (cm³)
A	26	32	37	31.6	37 − 26 = 11
B	47	42	57	48.6	57 − 42 = 15
C	68	67	70	68.3	70 − 67 = 3
D	89	87	82	86	89 − 82 = 7

● Each column must have a heading, including units.

● Mean (average) – add together all the data values and divide by the total number of values.

● Range – this is used to check the accuracy of the result. Subtract the smaller number from the larger number. This shows how spread out the data is (the greater the spread, the lower the accuracy).

Presenting data

Scientists must present their data in a meaningful manner so it is easier to see patterns and relationships in the data.

Data can be presented as a bar chart, a line graph, a pie chart, a flow chart or a Sankey diagram:

Bar chart

● Draw it nice and big.

● Label both axes.

● Include units.

● Leave a gap between categories.

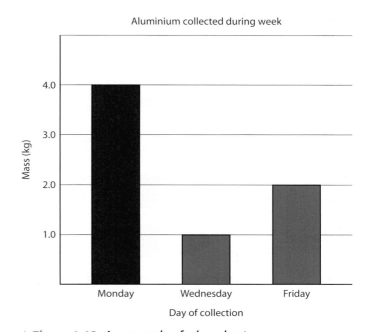

▲ Figure 1.12 *An example of a bar chart*

Line graph

● When plotting use a sharp pencil.

● The dependent variable (what you measure) goes on the *y*-axis.

● The independent variable (what you change) goes on the *x*-axis.

● Label both axes and include units.

● When drawing a line, draw through as many points as possible.

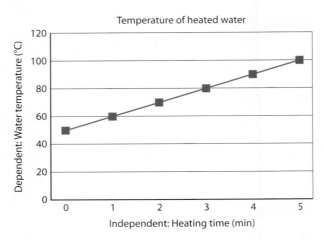

▲ **Figure 1.13** *An example of a line graph*

Pie chart

A pie chart is a circular two-dimensional graph divided into sections (slices). Each slice of the pie is relative to the size of that category in the group as a whole.

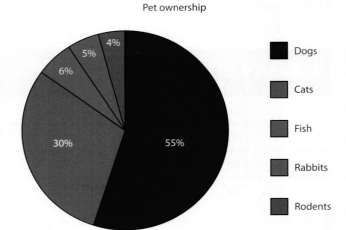

▲ **Figure 1.14** *An example of a pie chart*

Flow chart

A flow chart is a diagram made up of boxes and arrows. It is a step-by-step series of stages in a process, where the last stage is the product.

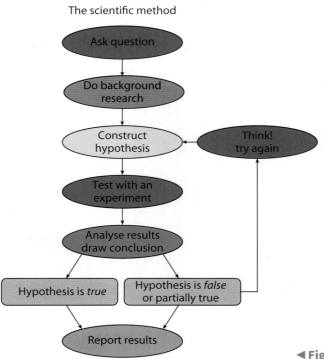

◀ **Figure 1.15** *An example of a flow chart*

Sankey diagram

A Sankey diagram is a type of flow chart where the width of the arrows is proportional to the flow quantity. This diagram can be used to show energy transfer, where the thicker the line or arrow, the greater the amount of energy involved.

Did you know?

Matthew H. Sankey (1853–1925) was an Irish-born engineer from Co. Tipperary. He was the first person to use Sankey diagrams, which is why they were named after him.

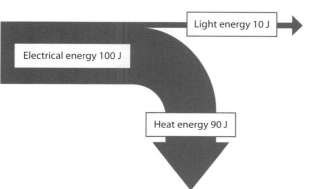

▲ Figure 1.16 *A Sankey diagram showing the energy transfer for a filament bulb*

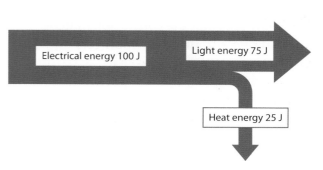

▲ Figure 1.17 *A Sankey diagram showing the energy transfer for an energy-saving bulb*

Interpreting data

Interpreting data involves looking at the data and saying what pattern you can see.

A **correlation** is the relationship between the two sets of data (variables).

Positive correlation (linear)

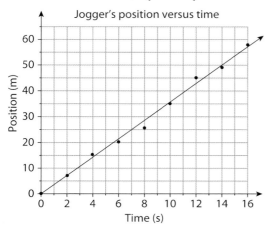

▲ Figure 1.18 ***Directly proportional:** as one variable increases the other variable increases; the graph is a straight line, through the origin, where both the variables increase or decrease in the same ratio*

Inverse correlation

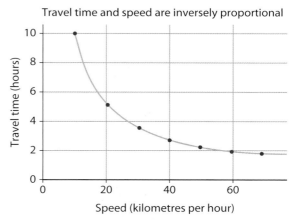

▲ Figure 1.19 ***Inversely proportional:** as one variable increases the other variable decreases*

No correlation

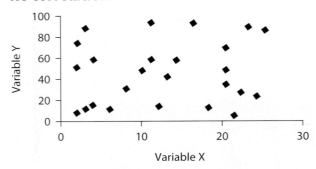

▲ Figure 1.20 **No correlation: no relationship between variables**

The data obtained in any investigation should be **analysed** to reach a suitable **conclusion**.

Conclusion

The conclusion is a summary of the findings in the investigation.

Forming a conclusion involves looking at the data and highlighting any patterns you can see. It is important that the conclusion matches the data it is based on. The conclusion should either support or contradict the hypothesis.

Evaluation

The evaluation is an analysis of the whole investigation.

The analysis should:

- Try to explain any unusual or strange observations that may have arisen

- Include consideration of anything that was hard to do or caused difficulty during the investigation

- Give rise to a discussion of how the investigation could be improved or altered if it were to be repeated, so that more information could be obtained on the topic under investigation.

An investigation must have a conclusion and an evaluation, as it shows that you have a really good understanding of what the investigation was about.

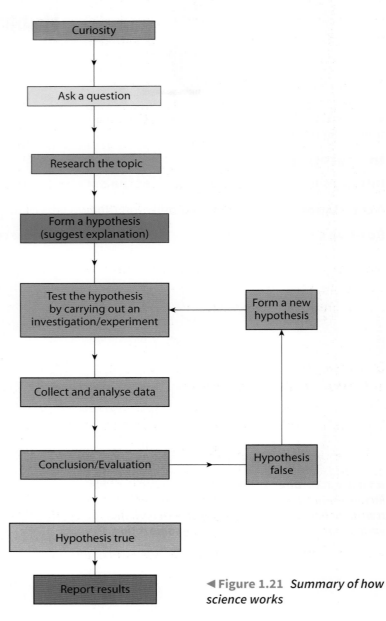

◄ Figure 1.21 **Summary of how science works**

Reviewing and reflecting on investigations

By thinking back over the skills, methods and ideas used to carry out a series of investigations, you should become better at applying scientific learning and skills in new and varied ways. In particular, you should be able to think and act like a scientist.

This means you should be able to identify questions that are suited to scientific investigations. You should then be able to form a prediction, make a hypothesis that can be tested by investigation and carry out a proper scientific investigation of a new, unfamiliar problem.

Scientific ideas change over time

Science is not a fixed, unchanging set of ideas. It changes all the time. As a result of carrying out investigations, our hypothesis is supported or contradicted. Over time a new hypothesis may arise to replace an old, unsupported hypothesis. This means that scientific thinking is constantly changing in line with new investigations that are carried out.

Communicating in science

How to communicate research

An important aspect of science is the ability to tell others what you did, how you did it and what you have discovered. This often involves writing a report of your investigation. In your report it is important that you present your information in a form that is clear, accurate and easy for others to understand.

This may involve a written report, the use of diagrams and photographs, tables to show any numerical data you obtained, or the use of graphs, pie charts or bar charts. Sometimes it involves preparing a poster to outline your work or telling others about your work using a slide presentation or other multimedia resources.

You will have to adapt your presentation to suit the people to whom you are reporting. For example, a report to your class who shared the investigation with you might be different from reporting to another class or a group of parents.

Conduct research

When carrying out an investigation it is important to find out as much as you can about the topic before you start. This involves researching it using books, libraries, internet and media (such as newspapers, scientific magazines or TV programmes), or any other relevant sources.

Evaluating media-based arguments

Of course, you cannot always believe all you see or read. It is important that you make judgements as to **how reliable or accurate** a source is. A properly conducted scientific report is much more valid than a newspaper report giving a person's (or a group's) point of view. **It is very important to be able to detect that a source may be unfair or show bias.**

Bias in an article shows only one point of view and does not give equal chance to different points of view.

Very often media reports on a scientific issue are based on information given to the media by groups who want to promote their own ideas and plans. It is important to be aware of the source of the information and of the reasons for releasing the information. This is true for all media sources, but it is especially true for the internet.

Some of the main features to look for in an internet source you can trust are shown in the table below.

How to tell if a website is credible	
Author	The name of the author is given
Date	The date is given for all research findings that are listed (regularly revised)
Source	Articles give the source of the information presented (possibly with links to support them), so you can tell that the information is not just personal opinion
Domain	In general, websites from universities (.edu), governments (.gov) and organisations such as the BBC and NASA are more reliable; some domains, such as .com, .org and .net can be purchased and used by any individual
Site design	A well-designed site can indicate a more reliable source
Writing style	Good grammar and spelling are an indication that the site may be credible

Contribution and impact of scientists on society

The nature of science means that it is important to be aware of the role scientists have played in making the world a better place. Through their discoveries and inventions, they have expanded our knowledge and understanding of how things work.

◄ **Figure 1.22** *Students studying in a library*

They have allowed more food to be produced, more diseases to be controlled, new materials to be designed, new technologies to be available and new understandings to be made about our own planet and the rest of the known universe.

You should be able to research and present information on what exactly different scientists have achieved. Some of these scientists are now legends of history. However, many major discoveries are being made by scientists who are still living.

Most of these achievements have been for the better but, sadly, sometimes scientific discoveries may be used for negative reasons or have negative results. For example, the invention of engines that could burn petrol has given rise to cars, buses and fast means of transport. However, it has also resulted in carbon dioxide levels rising, which are contributing to global warming and climate change.

Role and importance of science in society

Science and society are deeply interlinked. It is obvious that **science affects society by developing new discoveries, processes and materials**. Science does not exist simply for itself. It should try to provide solutions that help make the world a better place for everyone. This has been done by developments such as electricity, electronics, digital technologies, communications, disease control, improved healthcare, new materials and drugs, discoveries about our solar system (and beyond it) and new methods to supply our energy needs as oil and other fuel supplies run out.

▲ **Figure 1.23** *Scientist Stephen Hawking (1942–2018)*

However, the link between science and society is a two-way process. Society also relates to science and scientists. **Society often guides or encourages scientific research in different areas.**

This can happen due to laws being passed, public money being made available to fund science and the general interests, values and public opinion as to what science needs to do next.

In addition, scientists are influenced by the culture in which they grew up. For example, scientists may not want to carry out certain types of research because it goes against what they believe in.

Science has had a huge role in making the world a better place. The role of science will be even more important in the future as we try to come to terms with our growing human population numbers, the need for new forms of energy, our desire to improve our health, our attempts to control disorders such as cancer and Alzheimer's disease, and the need to limit the effects of global warming.

These are all huge and complex problems. Remember, however, that science starts in a very simple way: by being curious and asking questions. As the famous scientist Stephen Hawking said:

'Look up at the stars and not down at your feet. Try to make sense of what you see and wonder about what makes the universe exist. Be curious.'

Summary questions

1.1 Indigestion is caused by too much hydrochloric acid in the stomach, which causes a burning feeling. Indigestion tablets are designed to neutralise this acid and soothe the pain.

Two students decided to carry out an investigation on indigestion tablets. Their research question was 'Do more expensive brands of indigestion tablets neutralise more acid?'.

(a) Suggest what their hypothesis might be.

(b) State the following for this investigation.

   (i) Independent variable

  (ii) Dependent variable

 (iii) Fixed variables

  (iv) Control

(c) Here is a table of their results:

Brand	Cost per packet (euros)	Cost per tablet (cents)	Volume of acid neutralised (cm³)	Average
A	1.35	0.13	19, 18, 19	
B	1.12	0.11	22, 21, 20	
C	1.20	0.12	18, 17, 19	

   (i) Why did they repeat each experiment three times?

  (ii) Calculate the average for each brand.

 (iii) Draw a bar chart showing their results (put the Brand on the *x*-axis and the Volume of acid on the *y*-axis.)

  (iv) Which brand of tablet was most effective at neutralising the acid?

   (v) Did the results of this investigation support your suggested hypothesis?

● 1.2 This table shows the power consumption comparison between three different types of television.

Screen size (inches)	LED (watts)	LCD (watts)	Plasma (watts)
15	15	18	------
20	24	26	------
24	40	50	------
30	50	60	150
37	60	80	180
42	80	120	220
50	100	150	300

(a) Plot a line graph showing the data for each television (remember the independent variable goes on the *x*-axis).

(b) Look at the graph and state the relationship between screen size and consumption of energy.

(c) Which TV is more energy efficient (use data collected to justify your conclusion)?

● 1.3 This Sankey diagram represents the energy conversion in a filament bulb.

(a) Identify:

   (i) Input energy

   (ii) Useful energy

   (iii) Wasteful energy

(b) Calculate the % efficiency using the following formula:

$$\% \text{ efficiency} = \frac{\text{useful energy}}{\text{input energy}} \times 100$$

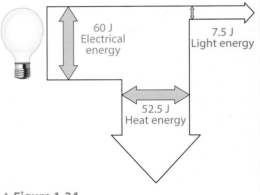

▲ **Figure 1.24**

● 1.4 This table shows the height of seedlings after three weeks using different fertilisers.

Fertiliser	Growth of seedlings (mm)
A	10.5
B	14.5
No fertiliser	4.5

(a) Identify the following for this investigation.

   (i) Independent variable

   (ii) Dependent variable

   (iii) Control

(b) Analyse the data in the table and write a conclusion, using the data to justify it.

 Log on to www.edcolearning.ie for Additional Summary Questions

BIOLOGICAL WORLD

LEARNING OUTCOMES: LO

BW1. Students should be able to investigate the structures of animal and plant cells and relate them to their functions

BW2. Students should be able to describe asexual and sexual reproduction; explore patterns in the inheritance and variation of genetically controlled characteristics

BW3. Students should be able to outline evolution by natural selection and how it explains the diversity of living things

BW4. Students should be able to describe the structure, function, and interactions of the organs of the human digestive, circulatory and respiratory systems

BW 5. Students should be able to conduct a habitat study; research and investigate the adaptation, competition and interdependence of organisms within specific habitats and communities

BW6. Students should be able to evaluate how human health is affected by: inherited factors and environmental factors including nutrition; lifestyle choices; examine the role of microorganisms in human health

BW7. Students should be able to describe respiration and photosynthesis as both chemical and biological processes; investigate factors that affect respiration and photosynthesis

BW8. Students should be able to explain how matter and energy flow through ecosystems

BW9. Students should be able to explain human sexual reproduction; discuss medical, ethical and societal issues

BW10. Students should be able to evaluate how humans can successfully conserve ecological biodiversity and contribute to global food production; appreciate the benefits that people obtain from ecosystems

LIVING THINGS AND CELLS

LO: BW1

Learning intentions

At the end of this chapter you will be able to:

✓ Investigate the difference between living and non-living things

✓ Classify living things into different groups

✓ Investigate the structures of animal and plant cells and their functions

✓ Use a microscope to see the structure of animal and plant cells.

Keywords

- organism
- vertebrate
- invertebrate
- diversity
- biodiversity
- cell
- zygote
- nutrition
- excretion
- response
- reproduction
- cell membrane
- nucleus
- cytoplasm
- mitochondrion
- vacuole
- chloroplasts
- microscope

What are living things?

An organism is a living thing.

In general, living things must have all the features or characteristics shown in Table 2.1.

Table 2.1 The characteristics of all living things

Characteristic	Meaning
Cells	The basic building blocks of living things
Nutrition	The way in which living things get their food
Excretion	The way in which living things get rid of wastes that they produce
Response	The way in which living things react to changes in their surroundings
Reproduction	The way in which living things produce new living things

▶ Figure 2.1 *Living things include plants and animals*

▼ *Figure 2.2 Characteristics of all living things*

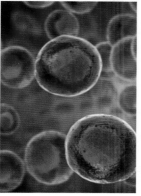
Cells

Nutrition: a rabbit eating lettuce

Excretion: a person breathing out

Response: a chameleon responds slowly

Reproduction: a swan and cygnets

 Questions

2.1 **Separate the following into living and non-living things:**

a stone   *a baby*   *a pen*   *a weed*   *a dog*

water   *ice*   *smoke*   *a fly*   *a jellyfish*

2.2 **Why is it difficult to say whether an egg or a piece of fruit is living or non-living?**

BIOLOGICAL WORLD

Some people claim that movement, growth and respiration (which is the release of energy from food) are also characteristics of living things.

However, plants do not move (from place to place), animals continue growing throughout their lives but at a much slower pace, and the spores of bacteria can remain (be dormant) without the need for energy for long periods of time.

> **? Question**
>
> **2.3** Find some other examples of living things that do not move, grow or get energy from food.

Different types of living things

Living things are classified into groups. This is not unlike music which can be classified (or grouped) under headings such as new releases or compilations. **In general there are five major groups of living things**, as show in Table 2.2.

Table 2.2 **Groups of living things**

Group of living things	Examples
Bacteria	Tiny microscopic living things. Some cause disease, some cause decay, some are used to produce valuable substances
Fungi	Mushrooms, moulds and yeast
Plants	Trees, grasses, flowers
Animals	Humans, fish, insects
Others (Protists)	Seaweeds, amoeba

Each of the five groups shown in Table 2.2 can be sub-divided into many smaller groupings. For example, animals can be classified as:

● **Vertebrates – animals that have backbones**

● **Invertebrates – animals that do not have backbones.**

Examples of vertebrates and invertebrates are shown in Table 2.3.

▼ Figure 2.3 *Different types of living things*

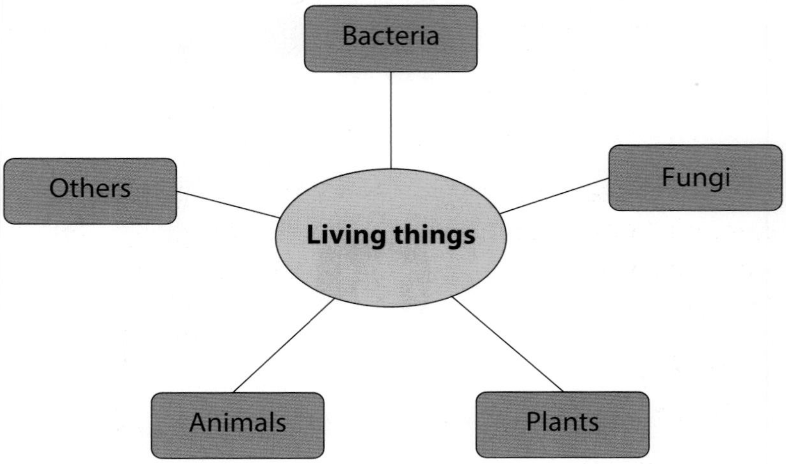

Table 2.3 **Types of living things**

Vertebrates	Invertebrates
Horse	Spider
Seagull	Earthworm
Frog	Fly
Snake	Jellyfish

▲ Figure 2.4 *Vertebrates are animals that have a backbone*

▲ Figure 2.5 *Invertebrates are animals that do not have a backbone*

? Questions

2.4 **(a)** Work in groups and name three plants and three animals with three, four, five and more than five letters in their name.

(b) Think of an animal in each case whose name starts with the letter a, then b, then c, and so on. How far along the alphabet can you go with your list?

2.5 Work in groups to answer the following questions.

(a) In what way might cars be classified? (For example, by price, by colour.)

(b) In what way might films or movies be classified?

Diversity of living things

Biodiversity means the range of living things.

There is a huge range (or **diversity**) of living things on Earth. For example, there are many different types of plants, birds, fish and insects. Each of these living things needs special conditions in which to grow. Unfortunately, many of these conditions are being lost due to human activities. For example:

● Woodlands are destroyed for housing and roads.

● Forests are being lost to supply wood for building.

● Lakes are destroyed by pollution.

The resulting loss of biodiversity will be examined in chapter 12.

? Question

2.6 What other negative impacts to the environment can you think of in addition to the above examples?

Cells

Living things are made of cells. Cells are the basic building blocks of all living things. Most cells are too small to be seen with the naked eye. They can be seen only using a microscope.

Cells can divide to form two cells. This is called cell division. Living things grow by cell division. For example, humans grow from a single cell (called a **zygote**) by cell division. As a result, an adult human has an estimated forty million million cells.

Animal cells

Animal cells have three main parts:

- A **cell membrane**
- A **nucleus**
- **Cytoplasm**.

Cell membrane

The cell membrane is a very thin layer that surrounds the cell.

Its function (i.e. what it does) is to hold the cell contents in place and control what passes into and out of the cell. For example:

- When we exercise, our muscle cells allow glucose and oxygen to pass in from our blood vessels to supply energy to the cells.

- Wastes can pass out into the blood through our cell membranes so that we can remove the waste from our bodies.

Nucleus

**The nucleus is normally round.
Its function is to act as the control centre of the cell.**

The nucleus controls the cell by means of strands called chromosomes. Each chromosome has many genes.

Each gene is made of DNA and controls one particular feature or characteristic. These features or characteristics are passed on (or inherited) from parents to their children. For example, humans have genes to control features such as eye colour, the formation of nails, height and the formation of fingers and toes.

> **Did you know?**
>
> Eggs are single cells.
> An ostrich egg is the largest cell known.

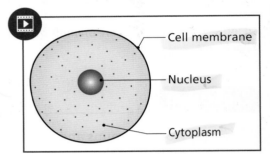

▲ **Figure 2.6** *A typical animal cell*

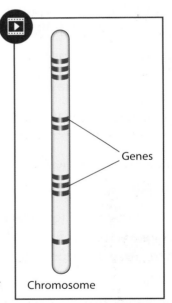

▲ **Figure 2.7** *The relationship between chromosomes and genes*

> **? Questions**
>
> **2.7** Suggest why sperm and egg cells have half the number of chromosomes as ordinary body cells.
>
> **2.8** Think of a new-born baby and list at least ten features that the baby inherits from its parents.

> **Did you know?**
>
> Human cells have 46 chromosomes. These chromosomes contain around 20 000 genes. However, sperm and egg cells have only 23 chromosomes.

Cytoplasm

Cytoplasm is a watery liquid found between the nucleus and the cell membrane.

Its functions are to carry out some cell reactions and to support tiny cell structures.

These structures carry out many of the vital processes of the cell. They are too small to be seen using a light microscope. (We look at light microscopes later in this chapter.)

One such structure is the **mitochondrion** (plural mitochondria). These tiny structures supply energy to the cell.

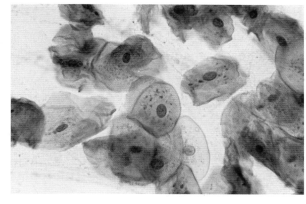

▲ Figure 2.8 *Human cheek cells as seen through a light microscope*

Plant cells

Plant cells have five main parts:

- A **cell wall**
- A **cell membrane**
- A **nucleus**
- **cytoplasm**
- A **vacuole**.

Cell wall

A cell wall is found outside the cell membrane in plant cells.

The function of the cell wall is to give strength to the plant cell. This is needed as plants, unlike many animals, do not have strong skeletons. The cell walls make plant cells stronger and less flexible than animal cells.

The material in cell walls is called cellulose. This forms everyday substances such as paper, cardboard and cotton.

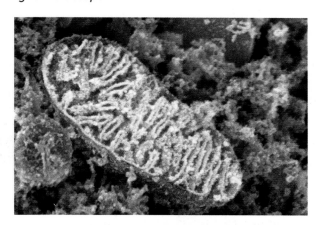

▲ Figure 2.9 *The inside of a mitochondrion*

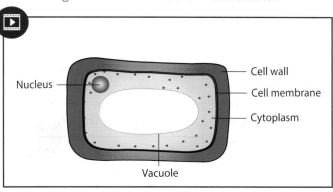

Nucleus — Cell wall — Cell membrane — Cytoplasm — Vacuole

▲ Figure 2.10 *A typical plant cell*

---

② Question

2.9 Why can animal cells (such as skin cells) be stretched, but plant cells (such as lettuce or cabbage leaves) cannot be stretched?

Cell membrane

Plant cell membranes are similar to animal cell membranes.

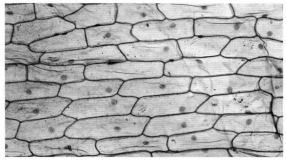

▲ Figure 2.11 *Onion cells as seen using a light microscope*

Nucleus

The nucleus is almost the same in plant and animal cells. However, the genes present in plant cells are different from those found in animal cells.

For example, plant cells have genes for features such as forming a cell wall and making the green chemical (chlorophyll) found in many plant cells.

Cytoplasm

The cytoplasm in plant cells is similar to cytoplasm in animal cells. However, plant cytoplasm may contain tiny green structures (**chloroplasts**), which allow the plant to make its own food in a process called photosynthesis.

Vacuole

A vacuole contains liquid. If the vacuole is full of liquid, it forces the cytoplasm to push out against the cell wall.

In this way the function of the vacuole is to give strength to the cell. Normally vacuoles cannot be seen using a light microscope.

Table 2.4 Function and location of cell structures

Cell structure	Function	Found in
Cell membrane	● Retains cell contents ● Controls what passes in and out of the cell	Animals and plants
Nucleus	● The control centre of the cell	Animals and plants
Cytoplasm	● Carries out some cell reactions ● Supports tiny cell structures	Animals and plants
Mitochondrion	● Supplies energy to the cell (by respiration)	Animals and plants
Cell wall	● Gives strength to the cell	Plants only
Chloroplast	● Makes food (by photosynthesis)	Plants only
Vacuole	● Gives strength to the cell	Plants only

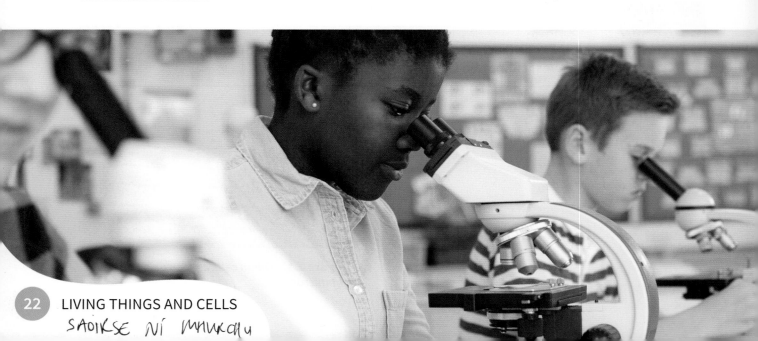

SAOIRSE NÍ MHURCHU

The light microscope

A **microscope** is used to view objects that are too small to be seen by eyesight alone.

The term 'magnification' means how many times larger the object appears to be when viewed under the microscope.

The parts of a microscope

Eyepiece lens

The eyepiece is the lens that is nearest to your eye. If it is marked ×10 it makes the object ten times larger (that is, it magnifies the object by ten).

Focus knobs

The coarse focus knob is used to see the image clearly at low magnification. The fine focus knob is used for delicate focusing at high power.

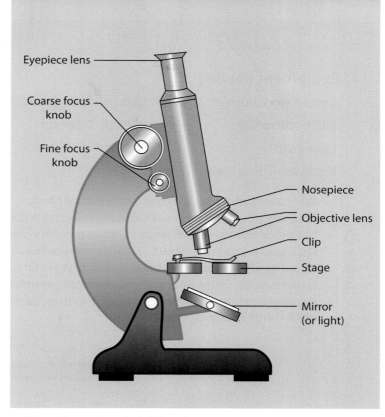

▲ Figure 2.12 *A typical light microscope*

Objective lens

Each objective lens has a different magnification. The total magnification is found by multiplying the powers of the eyepiece and objective lenses being used.

power of eyepiece × power of objective lens = total magnification

For example: An eyepiece marked ×10 and an objective lens marked ×20 will give a total magnification of ×200.

Nosepiece

The nosepiece can rotate to move the different objective lenses into position.

Stage

The stage is used to support the microscope slide. It has a hole in the centre to allow light to pass through.

Clips

The clips are used to hold the microscope slide in place.

Mirror or light

The mirror is used to reflect light from a lamp up through the object. Some microscopes have a light instead of a mirror.

Activity 2.1 How can we examine animal cells?

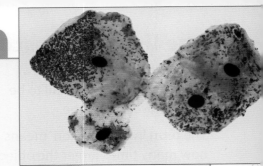

Equipment needed

Cotton wool buds or wooden spatula (lollypop stick)

Microscope slide   Pen or pencil or seeker

Cover slip   Tissue paper/filter paper

Methylene blue stain   Microscope

▲ **Figure 2.13** *Cheek cells (at high power)*

Safety

- Take care when placing the cover slip as it could break.
- Take care when using the focus knobs not to lower the objective lens onto the slide as it could crack.
- Use cotton wool buds at all times, to obtain the cheek cells.
- Dispose of the cotton wool bud or spatula immediately after the slide has been prepared.
- Do not handle the cotton wool bud or spatula at any time during this activity.
- Do not pass the cotton wool bud or spatula to any member of your class during this activity.
- Pay attention to your teacher at all times regarding how to prepare your slide and the use and disposal of the cotton wool bud or spatula.

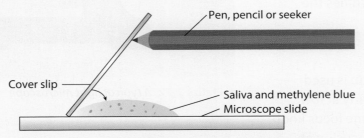

▲ **Figure 2.14** *Adding a cover slip to a microscope slide*

➡ Conducting the activity

Preparing the slide

1. Gently scrape the inside of your mouth with the cotton wool bud (or the wooden spatula).
2. Scrape the saliva (which now contains cheek cells) onto the centre of a microscope slide.
3. Add three or four drops of methylene blue stain to the saliva (this stain highlights parts of the cell, especially the nucleus).
4. Lower a cover slip slowly at a 45 degree angle over the cheek cells as shown above.
5. Use tissue paper to soak up any of the stain that may be outside the cover slip.

Viewing the slide under a microscope

1. Switch on the microscope light (or adjust the mirror so that light is shining through the opening in the stage of the microscope).
2. Turn the nosepiece so that the lowest power objective lens is in place.
3. Place the slide in the centre of the microscope stage and use the clips to hold it in place.
4. Look at the stage from the side and turn the coarse focus knob so that the low-power objective lens moves as close as possible to the slide. (Be careful with the lens.)
5. Look through the eyepiece and turn the coarse focus knob slowly so that the cells become visible.
6. If necessary, move the slide slightly so that you can see the best sample of cells.
7. In the space provided in your Activity Book, draw a diagram of the cells that you can see. Label the three main parts of one of the cells.
8. Turn the nosepiece to a higher power lens and use the fine focus knob to get a clear image of one of the cells.
9. In the space provided in your Activity Book, draw this cell and label three main parts.
10. Observe the cheek cells for features such as:
    - Are they all the same shape?
    - Are they all the same size?
    - What colour is the cytoplasm?
    - What colour is the nucleus?
    - Can you see any particles in the cytoplasm?

Activity 2.2 How can we examine plant cells?

 Equipment needed

Knife
Onion
Forceps
Microscope slide
Cover slip

Iodine solution
Pen or pencil or seeker
Tissue paper/filter paper
Microscope

Safety
- Take care when placing the cover slip as it could break.
- Take care when using the focus knobs not to lower the objective lens onto the slide as it could crack.

➡ **Conducting the activity**

Preparing the slide

1. Cut an onion into small pieces.
2. Using a forceps, peel a thin layer of cells from the inner curve of a piece of onion.
3. Place the onion cells on a microscope slide.
4. Add three or four drops of iodine solution onto the cells (iodine stains and highlights parts of the cell, especially the nucleus).
5. Lower a cover slip slowly at a 45 degree angle over the cells as shown in Figure 2.14.
6. Use tissue paper to soak up any of the stain that may be outside the cover slip.

Viewing the slide under a microscope

1. Switch on the microscope light (or adjust the mirror so that light is shining through the opening in the stage of the microscope).
2. Turn the nosepiece so that the lowest power objective lens is in place.
3. Place the slide in the centre of the microscope stage and use the clips to hold it in place.

4. Look at the stage from the side and turn the coarse focus knob so that the low-power objective lens moves as close as possible to the slide. (Be careful not to damage the slide or the lens.)
5. Look through the eyepiece and turn the coarse focus knob slowly so that the cells become visible.
6. If necessary, move the slide slightly so that you can see the best sample of cells.
7. In your Activity Book draw a diagram of the cells that you can see. Label the main parts of one of the cells.
8. Turn the nosepiece to a higher power lens and use the fine focus knob to get a clear image of one of the cells.
9. In your Activity Book draw this cell and label the main parts.

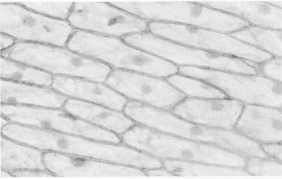

▲ **Figure 2.15** *Onion cells*

Summary questions

BIOLOGICAL WORLD

● **2.10** The features of living things are: response, nutrition, excretion, reproduction, cells. Write out the passage below and insert each of these features into the correct space.

The building blocks of living things are _____. Getting rid of wastes is called _____. The way in which living things get food is _____. Living things producing new living things is called _____. Living things reacting to change is called _____.

● **2.11** State a main function for each of the following parts of a cell:

(a) Cell membrane

(b) Nucleus

(c) Cell wall

(d) Mitochondrion

(e) Vacuole

(f) Chloroplast.

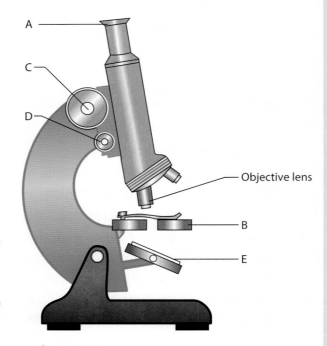

▲ **Figure 2.16**

● **2.12** (a) Name the parts of the microscope labelled A, B, C, D and E in Figure 2.16.

(b) If the objective lens is marked ×20 and part A is marked ×20, what is the total magnification?

(c) If the objective lens is marked ×10 and the total magnification is ×100, what is the magnification of part A?

● **2.13** Answer the following in respect of how you investigated animal cells.

(a) What type of animal cells did you investigate?

(b) How did you get the animal cells?

(c) What stain did you use?

(d) Why did you use a stain?

(e) When you first examined the cells, did you use the high-power or low-power objective lens?

● **2.14** Answer the following in respect of how you investigated plant cells.

(a) What type of plant cells did you investigate?

(b) How did you get the plant cells?

(c) What stain did you use?

(d) What colour were the nuclei?

 Log on to **www.edcolearning.ie** for Additional Summary Questions

Assessment questions

2.15 Answer these questions on microscopes. **(30 marks)**

   (a) Give one benefit of using a microscope.

   (b) Microscopes are good for examining thin structures (such as cheek cells) but are not good for thick structures.

     (i) Why is this?

     (ii) What colour will thick objects appear under the microscope?

   (c) If the focus knobs or wheels on a microscope did not work, what problem would you have in viewing objects?

   (d) Anton van Leeuwenhoek was a Dutchman who is credited with first using microscopes. In the 1670s he discovered tiny structures such as single-celled living things, cell vacuoles, sperm cells and the structure of muscle cells.

     (i) There was no electricity at the time, so what source of light might he have used?

     (ii) In what kind of cells did he discover vacuoles?

2.16 Question from SEC Junior Cycle Science sample paper **(15 marks)**

All biological organisms are made up of cells.

   (a) Name the instrument shown in the picture on the right (Figure 2.17), which is used to examine cells.

   (b) Name the labelled part of the instrument (A), which makes the cells look bigger.

   (c) Figure 2.18 shows cells from an onion, which are typical plant cells.

     Draw one cell from Figure 2.18 and label any one part of it.

   (d) State the function of the part of the cell you have chosen in (c) above.

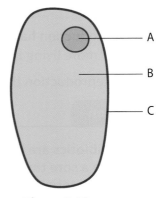

▶ **Figure 2.17**

A

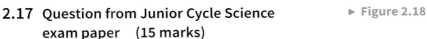

▶ **Figure 2.18**

2.17 Question from Junior Cycle Science exam paper **(15 marks)**

The diagram Figure 2.19 shows an animal cell.

   (a) Which of the words listed below correspond to the labels A, B and C?

     Cytoplasm   Cell membrane   Nucleus

   (b) Which of the three named parts controls the activities of the cell?

   (c) A student was asked to examine animal cells in the laboratory. Which of the following instruments should the student use?

     Telescope   Microscope   Periscope

A

B

C

▲ **Figure 2.19**

 Log on to **www.edcolearning.ie** for Additional Assessment Questions

 PowerPoint summary  **Weblinks**

CHAPTER 3

PASSING ON CHARACTERISTICS

LO: BW2

Learning intentions

At the end of this chapter you will be able to:

✓ Describe asexual and sexual reproduction

✓ Explain characteristics and variation

✓ Explore patterns in inheritance and variation.

Keywords

- asexual and sexual reproduction
- gametes
- zygote
- fertilisation
- characteristics
- variation
- DNA
- genes
- chromosomes
- dominant
- recessive
- genotype
- phenotype
- pedigree chart

Reproduction

The formation of new living things is called reproduction. This is one of the characteristics of living things. There are two types of reproduction, asexual and sexual:

● **Asexual reproduction is the formation of living things from one parent only**

● **Sexual reproduction is the production of living things by combining cells from two parents.**

Asexual reproduction

Asexual reproduction happens when one cell splits into two, or when one organism divides to form two or more living things. Asexual reproduction does not require sex cells to join together.

In asexual reproduction the offspring are identical to the parent cell or cells.

> **? Question**
>
> **3.1** Antibiotics are drugs that kill bacteria. Bacteria do not reproduce sexually. If you have a sore throat and the antibiotic is effective, why would you expect it to kill all the bacteria?

Examples of asexual reproduction

(a) Bacteria are single-celled organisms. When they divide they form two identical cells.

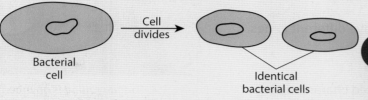

Bacterial cell → Cell divides → Identical bacterial cells

▲ **Figure 3.1** *Asexual cell division*

(b) Strawberry (and buttercup) plants produce special stems (called runners), which grow overground from the base of the parent plant.

Some distance away from the parent plant, the runners form new plants, which are identical to the parent plant.

▲ **Figure 3.2** *Strawberry plant with runners*

Sexual reproduction

A gamete is a sex cell.

Sexual reproduction involves two sex cells (or **gametes**) joining together to form a single cell (called a **zygote**).

Fertilisation is the joining or fusion of sex cells.

As a result of sexual reproduction the offspring formed have features or characteristics of both parents. This means the offspring are not identical to the parents. This is the main benefit of sexual reproduction.

The most common way animals reproduce is by sexual reproduction (see chapter 11). Plants can reproduce sexually or asexually.

⍰ **Question**

3.2 What are the names of the gametes found in humans?

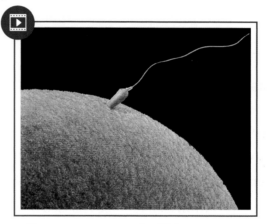

▲ **Figure 3.3** *A sperm fertilising an egg*

⍰ **Questions**

3.3 Would you expect bacteria to have gametes? Explain your answer.

3.4 Brothers (or sisters) may be very similar. However, they normally show some differences due to being formed by sexual reproduction. List five differences that are often visible between brothers or sisters.

3.5 What inherited differences might there be between dog pups from the same parents?

Passing on characteristics

Characteristics are traits or features of an organism that can be passed on from parents to their offspring. Characteristics are controlled by genes (which are found on chromosomes).

Genes are passed from parents to their offspring during reproduction.

In asexual reproduction the parent passes exact copies of its genes to the offspring. This is why the offspring are genetically identical to the parent. For example, strawberries that reproduce by runners will taste, look and grow the same as the strawberries on the parent plant.

In sexual reproduction the offspring have different genes.

Examples of characteristics

Humans have many genetically controlled characteristics. These include:

▲ **Figure 3.4** *Tongue rolling is an inherited trait*

- Eye colour
- Having two eyes
- The presence or absence of freckles
- Having one heart
- The ability to roll the tongue.

Plant characteristics controlled by genes include:

- Colour of the fruit
- Colour of the petals
- Taste of the fruit
- Height of the plants.

⑦ Questions

3.6 Discuss the following question in groups and then report back to the class. Growers often prefer fruit that has developed by asexual methods as it is more similar. What features might the grower prefer to be similar in the fruit?

3.7 Plants that reproduce asexually are often all killed by a new fungus infection. Explain why plants that reproduce sexually may not all be killed by a new fungus.

Variation

Humans have many characteristics in common. They have one heart, two eyes and the ability to produce chemicals such as saliva, sweat and hair.

However, humans also have some differences (or variation). There are two types of variation:

- **Genetic (inherited)**
- **Non-inherited (acquired)**.

Genetic variation is differences passed on from parents to their children by genes. This means that genetic variation is inherited from the parents. For example, eye colour, the length of our eyelashes and the presence or absence of freckles are all inherited from our parents.

Non-inherited variation is differences that are not controlled by genes. These variations do not pass from parents to their children. They have to be learned or practised. For example, speaking a language, using a computer, reading or tying a lace are non-inherited variations.

⑦ Questions

3.8 (a) Inherited variations are controlled by genes. Name the chemical of which genes are made.

(b) In what part of the cell is this chemical normally found?

3.9 Why is the ability to ride a bicycle or play a musical instrument not considered to be genetic variation?

Activity 3.1 How can we investigate some inherited traits?

Note

It is difficult to find human traits that are clearly of one form or another. Most of the following traits are thought to be controlled by single genes. However, it may be difficult to judge some of the following features and put them into a particular category.

➡ Conducting the activity

1. Answer the following questions about yourself by ticking the relevant box on the copy of the chart below in your Student Activity Book.

   (a) Do you have attached earlobes (do your earlobes attach directly to the side of your head) or detached earlobes (where the earlobes are not attached to the side of your head)?

   (b) Can you roll your tongue at the sides to form a tube shape or not (as in Figure 3.4)?

   (c) Do you have dimples in your cheeks or no dimples?

   (d) Are you left-handed or right-handed?

   (e) Do you have freckles or no freckles?

   (f) Do you have naturally curly or straight hair?

   (g) When you join your hands together by inter-locking your fingers is your left thumb or right thumb on top?

   (h) Does your hairline form a point at the centre of your forehead (called a widow's peak) or do you have a straight hairline?

Trait	Individual results Tick the correct boxes below	Class result totals
Attached ear lobes		
Detached ear lobes		
Tongue roller		
Not a tongue roller		
Dimples		
No dimples		
Left-handed		
Right-handed		
Freckles		
No freckles		
Curly hair		
Straight hair		

Table continues over page

Trait	Individual results Tick the correct boxes below	Class result totals
Left thumb on top		
Right thumb on top		
Pointed hairline		
Straight hairline		

2. Combine all the results from your class and put the total number showing each trait into the table.

3. Of the pairs of traits investigated:

   (a) Which trait was the most common?

   (b) Which trait was closest to a 50:50 ratio?

Chromosomes and genes

Chromosomes are thread-like structures found in the nucleus of each plant and animal cell. Most of the time chromosomes cannot be seen in a nucleus because they are stretched out into extremely long, thin threads. Most human cells have 46 chromosomes.

When cells divide, the chromosomes become shorter and thicker and can be seen using a microscope. At this time each chromosome looks like a tiny, thin thread. Chromosomes are made of a chemical called deoxyribonucleic acid (**DNA**) and protein.

Genes are short sections of DNA located on chromosomes. Genes control the production of inherited characteristics. Examples of human genes include:

- The gene to make acid in our stomach

- The gene to make the coloured chemical (pigment) in our eyes.

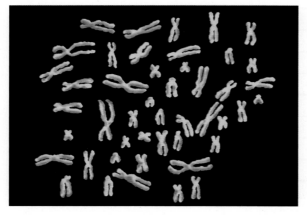

▲ Figure 3.5 *The 46 chromosomes from a human cell*

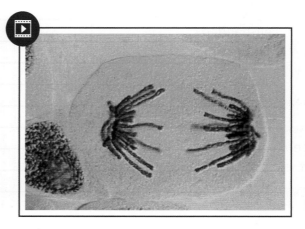

▲ Figure 3.6 *A dividing cell showing chromosomes*

Patterns of inheritance

The inheritance of genetic characteristics often follows a pattern. This is because of the way in which genes may be inherited from each parent. The pattern of inheritance is best understood by following the outcomes of sample genetic crosses.

Introduction to genetic crosses

Eye colour in humans is controlled by a gene. The gene has two versions:

- The **dominant** version, represented as B, causes brown eyes
- The non-dominant version (also called the **recessive** version), represented as b, causes blue eyes.

This information is often shown as:

- B = brown eyes (dominant)
- b = blue eyes (recessive).

Normally the first letter of the dominant version is used; e.g. for brown eyes, B is used.

The dominant version prevents the recessive version of the gene from working.

Genotype is the genes an organism possesses.

In terms of eye colour, each person has two copies of the gene. This means they may have the following combinations:

Gene version (or genotype)	Eye colour
BB	Brown eyes
Bb	Brown eyes
bb	Blue eyes

Phenotype is what the organism looks like. For example, the eye colour is the phenotype.

In sexual reproduction the number of genes is halved during the production of the gametes (sperm and eggs, also known as sex cells). This means the gametes each contain only one version of the gene.

A person with the combination …	Will produce gametes (or sex cells) with …
BB	a single B
Bb	either B or b
bb	a single b

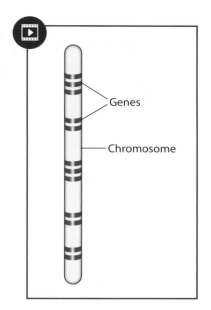

▲ Figure 3.7 *Genes on a chromosome*

ⓘ Information

Genetic crosses

Cross 1
Question

Show the pattern in eye colour of a family in which one parent is BB and the second parent is bb.

Answer

B = Brown eyes
b = Blue eyes

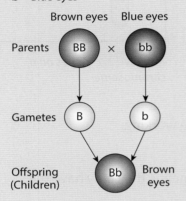

▲ **Figure 3.8** *Genetic cross – eye colour*

In this case all the children will have brown eyes.

Cross 2
Question

Show the pattern of inheritance in eye colour in the following family: a brown-eyed parent who is Bb and a blue-eyed parent.

Answer

B = Brown eyes
b = Blue eyes

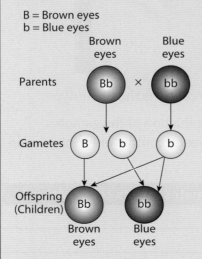

▲ **Figure 3.9** *Genetic cross – eye colour*

Cross 2 can also be shown using a Punnett square:

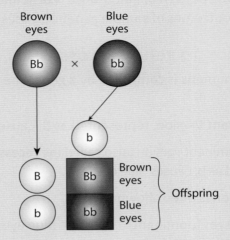

▲ **Figure 3.10** *Genetic cross – eye colour*

In this cross there is an equal chance of a brown-eyed or a blue-eyed child. In other words, there is a 50% (or 1 in 2) chance of a brown-eyed or a blue-eyed child.

Cross 3
Question

Show by diagrams the pattern of inheritance in eye colour for a family in which both parents are brown-eyed (Bb). From the cross predict the percentage chance of the couple having a blue-eyed child.

Answer

B = Brown eyes
b = Blue eyes

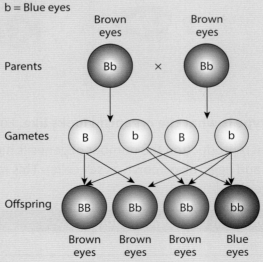

▲ **Figure 3.11** *Genetic cross – eye colour*

Cross 3 can also be shown as:

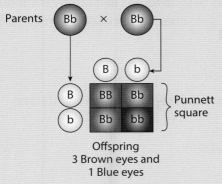

▲ **Figure 3.12** *Genetic cross – eye colour*

In this cross there is a 25% (or 1 in 4) chance of the couple having a blue-eyed child.

Cross 4

Question

Freckles are caused by the dominant version of a gene (F). Lack of freckles is caused by the recessive version of the gene (f).

(a) Which two of the following genetic combinations could a person with freckles have?

FF   Ff   ff

(b) What genetic combination must a person with no freckles have?

(c) If a couple are both Ff, what is the chance of them having a child with freckles? Explain your answer by showing the genetic cross.

Answer

F = Freckles
f = No freckles

(b) Person with no freckles is ff

(c)

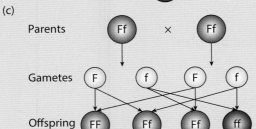

▲ **Figure 3.13** *Genetic cross – freckles*

The chance of this couple having a child with freckles is 75% (or 3:1). The same result would be obtained if this cross were drawn as a Punnett square.

Cross 5

Question

Full lips (B) are dominant to thin lips (b).

A couple, one with full lips and the other with thin lips, have two children. One of the children has full lips and the other has thin lips.

(a) What are the two possible genetic combinations of a person with full lips?

(b) Only one genetic combination produces thin lips. What is this combination?

(c) Show by diagrams how the pattern of inheritance of the couple and their children could occur.

Answer

B = Full lips
b = Thin lips

(a) Full lips could be   BB or Bb

(b) Thin lips must be   bb

(c)

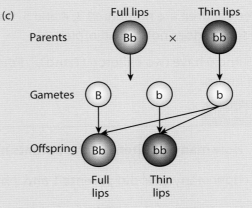

▲ **Figure 3.14** *Genetic cross – full lips and thin lips*

Pedigree studies

A pedigree chart is a diagram showing the physical appearances of individuals in a family from one generation to the next. Figure 3.15 below is an example of a pedigree chart (also called a family tree).

In a pedigree chart:

● A circle (O) represents a female; a square (□) represents a male

● A solid symbol represents an affected individual; an empty symbol represents an unaffected individual

● Roman numerals (I, II, III, etc.) represent the different generations

● Simple numbers or digits (1, 2, 3, etc.) represent individuals

● A horizontal line represents a couple that have offspring

● A vertical line links parents to offspring.

Figure 3.15 represents the appearance of dimples in a family. No dimples (D) is dominant to dimples (d).

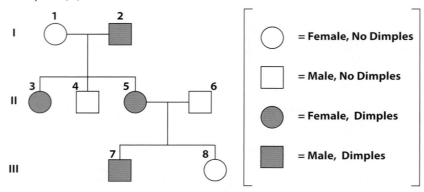

▲ Figure 3.15 *A pedigree chart or family tree*

The diagram shows three generations of a family (I, II, III). The parents are numbered 1 and 2. Person 1 is a female who does not have dimples. Person 2 is a male with dimples.

Their three children are numbered 3, 4 and 5. Both daughters (numbered 3 and 5) have dimples but their son (4) does not have dimples.

Persons 5 and 6 have two children (7 and 8). Person 7 is a male with dimples, person 8 is a female with no dimples.

---

⑦ Questions

3.10 How many children did the parents numbered 1 and 2 have?

3.11 How many girls did parents 1 and 2 have?

3.12 How many of the children of parents 1 and 2 had dimples?

3.13 How many grandchildren did parents 1 and 2 have?

3.14 What was the genetic combination of person 2?

3.15 Persons 3 and 5 had the same genetic combination. What was this?

3.16 What was the genetic combination of person 1?

3.17 What was the genetic combination of person 8?

Summary questions

3.18 A human cell normally contains 46:

    (a) Nuclei   **(b)** Genes   **(c)** Chromosomes   **(d)** Membranes.

3.19 Which of the following statements are true and which are false?

	Statement	True or false
(a)	Asexual reproduction requires two parents.	
(b)	Animals normally reproduce sexually.	
(c)	A tattoo is an inherited trait.	
(d)	An egg cell is a gamete.	

3.20 Hitchhiker's thumb refers to the shape of our thumb when we make a fist and extend our thumb into the air. A straight thumb (S) is dominant to a bent thumb (s).

    (a) Show the following crosses using diagrams.

        (i) SS × ss   **(ii)** Ss × ss   **(iii)** Ss × Ss

    (b) For each cross, state the percentage chance of a child with a straight thumb.

3.21 Bent little finger (B) is dominant over straight little finger (b). A man has the genetic combination Bb and his wife is bb.

    (a) What is the shape of the little finger of the man and his wife?

    (b) Show this cross by means of a diagram and predict the percentage chance of them having a child with bent little fingers.

3.22 Curly hair (C) is dominant to straight hair (c).

    (a) Using your knowledge of genes, explain why more people have curly hair than straight hair.

    (b) In a family, one parent is CC while the second parent is cc.

        (i) What type of hair has each parent?

        (ii) What is the chance that their next child will have curly hair? Draw a genetic cross diagram to explain your answer.

3.23 Dimples (D) are dominant to lack of dimples (d). If the parents have the combinations Dd and dd and they have four children, how many of the children do you expect to have dimples? Explain your answer by showing the genetic cross.

3.24 Gregor Mendel is the person who first discovered how the process of genetic inheritance works. Write a biography (life history) of Mendel to include:

- His dates of birth and death
- His nationality
- His background
- Where he lived and worked
- The value of his discoveries.

Assessment questions

3.25 In humans, brown eyes (B) are dominant to blue eyes (b). Both parents have brown eyes and have the genetic combination Bb. **(30 marks)**

   (a) What is the genotype of each parent?

   (b) What is the phenotype of each parent?

   (c) Their first child has blue eyes. What is the genotype of this child?

   (d) Write out the cross that shows how these two brown-eyed parents could have had a blue-eyed child.

   (e) What is the percentage chance that their next child will have blue eyes?

3.26 Question from Junior Cycle Science exam paper (15 marks)

Sickle cell anaemia is an inherited human disease. It causes the body to produce red blood cells that have an irregular shape. The gene for the disease is passed on from generation to generation.

Examine the pattern of inheritance for sickle cell anaemia shown in the family tree below (Figure 3.17) and answer the questions that follow.

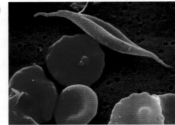

▲ Figure 3.16

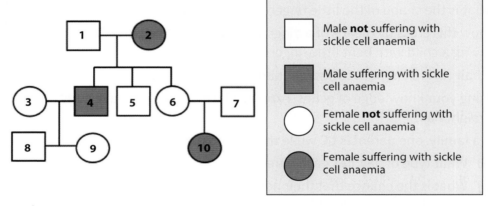

▲ Figure 3.17

   (a) Square **1** and circle **2** are a couple with children. How many children do they have?

   (b) Some non-sufferers may be carriers of the disease. This means that they have inherited the sickle cell gene, but they don't suffer from the disease. What evidence is there from the diagram that persons **6** and **7** are both carriers?

   (c) Suffering from sickle cell anaemia is an example of a genetically controlled characteristic. Classify the characteristics below as being either genetically controlled or **not** genetically controlled.

Characteristic
Eye colour
How to ride a bike

   (d) Complete this sentence: The function of red blood cells is to ...

      Fight infection   Clot blood   Carry oxygen.

 Log on to www.edcolearning.ie for Additional Assessment Questions

PowerPoint summary   **Weblinks**

THE ORIGINS OF LIVING THINGS

LO: BW3

CHAPTER 4

Learning intentions

At the end of this chapter you will be able to:

✓ Outline the process of evolution by natural selection

✓ Explain how evolution leads to the diversity of living things.

Keywords

- biodiversity
- fossils
- extinct
- natural selection
- species
- mutation
- evolution
- struggle for existence
- adaptation

Introduction

Biodiversity means there are many different types of living things.

Humans have often wondered where all these types of life came from. Were they always present on Earth? Will they always be here?

Evidence from **fossils** (which are the remains of very ancient living things) tells us that some types of living things have been wiped out.

Also there are no fossils of some modern living things.

This suggests that some living things disappear (become **extinct**) and new types of living things emerge, i.e. that life on Earth changes.

▲ Figure 4.1 *Fossils*

? Questions

4.1 Name two types of living things that were on Earth but are no longer present (i.e. they are now extinct).

4.2 Name two extinct animal species from Ireland.

4.3 Research how long ago modern humans are thought to have arisen.

Charles Darwin

There are a number of suggestions as to how the variety of living things may have arisen. However, the most widely accepted explanation based on evidence is the **theory of evolution by natural selection**. This theory was first put forward by Charles Darwin (in association with Alfred Russel Wallace) in 1859.

4.4 Write a short biography of Charles Darwin. Include a couple of sentences on each of the following:

- His childhood
- His studies
- The famous ship journey he took
- The islands off South America that he visited
- His health.

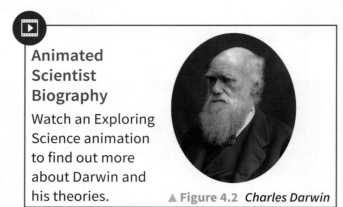

Animated Scientist Biography

Watch an Exploring Science animation to find out more about Darwin and his theories.

▲ Figure 4.2 *Charles Darwin*

Evolution by natural selection

Evolution is the process by which different kinds of living things develop from earlier forms by genetic changes over long periods of time.

Before we examine Darwin's theory of evolution, we need to look at a couple of important terms: **species** and **mutation**.

Species

A species is a group of living things that can reproduce together to produce offspring which themselves can reproduce.

For example, humans are a species; dogs are a species; so are daffodils, cabbages, cats and rabbits.

A cat and a rabbit cannot reproduce together, which is how you know they are different species.

The members of a species have similar genes and so they have many characteristics in common. However, the members of a species may show variations that are inherited because they are caused by changed genes.

4.5 A cocker spaniel and a poodle can breed together to produce a cockapoo (a 'designer' dog). A poodle and a cat cannot breed together. What does this tell you about:

(a) Cocker spaniels and poodles?

(b) Poodles and cats?

4.6 Name two other 'designer' dogs that humans have developed.

Mutation

A mutation is a change in a gene.

We know that the characteristics of an organism are controlled by genes and that genes are passed from parents to their offspring during reproduction.

The genes in the members of a species are different due to mutations and due to events that occur in sexual reproduction.

For example, while humans are similar in having two eyes, they show variations in eye shape and eye colour. These variations are passed on to the next generation because they are inherited, or gene-controlled, variations.

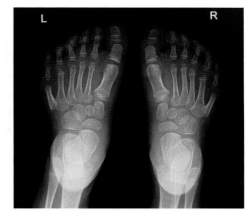

▲ Figure 4.3 *Most humans have five toes: if the gene is altered the person may have extra toes*

Theory of evolution

Darwin's theory of **evolution** is based on three things he noticed (called observations), and from these he made two predictions (called hypotheses; see chapter 1).

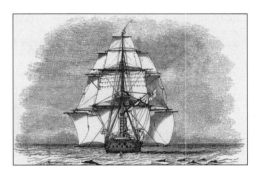

▲ Figure 4.4 *Darwin's ship, HMS* **Beagle**

(i) Information

Darwin's theory of evolution

Observation 1

Living things produce huge numbers of offspring. For example, a tree may produce thousands of seeds, or a fly may lay thousands of eggs.

Observation 2

The environment (or surroundings) can support only a limited number of living things. For example, there is not enough space for all the seeds to grow or there may not be enough food for all the flies to live.

Observations 1 and 2 lead to hypothesis 1 below.

Hypothesis 1

If more living things are produced than can survive, they will struggle to get scarce resources. Darwin called this the **struggle for existence**. It is now often called competition for scarce resources.

For example, seeds may struggle to get enough space and light to grow; the flies may struggle for food and water.

▲ Figure 4.5 *A dandelion with many seeds*

Observation 3

Darwin studied animals such as pet pigeons and cows on farms. Also, on his voyage around the world he noticed that species showed inherited variations. He realised that species could have differences that they would pass on to their offspring.

Observation 3 leads to hypothesis 2 below.

▲ Figure 4.6 *Variations in pet pigeons*

Hypothesis 2

Suitable variations

Darwin realised that some of the variations would help the living thing to survive better. For example, if some seeds produced longer or bigger roots, those seeds would grow better; if some flies developed wings more quickly, they could fly away to get more food.

An adaptation is a characteristic that helps an organism to survive and reproduce.

Living things that are best suited, or adapted, to their environment survive more easily. If they survive, they have a better chance of reproducing and so passing on their genes (and their suitable variations) to the following generations.

Unsuitable variations

However, some variations do not help living things to survive better. These living things are not adapted to their environment and so may die. This means they do not pass their genes (and unsuited variations) on to the next generations.

Natural selection is the way in which organisms whose variations are suited to their environment survive and reproduce.

Nature selects those organisms that are best suited (or adapted) to their environment.

Table 4.1 **Summary of the theory of evolution by natural selection**

Observation	Hypothesis
1 Living things produce large numbers of offspring	A Living things struggle to survive
2 The environment can support only a limited number of living things	
3 The members of a species have inherited (genetic) variations	B Nature selects the organisms with variations that help them to live in the environment
	These organisms survive and reproduce to pass on their genes and their variations

⑦ Question

4.7 **Find out three major adaptations that have allowed humans to survive in their environment.**

4.8 Read about the changes in peppered moths and then answer the questions that follow.

Before the Industrial Revolution (which began around 1760) most of the peppered moths in the north of England were light coloured. This meant they were hard to see on the light-coloured bark of the trees that were covered in lichen (a fungus combined with an algae).

During the Industrial Revolution, for the first time a huge amount of pollution was emitted. This killed off most of the lichens. The bark of the bare trees was now dark coloured. By the 1860s most of the moths were dark coloured.

After more recent pollution control measures were put in place, the lichens grew back on the bark of the trees.

In summary:

Timescale	Moth colour
Before 1760	Light
1760 to 1860	Some light, some dark
After 1860	Mostly dark
Now	?

▲ Figure 4.7 *The light-coloured moth is hard to see on the lichen-covered tree*

▲ Figure 4.8 *The light-coloured moth is very visible on the tree with no lichens*

4.9 Answer the following questions based on the information above.

(a) What was the evolutionary change that took place in the moths between 1760 and 1860?

(b) What was the cause of this change?

(c) What might have happened to any light-coloured moths in the late 1800s?

(d) Predict the colour of the moths in recent years. Give a reason for your answer.

(e) Explain how the changes in the moths provide evidence for the theory of evolution by natural selection.

Evolution and the diversity of life

Evolution by natural selection has given rise to all of the different types of living things on Earth today.

This happens when a single species evolves to form two (or more) different species. These two species then evolve to form even more species. In time, huge numbers of species may develop from the original species.

Did you know?

Galápago is the Spanish word for tortoise.

New species

As an example of how new species form, consider the finches on the Galápagos Islands. Darwin studied these birds on his voyage on HMS *Beagle*. He noticed that the finches on the different islands were similar in many ways, but they showed differences in many features, especially their beak shapes.

Ground finch
(feeds on
hard seeds)

Warbler finch
(feeds on
insects)

Cactus finch
(feeds on
cactus seeds)

▲ **Figure 4.9** *Finches*

Darwin concluded that the original finches must have got to the islands from the mainland of South America. On each island the conditions were different. This meant that:

● Where hard seeds were available, those birds with a short, strong beak were better suited to feeding

● If there were many insects, birds with a sharper and more slender beak were better suited to feeding

● On an island with many cactus plants, finches with a long, pointed beak were better suited to getting cactus seeds.

On each island those finches that had a beak that was not well suited to feeding on that island got less food. As a result, they died out. Those birds with a beak that was most suited to getting the available food survived. When these birds reproduced they passed on their beak shape to the next generation.

Darwin concluded that from a single species of finch that flew (or was blown) in from the mainland, many different types of finch evolved. The new beak shapes arose when genes became altered, or mutated.

This type of process has happened all over the world to different living things over very long periods of time to produce the wide range of species or biodiversity found on Earth today.

? Questions

4.10 Research the following:

(a) What country is nearest to the Galápagos islands?

(b) How far is this country from the Galápagos islands?

(c) Suggest why the finches did not evolve into as many species in their country of origin.

4.11 Read this information on the evolution of Galápagos tortoises and then answer the questions that follow.

On one of the Galápagos Islands Darwin noticed that most of the giant tortoises had shells with low neck collars. However, he noticed a few tortoises on drier land with less plants, had higher neck collars. All the tortoises feed on plants.

Darwin predicted that in the future (possibly as a result of a long period with no rain) the tortoises with high neck collars would survive better. Over the last hundred or more years the tortoises with low neck collars have become extinct on that island, but many of those with high neck collars have survived.

(a) How would a lack of rain affect the number of plants on the island?

(b) What advantage might a high neck collar provide for a tortoise in drier conditions?

(c) Apply your knowledge of the theory of evolution to explain why tortoises with high neck collars survived and those with low neck collars died out.

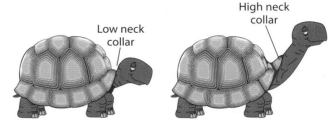

▲ Figure 4.10 *Two tortoises*

4.12 'Living things that do not reproduce are an evolutionary dead end.' Explain why this is the case.

4.13 David and Amanda wanted their future children to be big and strong. So they went to the gym every day for a year and developed really big, strong muscles so that their children would inherit big, strong muscles.

Discuss this with your partner. Do you think their children would have big, strong muscles as a result of their parents' working out in the gym? Explain your answer.

Timeline for biodiversity

The planet Earth formed about 4.6 billion years ago. The first forms of life on Earth appeared about 3.8 billion years ago. They were tiny, single-celled bacteria that lived in the sea. For about 90% of Earth's history, living things were found only in the sea or in watery environments.

About 500 million years ago the first plants and fungi grew on land. It is only since then that all the modern life forms have developed.

For example, dinosaurs first appeared about 220 million years ago, birds 140 million years ago, and humans only 200 000 years ago. The examples given show that evolution normally takes place over long periods of time.

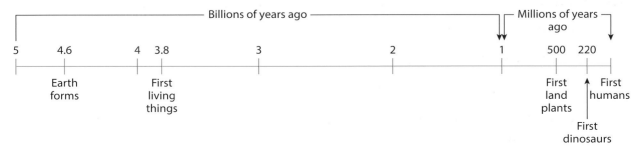

▲ Figure 4.11 *A simple timeline for evolution*

Summary questions

● 4.14 Write out the following passage and insert the correct words from the list below in the correct spaces.

| extinct | bacteria | biodiversity | species | fossils |

The range of different organisms on Earth is called _____. Those living things that can successfully reproduce together are called a _____. Some types of living things no longer survive on Earth; they are said to be _____. The remains of those once-living things are called _____. The oldest forms of life are thought to be _____.

 4.15 Write out the following passage but only use one word from each of the bracketed lists of words.

Darwin proposed a theory of evolution by (accidental / natural / sexual) selection. He proposed that all modern living things have evolved from (complex / simple / asexual) forms of life. It is now believed that the first living things were formed about (four thousand / four million / four billion) years ago. Darwin's theory says that living things that are best (mutated / coloured / adapted) to their surroundings would live (longer / forever / briefly) and reproduce to pass on their (energy / abilities / genes) to the next generation.

📝 Log on to **www.edcolearning.ie** for **Additional Summary Questions**

Assessment questions

4.16 In the 1800s a famous British scientist went around the world on the voyage of the *Beagle*. On the Galápagos Islands he found many species of birds called finches. He suggested that the different species of finches had evolved from a single type of finch that had arrived on the islands years earlier.

(15 marks)

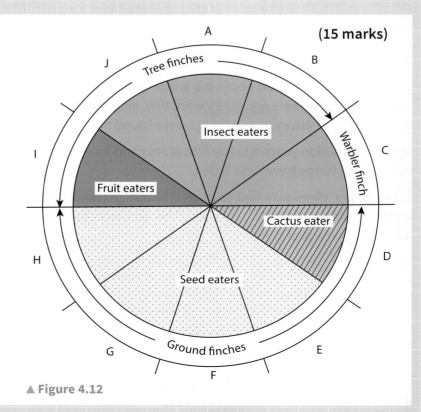

▲ Figure 4.12

(a) Name the scientist who first proposed the theory of evolution.

(b) He proposed that evolution had occurred by a process called natural _____.

(c) Figure 4.12 shows some information about the different types of finches which are labelled A to J.

Answer the following questions based on this diagram.

  (i) How many species of finch are represented on the diagram?

 (ii) How many species of finch eat plant material?

(iii) How many types of ground finch are shown?

(iv) Which type of finch might be best adapted to very dry conditions?

 (v) Give two pieces of information about finch type I.

4.17 Humans need vitamin D to help them absorb calcium. Vitamin D can be made in the skin if it is exposed to ultraviolet radiation, which is found in sunlight. **(15 marks)**

Human skin can also make melanin, which is a brown/black pigment. Melanin helps protect the skin against the harmful effects of ultraviolet radiation. The main harmful effect is that this radiation causes mutations in the skin, which may lead to cancer.

In people living in countries near the equator the skin contains large amounts of melanin, resulting in a dark skin colour. Over thousands of years humans have moved farther away from the equator. This has resulted in a lower production of melanin, which causes a lighter skin colour.

(a) Name a vitamin produced by the skin in humans.

(b) What is the function of the vitamin named above?

(c) What is the advantage of melanin?

(d) Suggest a disadvantage of too much melanin for a person living far from the equator.

(e) Suggest a disadvantage of too little melanin for a person living near the equator.

PowerPoint summary   Weblinks

CHAPTER 5

THE PATH OF FOOD

LO: BW4

Learning intentions

At the end of this chapter you will be able to:

✓ Describe the structure of the organs of the digestive system

✓ Describe the functions of the organs of the digestive system

✓ Describe the interaction of the digestive and circulatory systems.

Keywords

- digestion
- enzyme
- catalyst
- amylase
- maltose
- oesophagus
- peristalsis
- fibre
- stomach
- organ
- small intestine
- liver
- bile
- pancreas
- large intestine
- faeces
- egestion

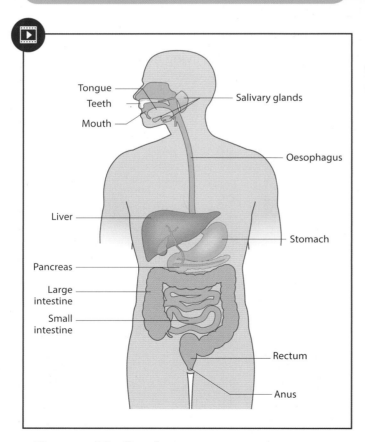

▲ Figure 5.1 *The digestive system*

Introduction

The main steps in getting and using food are:

1. **Ingestion:** taking in food

2. **Digestion:** breaking down food

3. **Absorption:** taking digested food from our intestines into our blood

4. **Assimilation:** using the food in the cells of the body

5. **Egestion:** discharge of undigested waste.

The alimentary canal is a tube that runs from the mouth to the anus. Food is one of our most basic needs.

We need food for three main reasons:

● To give us energy   ● To provide the raw materials for growth   ● To allow us to repair the body.

Our digestive system (which consists of the alimentary canal and some other glands) allows us to convert food into a form that the body can use easily. Our digestive system breaks our food into smaller molecules. These molecules can then pass from our intestines into our blood.

The blood carries the food molecules to all parts of the body. Any food that does not pass into our blood is removed (or egested) from our bodies as waste called faeces.

> **? Questions**
>
> Most humans are between 1.5 and 2 metres tall. Our digestive system is up to 9 metres long.
>
> **5.1** How, do you think, can such a long tube fit into a person's body?
>
> **5.2** What problem might this arrangement cause for the movement of food through our digestive system?

The functions of the parts of the digestive system

Mouth

The function of the mouth is to take in and digest food. Two types of **digestion** take place in the mouth:

● **Physical digestion**

● **Chemical digestion.**

What is physical digestion?

Physical digestion is the breakdown of food using mechanical or physical methods.

An example of this occurs in the mouth when the teeth cut and chew food into smaller pieces. The smaller pieces of food have a larger surface area and can be more easily broken down later in the rest of the digestive system.

Teeth

There are four types of teeth in the adult human jaw. The sequence of the teeth from the front to the back of the jaw is shown in Figure 5.2 and given in Table 5.1.

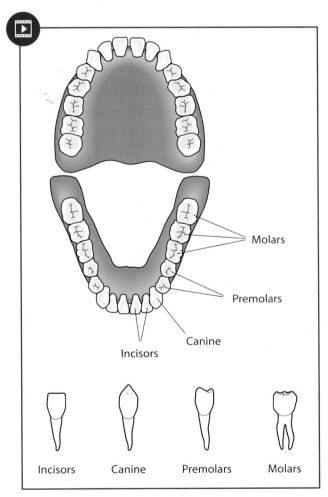

Molars

Premolars

Canine

Incisors

Incisors   Canine   Premolars   Molars

▲ Figure 5.2 *The location and types of teeth in the human jaw*

Table 5.1 Teeth in an adult human jaw

Teeth — from the front to the back of the jaw	Appearance and function
Incisors	Sharp edges, like a chisel Used to cut, slice and nibble food
Canines	Long and pointed Used to grip and tear food
Premolars	Large with flat surfaces Used for chewing, crushing and grinding food
Molars	Larger than premolars Used for chewing, crushing and grinding food

? Questions

5.3 We are advised to chew food many times before swallowing it.

(a) Why might this be important?

(b) What problems might arise for a person who does not chew food thoroughly?

5.4 If a person loses most of their premolar and molar teeth, what problem would they have?

5.5 Some animals have large incisors and others have large canine teeth. Name one animal in each case and find out why they have such teeth.

What is chemical digestion?

Chemical digestion is the breakdown of food using enzymes (or hydrochloric acid in the stomach). We will examine different kinds of food in chapter 9.

An enzyme is a chemical (made of protein) produced by the body that speeds up chemical reactions in the body without the enzyme being used up.

Scientists give the name **catalyst** to substances that speed up reactions. Enzymes are called biological catalysts.

Salivary glands are located in the cheeks and under the tongue. They produce liquid called saliva. Saliva helps to soften and moisten food.

Saliva also contains an enzyme called (salivary) **amylase**.

Amylase breaks down starch and turns it into a simple sugar called **maltose**.

$$starch \xrightarrow{amylase} maltose$$

Our digestive system produces many enzymes, each one breaking down a different type of food. Just as amylase breaks down starch, another enzyme then breaks down maltose into an even simpler sugar (called glucose).

? Question

5.6 Why do we need to soften and moisten food before we swallow it?

▶ Activity video

Did you know?

Many washing powders and detergents contain enzymes to break down food stains in a short space of time and at a very low temperature.

Oesophagus

The oesophagus, or food pipe, is a muscular tube. It forces food down from the mouth to the stomach using a wave of muscular action (called **peristalsis**). Peristalsis also pushes food through the rest of our intestines.

This muscular action is stimulated by **fibre** (also called roughage) in our diet. Fibre is material that is not broken down or digested by enzymes in our digestive system. Good examples of fibre include: fruit, vegetables, cereal grains, brown bread, muesli and porridge.

> ### ⑦ Questions
>
> **5.7** We are told we should eat between five and seven portions of fruit and vegetable every day. Find out:
>
> **(a)** How big a portion should be
>
> **(b)** What the benefits are of eating so many fruits and vegetables
>
> **5.8** If a person standing on their head eats food, the food has to travel upwards. Find out:
>
> **(a)** What force the food is going against
>
> **(b)** How the person can still swallow food.
>
> **5.9** Astronauts in space experience low (or micro) gravity conditions. Can food pass through their digestive systems in the normal way? Explain your answer.

Stomach

The stomach is a muscular bag that holds food for a few hours. Hydrochloric acid in the stomach kills bacteria and also softens food. The stomach produces enzymes that chemically digest food. The stomach also churns and physically digests and mixes the food.

The stomach is an **organ**. An organ is a structure in a living thing that carries out a particular function (or functions).

> ### ⑦ Question
>
> **5.10** Food stays in our stomachs for up to 4 hours. If food passes too quickly through the stomach a person may get many intestinal infections. Why might this happen?

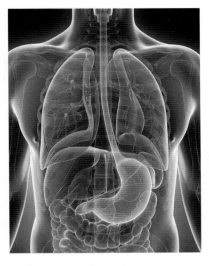

▲ Figure 5.3 *The stomach*

Small intestine

The small intestine is a long tube (about 6 metres) but it has a narrow diameter (about 2.5 centimetres). It has two functions:

- Digestion
- Absorption.

The small intestine produces many enzymes that complete the breakdown of food. Most digestion takes place in the part of the small intestine just below the stomach.

In the rest of the small intestine the food is absorbed from the intestine into the bloodstream. Digested food is then transported all over the body by the blood.

Two organs, the liver and the pancreas, help to digest food. They pass their products into the small intestine.

Liver

The liver is a complex organ that carries out a range of functions. One of its many functions is to produce a liquid called **bile**.

Bile passes from the liver into the small intestine. Bile helps to digest fat in the small intestine.

The liver is the largest organ inside the body.

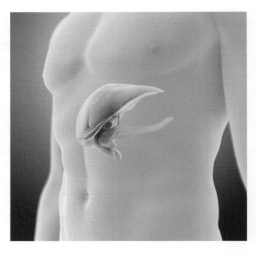

▲ Figure 5.4   *The liver (with the pancreas below it)*

> **? Question**
>
> **5.11** People who have pain and discomfort after eating fried or fat-rich food are often suspected of having a liver problem. Explain why this might be suspected.

Pancreas

The pancreas produces many digestive enzymes. These enzymes pass from the pancreas into the small intestine, where they help to digest food.

The salivary glands, the liver and the pancreas are glands attached to the digestive system. They are called associated glands.

Large intestine

The large intestine is about 1.5 metres long. It is about twice the diameter of the small intestine.

The material entering the large intestine contains a lot of liquid along with unabsorbed waste material. The large intestine takes water back into the bloodstream (reabsorbs water). The semi-solid waste material left in the large intestine is called **faeces**.

- If too much water is taken back, the waste becomes too solid, in a condition called constipation.

- If too little water is taken back, the waste becomes liquid and we suffer from diarrhoea.

Faeces are stored in the rectum and pass out of the intestine through the anus. The loss of unabsorbed material is called **egestion**.

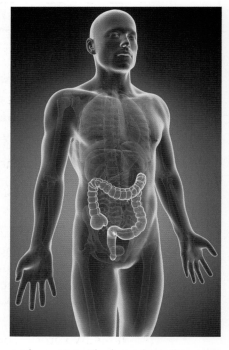

▲ Figure 5.5   *The large intestine*

> **? Questions**
>
> **5.12** Research fibre in the diet:
>
>   **(a)** Find out why a low-fibre diet might cause us to feel bloated and full.
>
>   **(b)** High-fibre diets are thought to reduce the risk of bowel cancer (cancer of the large intestine). Find out why this might be the case.
>
> **5.13** Why might children with diarrhoea often suffer from dehydration?

Summary questions

● 5.14 Copy out the table below and use the structures listed below to complete the table.

liver   oesophagus   large intestine   stomach

mouth   pancreas   small intestine   salivary glands

Structure	Function
	Ingests food Physical digestion (by teeth) Chemical digestion (by amylase)
	Pushes food from mouth to stomach (by peristalsis)
	Physical digestion (churns food) Chemical digestion (enzymes) Kills bacteria and softens food (hydrochloric acid)
	Chemical digestion (enzymes) Absorption (into the bloodstream)
	Reabsorbs water (into the blood) Stores waste faeces (in the rectum) Egests (passes out) faeces (through the anus)
	Make saliva (which has the enzyme amylase)
	Makes bile (which breaks down fats)
	Makes enzymes (to digest food)

● 5.15 **(a)** The following processes are involved in getting and using food. Rewrite the five processes in the correct order.

digestion   ingestion   absorption   egestion   assimilation

(b) What is meant by the term 'digestion'?

(c) Why must we digest our food?

(d) What is the difference between physical and chemical digestion?

(e) Are the teeth used for physical or chemical digestion?

● 5.16 **(a)** Name the type of tooth labelled X on Figure 5.6.

(b) Which of the following best describes the function of this type of tooth: gripping food, chewing food or biting food?

(c) Name two other types of tooth.

(d) Why do we need teeth?

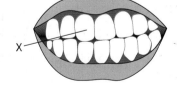

▲ **Figure 5.6** *Human teeth*

● 5.17 **(a)** Name an enzyme and say what it acts on and what it produces.

(b) Name two places in the body where we produce digestive enzymes.

(c) Name two parts of the alimentary canal where digestive enzymes work.

5.18 **(a)** Name the part of the digestive system labelled A on Figure 5.7.

(b) What is the benefit of peristalsis?

(c) Name two foods that stimulate peristalsis.

(d) What problem results from peristalsis not working properly?

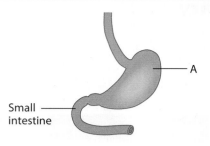

▲ **Figure 5.7** *Part of human digestive system*

Assessment questions

5.19 The passage below describes how we process food. Rewrite this passage and include the nine words below in the correct places in the passage. **(15 marks)**

faeces	absorb	ingest	rectum	stomach
peristalsis	digest	transported	egested	

When we _____ food we must chew it well to _____ it fully. We then force it through our digestive system by a process called _____. Hydrochloric acid in the _____ kills any bacteria in the food. Having digested the food we then _____ it in our small intestine. The digested food is then _____ around our body by the blood. Undigested waste, called _____, is stored in the _____ before it is _____ through the anus.

5.20 Fizzy drinks often contain high concentrations of glucose. Glucose is used by cells to give us energy. **(30 marks)**

(a) Name all the body parts that a molecule of glucose must pass through from when we drink it to when it arrives in a muscle cell in our leg.

(b) Name the two body systems involved in the passage of the glucose from the bottle to our muscle.

(c) Name the part of the body where the glucose passes from the first to the second body system.

(d) You are asked to make two sucrose solutions: one is a dilute solution and the second is a concentrated solution.

(i) What equipment will you need?

(ii) Describe how you will make the dilute glucose solution.

(iii) Compared to making the dilute glucose solution, what will you do differently when making the concentrated glucose solution?

Log on to **www.edcolearning.ie** for Additional Assessment Questions

PowerPoint summary   Weblinks

TRANSPORT IN THE BODY

CHAPTER 6

LO: BW4

Learning intentions

At the end of this chapter you will be able to:

✓ Describe the functions of the parts of blood

✓ Describe the structure and functions of the blood vessels

✓ Describe the structure and functions of the heart

✓ Describe the path of blood around the body

✓ Describe the interaction of the circulatory system with the digestive and respiratory systems.

Keywords

- plasma
- capillaries
- haemoglobin
- cardiac
- antibodies
- pulse
- platelets
- atria
- arteries
- ventricles
- veins
- pulmonary

How do materials pass around our body?

The human body needs a transport system to move materials from one place to another.

For example, food, oxygen and waste products have to be moved to and from all the cells in our body.

Our circulatory or transport system is made up of:

- Blood
- A system of tubes or blood vessels
- The heart, which is needed to pump blood through blood vessels.

What is in our blood?

Blood is made up of four parts, or components:

- Plasma
- White blood cells
- Red blood cells
- Platelets.

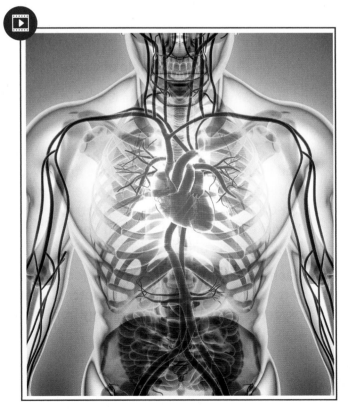

▲ Figure 6.1 *The circulatory system*

Plasma

Plasma is the liquid part of blood. It is a pale yellow colour and is mostly made of water.

Plasma transports many dissolved chemicals around the body. These chemicals may be:

- Useful materials, such as foods and water
- Wastes, such as carbon dioxide and salts.

Plasma also transports heat from one part of the body to another. Heat is produced by chemical reactions in all our body cells. By transporting heat, our blood plays an important role in maintaining our body temperature at 37°C.

Plasma also carries:

- Red blood cells
- White blood cells
- Platelets.

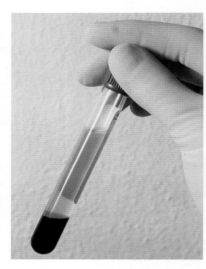

▲ Figure 6.2 *A blood sample separated into yellow plasma and red blood cells*

How plasma affects body temperature

When we are too hot, blood vessels in our skin expand (dilate). This means extra blood (plasma) is sent to our skin (especially to the face, causing it to go red). This allows more heat to pass out of our body and we cool down.

This can happen when we are ill. In this case our body temperature may rise (we have a fever). The high temperature helps to destroy the bacteria and viruses that are causing us to be ill.

When we are too cold, blood vessels in our skin become smaller. Blood also moves from our extremities to our core. This means we lose less heat from our body.

> **? Questions**
>
> 6.1 Apart from blood plasma there is another type of plasma.
>
> (a) What is the second type of plasma? (Hint: see States of matter in chapter 13.)
>
> (b) Give an example of where it may be found.
>
> 6.2 Since blood plasma is pale yellow, why is our blood red?

Red blood cells

Red blood cells are made in bone marrow located in the centre of bones. Red blood cells contain a red-coloured chemical (or pigment) called **haemoglobin**. To make haemoglobin we need iron. Our blood contains huge numbers of red blood cells.

Haemoglobin, and therefore red blood cells, carries oxygen. We will see in chapter 10 that oxygen is needed to release energy from food.

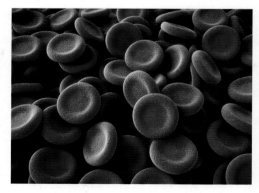

▲ Figure 6.3 *Red blood cells*

The path of oxygen

Oxygen enters our red blood cells in the lungs. It attaches to haemoglobin in the red blood cells. When blood reaches cells in other parts of our body (such as our muscles or the brain), haemoglobin releases the oxygen into these cells.

White blood cells

White blood cells are also made in bone marrow. White blood cells fight infection:

- Some white blood cells surround micro-organisms (such as bacteria and viruses) and destroy them

- Other white blood cells form proteins called **antibodies**. Antibodies help to destroy micro-organisms that have entered the body. Antibodies are very important in fighting infection.

? Question

6.3 Find out the answers to these questions on iron.

(a) Name any food in our diet that we need to eat in order to get iron.

(b) What is anaemia?

(c) How can you tell if someone is anaemic?

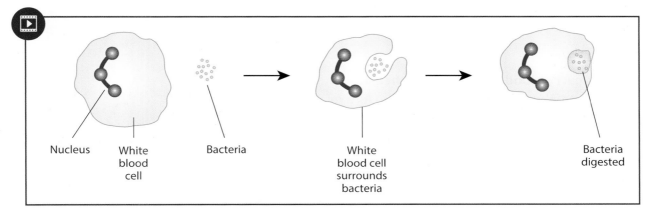

Nucleus White blood cell Bacteria White blood cell surrounds bacteria Bacteria digested

▲ Figure 6.4 *White blood cell destroying bacteria*

? Question

6.4 Since blood contains white blood cells, why is blood red and not white?

Platelets

Platelets are formed in bone marrow when large cells break down into smaller pieces. Platelets help to form blood clots. In this way they help to prevent:

- Loss of blood
- Micro-organisms entering the body.

? Question

6.5 Work in groups to find out what problems each of the following would cause. Each member of the group should report on at least one of these problems to the class group.

(a) A lack (or shortage) of iron

(b) A lack of red blood cells

(c) A lack of white blood cells

(d) A lack of platelets

(e) A lack of blood.

Why do we need blood?

We need blood for a number of reasons. Each of the four parts of blood has its own role (or function) as shown in Table 6.1.

Table 6.1 **What blood does**

Part of blood	Function
Plasma	Transports materials such as foods and wastes Transports heat around the body
Red blood cells	Transport oxygen
White blood cells	Fight infection
Platelets	Clot the blood

What are blood vessels?

There are three main types of blood vessel:

- Arteries
- Veins
- Capillaries

Arteries

Arteries carry blood away from the heart.
(Remember 'a' is for **a**rtery and for **a**way.) As a result of carrying blood away from the heart, there is a strong flow of blood in arteries. We say that the blood in arteries is under high pressure.

Veins

Veins carry blood to the heart. The blood flow, or pressure, in a vein is lower than in an artery.

Capillaries

Capillaries are tiny blood vessels. They are found between arteries and veins. There is a huge number of capillaries in the human body.

The walls of a capillary are very thin. They allow materials to pass into and out of the capillaries.

For example, in our intestines food passes into blood capillaries. This food is carried by the bloodstream to all the cells of the body. The food later passes out of the capillaries to enter the body cells.

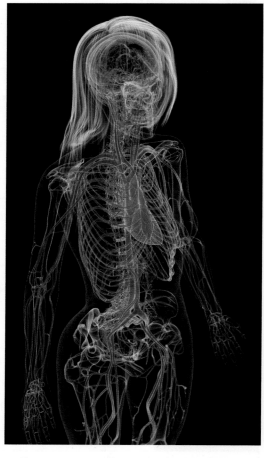

▲ **Figure 6.5** *Arteries and veins in a female*

> **?** **Question**
>
> **6.6** Apply your knowledge of arteries and veins to identify:
>
> **(a) Which of the two needs the thicker, stronger wall**
>
> **(b) Which of the two needs valves to prevent blood flowing backwards.**

The heart

The heart is about the size of a clenched fist. It is located between the middle and the left-hand side of the chest.

The heart is made of a special type of muscle called **cardiac** muscle. Cardiac muscle is very strong and does not tire easily. 'Cardiac' means anything related to the heart.

The heart contracts in order to pump blood around our body in blood vessels. The force of this blood in an artery causes a **pulse**.

When we are resting, the average rate of an adult heartbeat is 70 beats per minute. When we exercise, the heart beats faster. This causes blood and the materials it carries to move faster around our body.

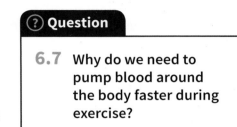

? Question

6.7 Why do we need to pump blood around the body faster during exercise?

Structure of the heart

Parts of the heart

Chambers: The heart contains four chambers. The top two are the right atrium and the left atrium (plural **atria**) and the bottom two are the right and left **ventricles**.

Septum: The two sides of the heart are separated by a muscular wall called the septum.

Heart valves: Valves in the heart make sure that blood can flow only in one direction. In this way, they are similar to valves in a car tyre or football (which let air pass in, but not out).

How blood flows through the heart

- Blood from the arms, legs and other parts of the body enters the right atrium of the heart through the vena cava. This blood is low in oxygen.

- The right atrium contracts to pump the blood down through a valve into the right ventricle.

- When the right ventricle contracts, the valve shuts to prevent the blood from going back into the right atrium. As a result, blood is pumped out of the heart in the **pulmonary artery** to the lungs.

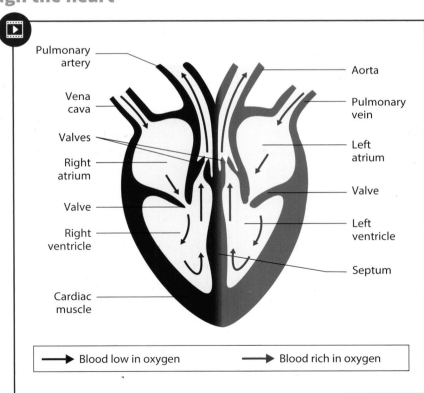

▲ Figure 6.6 **Structure and blood flow of the heart**

- In the lungs, the blood gains oxygen (and also loses carbon dioxide and water vapour).

- Blood from the lungs flows back into the left atrium of the heart through the **pulmonary vein**. This blood is now rich in oxygen.
- The left atrium contracts to pump the blood through a valve and into the left ventricle.
- The left ventricle contracts, the valve snaps shut and blood is forced out of the heart through the aorta. It then passes all around the body.
- Eventually this blood will lose oxygen to the body cells. It will return to the heart in the right atrium. The cycle then starts all over again.

The ventricles of the heart

- The right ventricle pumps blood from the heart to the lungs. This is a reasonably short distance, and so the muscular walls of the right ventricle are fairly thin.
- The left ventricle pumps blood from the heart all around the body. This is a very long distance, and so the muscular walls of the left ventricle are very thick.

Pulmonary artery and vein

- Most of the arteries in the body carry oxygen-rich blood. However, the pulmonary artery is an exception to this rule as it carries blood low in oxygen.
- Most of the veins in the body carry blood low in oxygen. However, the pulmonary vein is an exception to this rule as it carries oxygen-rich blood.

The two blood circuits

The circulatory system consists of two circuits:

- In the **lung circuit**, blood flows from the heart to the lungs and back to the heart
- In the longer **body circuit**, blood flows from the heart to the rest of the body and back to the heart again.

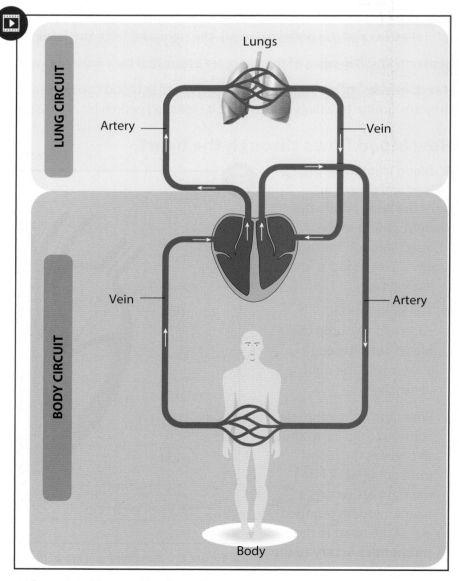

▲ Figure 6.7 *The two blood circuits*

What is a pulse?

When blood is pumped through the arteries, the pressure causes the arteries to expand. **This wave of pressure is called a pulse.**

A pulse can be felt in areas of the body where the arteries are close to the surface, for example at the wrist and in the neck. The pulse rate is used to measure the rate of heartbeat.

How exercise affects pulse rate

When we exercise, the cells in the body (especially in the muscles) need increased supplies of food and oxygen. In addition, the cells need to get rid of extra amounts of carbon dioxide and heat.

As a result, exercise causes the heart to beat faster and our pulse rate increases.

⁇ Questions

6.8   Why are the walls of the atria thinner (and weaker) than the walls of the ventricles?

6.9   Many people suffer from problems caused by damage to the valves in their heart. In terms of blood flow, what problems might they have?

6.10   Compare blood in the pulmonary artery and in the pulmonary vein in terms of:

   (a) Pressure

   (b) Oxygen and carbon dioxide content.

6.11   Why do most arteries contain oxygen-rich blood?

6.12   Why does blood in the pulmonary vein have lower pressure than the blood in the pulmonary artery?

✎ Activity 6.1   What is our resting heart rate?

🧪 **Equipment needed**

   A stopwatch or timer

➡ **Conducting the activity**

1. While you are resting, use the first finger and middle finger to locate your pulse in your wrist or neck. The pulse rate is a measure of the heart rate.

2. Count the number of pulses for one minute. (This is recorded as beats per minute – BPM.)

3. Repeat this three times.

4. Add the three values together and divide by 3 to get the average resting pulse rate. Getting an average rate is more reliable than taking a single reading.

5. Record your pulse rates in the copy of the table below that is in your Activity Book.

Number of pulses per minute at rest (BPM)	Total number of pulses in 3 minutes at rest (BPM)	Average pulse rate per minute at rest (BPM)

Activity 6.2 What is the effect of exercise on heart rate?

The plan is to record the heart rate at rest and then record the heart rate after exercise. This is done by counting the pulse rates at rest and after exercise.

Equipment needed

A stopwatch or timer

Safety	• The exercise should be carried out in a safe environment (i.e. where the person exercising cannot trip or come to harm). • The type of exercise should be controlled so that it is safe. • The person being tested should be in good general health.

➡ Conducting the activity

1. Record your resting pulse (or heart) rate as in activity 6.1. If you prefer, you can use the information (data) you collected in activity 6.1.

2. Provided you are fit and healthy, exercise strongly for 2 minutes (e.g. step up and down on a step or run on the spot).

3. Immediately after exercising count the number of pulses per minute.

4. Continue to record the number of pulses per minute until the rate returns to the average resting rate.

5. Record how long it takes for the pulse rate to return to normal after exercise.

6. Record your results in the copy of the table below that is in your Student Activity Book.

Number of pulses per minute at rest (BPM)	Total number of pulses in 3 minutes at rest (BPM)	Average pulse rate per minute at rest (BPM)	Pulse rates per minute after exercise (BPM)

What pathway around the body does the blood take?

Figure 6.8 is a model of the system that is used to circulate blood around the body.

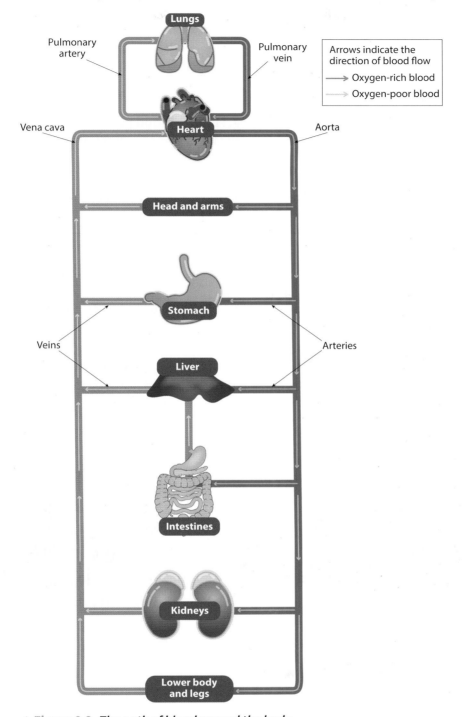

▲ Figure 6.8 *The path of blood around the body*

What happens to blood in different parts of the body?

Table 6.2 **What happens to blood in different parts of the body**

Organ	Blood gains	Blood loses
Lungs	Oxygen	Carbon dioxide and water
Intestines	Food, water and carbon dioxide	Oxygen
Head/arms	Carbon dioxide and water	Oxygen and food
Lower body/legs	Carbon dioxide and water	Oxygen and food

? Questions

6.13 Describe the changes in the blood that take place in:

   (a) The intestines   **(b)** The lungs.

6.14 Name the blood vessel that takes blood:

   (a) From the heart to the lungs   **(b)** From the arms and legs to the heart.

6.15 Blood pressure is measured in mm Hg. Human blood pressure is given as 120 mm Hg. The blood pressure in a giraffe is given as 300 mm Hg.

   (a) Why is the blood pressure of a giraffe so high?

   (b) Do you suspect that a giraffe has a large or a small heart? Explain your answer.

Summary questions

6.16 Write out the following passage and insert the words below to complete the passage.

   glucose   oxygen   vein   vena cava   heart   pulmonary

Blood flows from the heart to the lungs in the _____ artery. In the lungs the blood gains _____ and loses carbon dioxide. Blood flows back to the heart in the pulmonary _____.

Blood is then pumped from the _____ through the aorta. Some of this blood passes through the intestines, where it gains food such as _____. Blood from the intestines passes through the liver and flows into the _____. This vessel takes blood back to the heart.

6.17 **(a)** Name the four parts of blood.

   (b) Which part of our blood is a liquid?

   (c) Name the part of blood that is responsible for each of the following:

     (i) Fighting infection   **(iv)** Carrying heat

     (ii) Transporting glucose   **(v)** Making antibodies

    (iii) Preventing blood loss   **(vi)** Supplying oxygen to our cells.

6.18 **(a)** Copy out (or trace) the diagram of the heart shown in Figure 6.9.

    (i) Use blue arrows to show the path of low-oxygen blood.

    (ii) Use red arrows to show the path of high-oxygen blood.

   (iii) Use a pencil to label the four chambers of the heart.

   (b) Name the blood vessels labelled A and B.

   (c) Babies born with a hole in their heart often have a hole in structure C. What problem might these babies have as a result?

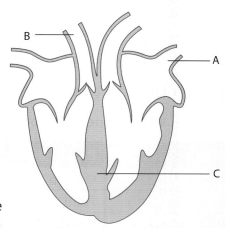

▲ Figure 6.9 *Diagram of the heart*

Assessment question

6.19 (45 marks)

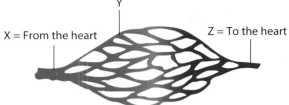

▲ Figure 6.10 *Blood vessels*

(a) Name the three types of blood vessel labelled X, Y and Z in Figure 6.10.

(b) The blood pressure in vessel X is higher than in vessel Z. Explain why this is so.

(c) Which type of blood vessel allows materials to pass in and out?

(d) Arteries tend to lose more blood when cut than veins do. Suggest a reason for this.

(e) Why can we not detect a pulse in a vein?

(f) Our pulse rate is often measured in our wrist or neck. Why is it measured in these places?

(g) Maria's pulse rate was measured three times when she was resting. Maria then ran for 5 minutes. After running she sat down and her heart rate was measured every minute until it returned to her resting rate. The results are shown below.

Minute number	1	2	3	4
Resting heart rate (BPM)	70	68	72	–
Heart rate after running (BPM)	96	84	78	70

(i) Calculate Maria's average resting heart rate.

(ii) How long did it take for Maria's heart rate to return to its resting rate after she stopped running?

(iii) Why did Maria's heart rate increase after she ran?

(iv) John's resting heart rate was 80 BPM. What does this suggest about the efficiency of John's heart compared to Maria's?

 Log on to **www.edcolearning.ie** for Additional Summary and Assessment Questions

CHAPTER 7

THE BREATHING SYSTEM

LO: BW4

Learning intentions

At the end of this chapter you will be able to:

✓ Explain why we breathe

✓ Describe the structure and functions of the breathing system

✓ Investigate the carbon dioxide levels of air breathed in and out

✓ Investigate our breathing rate at rest and after exercise.

Keywords

- inhale
- exhale
- respiration
- excretion
- trachea
- bronchus
- bronchiole
- alveolus
- diaphragm

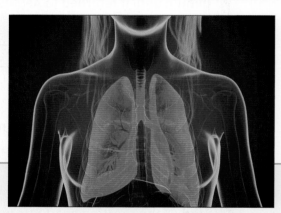

▲ Figure 7.1 *The positions of the lungs*

Why do we breathe?

✎ Activity 7.1

Question

What happens to our chests when we breathe?

➡ **Conducting the activity**

1. Place your hand on your chest.
2. Breathe in (**inhale**) and breathe out (**exhale**) deeply and slowly a few times.
3. What do you feel? Do you notice your hand changing position?
4. When you inhale does your chest get bigger or smaller?
5. When you exhale how does your chest change?

This is what takes place when we breathe:

- When we breathe in, air fills our lungs – this is why in Activity 7.1 your chest was getting bigger when you breathed in and smaller when you breathed out.

- Oxygen from the air passes from our lungs into our bloodstream.

- Red blood cells carry oxygen to all the cells of our body, where it is used to release energy from food. The release of energy from food is called **respiration** (and is explained in chapter 10).

- Carbon dioxide and water vapour are produced by respiration in each body cell. They enter the bloodstream and are carried in the plasma to the lungs.

- Carbon dioxide and water vapour pass from the blood into the lungs and are then breathed out. In this way the breathing system supplies oxygen for respiration and gets rid of the waste products of respiration (i.e. carbon dioxide and water).

Excretion is the getting rid of the waste products of reactions from the body.

Carbon dioxide and water vapour are excreted by the breathing system.

The breathing system is also called the respiratory system.

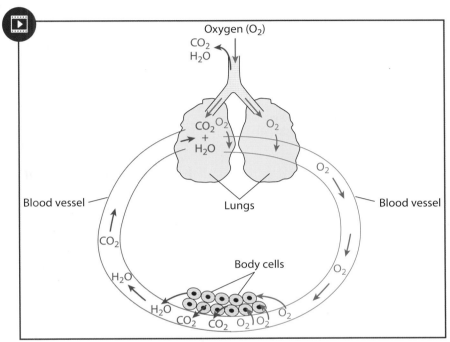

▲ **Figure 7.2** *Gas exchange between the lungs and body cells*

? Questions

7.1 Using figure 6.6 on page 59 if necessary, name the blood vessels that carry blood from:

    (a) The heart to the lungs

    (b) The lungs to the heart

    (c) The heart to the rest of the body

    (d) The body cells to the heart.

7.2 **(a)** Why does our body need oxygen?

    (b) Name two substances excreted by the body.

Did you know?

The left lung is slightly smaller than the right lung (to allow space for the heart).

The breathing system

The breathing system is made up of the following:

- Nose
- Trachea
- Bronchi and bronchioles
- Alveoli
- Diaphragm
- Ribs and intercostal muscles.

What are the functions of the parts of the breathing system?

Nose

We are supposed to inhale through our nose. The reasons for doing this are:

- Hairs and mucus trap dirt particles and bacteria in the nose

- Air is warmed and moistened as it passes through the nose. Warm and moist air helps oxygen to pass from the lungs into the bloodstream more easily.

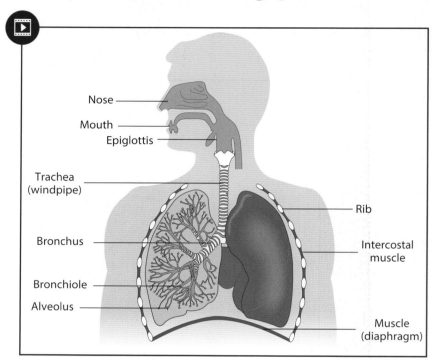

▲ Figure 7.3 *The breathing system*

Trachea

The trachea, or windpipe, carries air to and from the lungs. It is made of C-shaped rings of rigid cartilage (to prevent it from collapsing).

Bronchus and bronchioles

We have two bronchi. **Each bronchus carries air between the trachea and a lung.** The two bronchi subdivide many times to form tiny tubes called **bronchioles**. Bronchioles carry air to and from the air-sacs, or alveoli.

Alveolus

Each lung contains millions of tiny air-sacs called alveoli.
The function of each **alveolus** is gas exchange:

- Oxygen passes from the air in the alveolus into the blood vessels

- At the same time carbon dioxide and water pass from the blood vessels into each alveolus

- The gases pass in each direction by a process called **diffusion**. As an adaptation for diffusion each alveolus has a very thin lining, is moist and is surrounded by many tiny blood vessels called capillaries. For more on diffusion see chapter 13 in Chemical World.

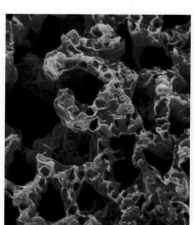

▲ Figure 7.4 *Each of our lungs contains millions of alveoli*

ⓘ Question

7.3 Research diffusion:

(a) What is meant by diffusion? (Hint: see chapter 13.)

(b) Find out if diffusion works better:

   (i) At high or low temperatures

   (ii) Across a dry or a moist surface.

(c) Based on your answers to part (b), how are our alveoli adapted to provide the conditions for diffusion to work best?

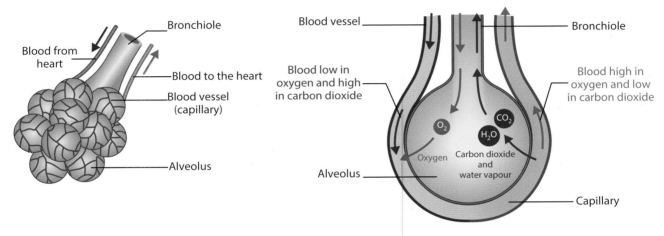

▲ Figure 7.5 *Gas exchange in an alveolus*

Diaphragm

The diaphragm is a sheet of muscle that forms the base of the chest. Along with the ribs and intercostal muscles (located between the ribs) the diaphragm causes air to move into or out of the lungs.

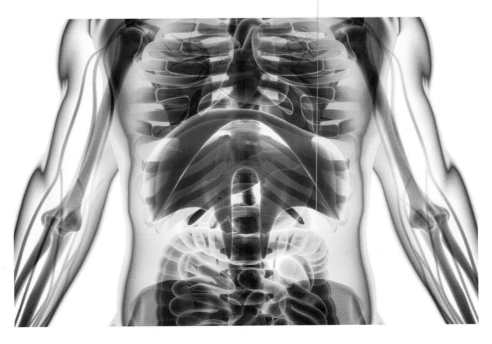

Activity 7.2 Can a model of the chest show how we get air in and out of the lungs?

🧪 **Equipment needed**

Large (2 litre is best) empty soft drink plastic bottle to represent the chest

Balloon to represent the lungs

Rubber bands

Plastic bag to represent the diaphragm

Scissors

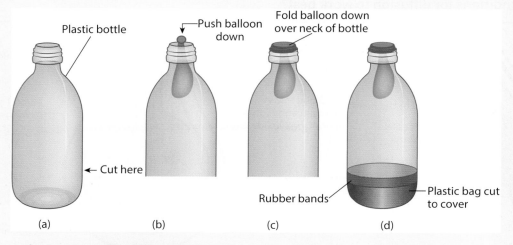

▲ **Figure 7.6** *Model of chest and lungs*

➡ **Conducting the activity**

This can be carried out alone, in pairs or in groups.

1. Cut around the plastic bottle about two-thirds of the way down and discard the bottom part.
2. Push the balloon down through the top or neck of the bottle.
3. Fold the top of the balloon down over the neck of the bottle.
4. Cut the plastic bag so that it covers the base of the bottle with about 4 cm spare all round.
5. Use the elastic bands to hold the plastic over the base of the bottle so that it is flat but loose.
6. Pinch the middle of the plastic cover at the end of the bottle and pull down gently. What happens to the size of the balloon? Does this represent breathing in or out?
7. Push up gently on the middle of the plastic cover. What happens to the size of the balloon? Does this represent inhalation or exhalation?
8. We have two lungs. This model has only one 'lung'. Discuss in a group how you might alter this activity so that you could make a model with two lungs.

❓ **Questions**

7.4 **(a)** Why do we have two bronchi?

(b) Suggest why we have so many alveoli.

(c) State two ways in which the structure of the alveolus is adapted to allow for gas exchange.

7.5 (a) Inhaled air contains lots of dust and disease-causing organisms. Suggest one way that these unwanted materials are prevented from entering the alveoli.

(b) Name the gas that passes from the alveoli into the blood.

(c) What part of the blood does this gas enter?

(d) Name an excretory product that passes from the blood into the alveoli.

(e) By what process do gases pass into and out of the alveoli?

What is the difference between air breathed in and air breathed out?

As a result of gas exchange in the alveoli, the contents of inhaled air are different from the contents of exhaled air. The approximate figures are given in Table 7.1.

Table 7.1 Makeup of inhaled air and exhaled air at rest.

Substance	Percentage in inhaled air	Percentage in exhaled air
Nitrogen	78	78
Oxygen	21	14
Carbon dioxide	0.04	5
Water vapour	Variable	Much higher than in inhaled air

(?) Questions

7.6 What is the normal concentration of carbon dioxide in the air?

7.7 Why does exhaled air contain more carbon dioxide than inhaled air?

7.8 The table below shows the exhaled carbon dioxide concentrations of three people. One of the people was resting, one was walking and the third was running. Answer these questions based on the figures in the table:

(a) From the table, match up the three people with the three activities.

(b) Which person would have the greatest demand for oxygen?

(c) Suggest why the person in part (b) required more oxygen. Identify in your answer any part(s) of the body that needed a higher supply of oxygen.

(d) Which person would have the lowest breathing rate (number of breaths per minute)?

(e) Why, do you think, did the person in part (d) require less oxygen?

Person	Percentage of carbon dioxide in exhaled air
A	7
B	4
C	9

 Activity 7.3 Can we compare the carbon dioxide levels of inhaled and exhaled air?

 Activity video

Limewater turns milky or cloudy in the presence of carbon dioxide. We will breathe in through one container of limewater and breathe out through a second container of limewater.

🧪 Equipment needed

Two test tubes

Two stoppers with holes

Tubing or straws

Clear limewater

➡️ Conducting the activity

1. Place equal volumes of clear limewater in two test tubes, A and B, as shown in Figure 7.7.
2. Suck air in through tube X and hold your breath for as long as possible.
3. Breathe air out through tube Y.
4. Repeat steps 2 and 3 until the limewater in one of the test tubes turns milky.
5. In which test tube did the limewater first turn milky? Record your answer in your Student Activity Book.
6. Why does the limewater in the second test tube eventually turn milky?

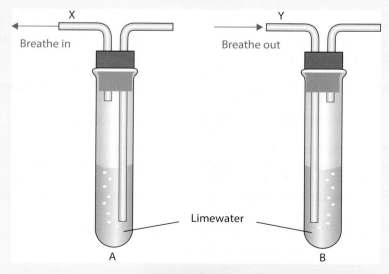

▲ Figure 7.7 *Comparing CO$_2$ concentration*

What is breathing rate?

The breathing rate is how many breaths a person or animal takes per minute. One breath is one inhalation and one exhalation.

Activity 7.4 How can we find our breathing rate at rest?

Equipment needed

A stopwatch

➡ **Conducting the activity**

1. Count the number of times you inhale per minute while you are at rest.

2. Repeat step 1 two more times, so you have three counts.

3. Add the three values together and divide by three. This gives the average number of breaths per minute at rest. This gives a more reliable result than a single measurement.

4. Record your breathing rate in the copy of the table below that is in your Student Activity Book.

Number of inhalations (breaths) per minute at rest	Total number of inhalations (breaths) in 3 minutes at rest	Average number of inhalations (breaths) per minute at rest

Did you know?

The normal breathing rate for an adult at rest is from 8 to 16 breaths per minute. For an infant, the normal rate is up to 44 breaths per minute.

? Questions

7.9 Why is the breathing rate of an infant greater than that of an adult?

7.10 **(a)** Research the breathing rates of other animals.

  (b) Can you see a pattern relating to breathing rate and the size of the animal? If so, then state the relationship.

  (c) Can you see a pattern relating to breathing rate and the lifespan of the animal? If so, then state the relationship.

7.11 In general, fitter people have lower breathing rates compared with less fit people. Their breathing rate also returns to normal faster after exercise than for unfit people. What does this suggest about the size of their lungs?

7.12 Breathing rates increase as people go higher up a mountain, even if they are inactively sitting in a car. Suggest an explanation (or hypothesis) for this change.

Did you know?

A hypothesis is a suggested explanation for something that we observe or notice. A hypothesis is tested by carrying out one or more experiments. The results of the experiment(s) will decide whether the hypothesis is true or false.

Activity 7.5 How can we investigate the effect of exercise on the rate of breathing?

Equipment needed

A stopwatch

➡ Conducting the activity

1. Record your resting breathing rate as in activity 7.4. If you prefer you can use the information (data) collected in activity 7.4. This value acts as a control or comparison.
2. Exercise strongly for 2 minutes (e.g. jump up and down on the spot or run on the spot).
3. Immediately after exercising count the number of inhalations (breaths in) per minute.
4. Continue to record the number of inhalations per minute until the rate returns to the average resting rate.
5. Note how long it takes for the breathing rate to return to normal after exercise.
6. Record your results in the copy of the table below that is in your Student Activity Book. On a separate sheet of graph paper, draw a graph to show the results you obtained (putting time after exercising on the x-axis and the number of breaths per minute on the y-axis).

Number of inhalations per minute at rest	Total number of inhalations in 3 minutes at rest	Average breathing rate per minute at rest	Breathing rates per minute after exercise

Summary questions

🔬 7.13 (a) Name three tubes that air passes through as it travels from our mouth to our lungs.

(b) Does inhaled air have a higher or lower concentration of oxygen than exhaled air?

(c) Gases pass through the walls of our alveoli by a process called _____.

(d) What gas combines with glucose in our cells to supply us with energy?

🔬 7.14 The diagram shows how a student could show that exhaled air has more carbon dioxide than inhaled air.

(a) Name the solution at S that is used to detect carbon dioxide.

(b) What effect has carbon dioxide on solution S?

(c) In which tube, X or Y, would you expect this effect to be seen first?

(d) Apart from carbon dioxide, name another waste product of respiration.

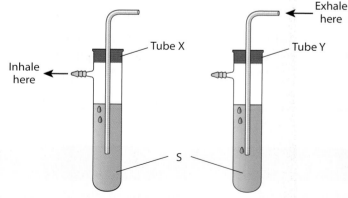

▲ Figure 7.8 Experiment to measure the carbon dioxide content of air

Assessment questions

7.15   Normal air has 78% nitrogen, 21% oxygen and 0.04% carbon dioxide.   **(15 marks)**

   (a) Would you expect exhaled air to have more or less oxygen than this?

   (b) Would you expect exhaled air to have more or less carbon dioxide than this?

   (c) When we breathe out onto a mirror it clouds up. What causes this to happen?

7.16   The bar chart in Figure 7.9 shows the breathing rate of three people, A, B and C, at rest and after exercise. Answer the following questions based on the bar chart.   **(30 marks)**

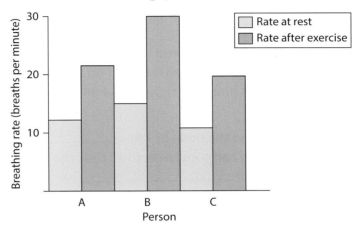

▲ **Figure 7.9**

   (a) Which person has the lowest breathing rate at rest?

   (b) Which person has the highest breathing rate after exercise?

   (c) Which person shows the greatest range of breathing rates?

   (d) What is the percentage increase in breathing rates for person A?

   (e) Calculate the average (mean) breathing rate for the three people:

   (i) At rest   **(ii)** After exercise.

   (f) Which person do you think is the fittest? Suggest two pieces of evidence from the chart in support of your answer.

7.17   John breathes in and out through the tube labelled X in Figure 7.10.   **(15 marks)**

   (a) Through which test tube will inhaled air pass?

   (b) Name a liquid that could be used in the test tubes to detect a difference in composition between inhaled and exhaled air.

   (c) After some minutes of breathing, how would the liquids in tubes A and B differ in appearance?

   (d) What conclusion could you reach based on this difference?

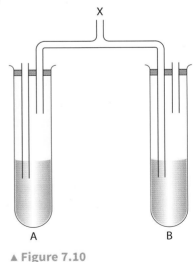

▲ **Figure 7.10**

7.18 **Question from SEC Junior Cycle Science sample paper** (15 marks)

The passage below explains how a cell gets the material it needs for respiration.

The names of five parts of the body are missing from the passage.

Here are the missing body parts:

heart   veins   small intestine   stomach   lungs

Write out the text inserting the names of the missing body parts.

> When we breathe we draw air into our _____ where the oxygen in the air is passed into our blood.
>
> After we swallow food it is first stored in our _____ for a few hours, where some digestion occurs. Then it travels on to our _____ where further digestion happens and glucose and other nutrients are absorbed into our blood.
>
> Blood is pumped around the body by our _____. The blood travels through arteries and capillaries to all the cells in our body. The blood then travels back through our _____.

7.19 **Question from Junior Cycle Science exam paper** (15 marks)

The diagram shows the human respiratory system.

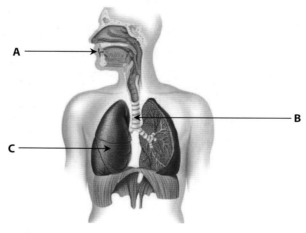

▲ **Figure 7.11**

(a) Draw and complete the table below in your science copy book by matching the words to the letters in the diagram.

Lung   Trachea   Liver   Oesophagus   Mouth

Letter	Part of respiratory system
A	
B	
C	

(b) Describe what happens in the respiratory system when a person breathes in.

Log on to **www.edcolearning.ie** for Additional Assessment Questions

 **PowerPoint summary**    **Weblinks**

THE STUDY OF A HABITAT

LO: BW5, BW8

Learning intentions

At the end of this chapter you will be able to:

- ✓ Identify different habitats
- ✓ Conduct a habitat study by:
  - ☐ Measuring environmental features
  - ☐ Using keys to name plants and animals
  - ☐ Collecting organisms in a habitat
  - ☐ Estimating the number of plants in a habitat
- ✓ Research and investigate adaptations, competition and interdependence of organisms in habitats and communities
- ✓ Explain how matter and energy flow through ecosystems.

Keywords

- ecology
- environment
- ecosystem
- habitat
- environmental (abiotic) factors
- identification key
- sweep net
- pitfall trap
- beating tray
- pooter
- ethics
- quadrat
- community
- adaptations
- competition
- interdependence
- producers
- consumers
- herbivores
- carnivores
- omnivores
- decomposers
- food chain
- food web
- energy flow
- matter flow

What are ecosystems and habitats?

Ecosystems

Ecology is the study of how plants and animals interact with each other and with their surroundings (or environment).

An ecosystem is a group of plants, animals and other organisms that interact with each other and with their environment.

The living world is divided into many ecosystems. Examples of major ecosystems are:

Deserts

Tropical rainforests

Grasslands

Seashores

▲ Figure 8.1 *Examples of major ecosystems*

Habitats

Normally an ecosystem is too large to study. Instead, a small, local part of the ecosystem called a **habitat** is studied.

A habitat is the place where an organism lives.

There are a wide variety of habitats that can be studied. These include:

- Grassland
- Rocky seashore
- Bog
- School field
- Hedgerow
- Woodland
- Local park
- Pond.

This chapter will deal with one sample habitat, a grassland.

⑦ Question

8.1 Answer these questions on habitats:

(a) What is the difference between an ecosystem and a habitat?

(b) Which is larger, an ecosystem or a habitat?

(c) Name three different types of habitat found in Ireland.

How to carry out a habitat study

The study of a local habitat is called fieldwork. If possible, the habitat should be visited during different seasons. This will show how the habitat changes over the course of a year.

There is a recognised countryside code, and when investigating any habitat it is important to follow this code.

ⓘ Information

The countryside code

- Get permission to enter private property.
- Close gates behind you.
- Do not disturb livestock.
- Do not damage gates, fences or crops.
- Do not light fires.
- Do not leave litter.
- Where possible you should 'leave only footprints and take only memories'.

▲ Figure 8.2 *Make sure you follow the countryside code*

⑦ Question

8.2 **The countryside code is simple, but very important.**

(a) Why is it important to follow the countryside code?

(b) Give three problems that might arise if people did not follow the countryside code.

The study of a habitat involves the following five steps:

1. Draw a simple map of the habitat (or photograph it, if possible).
2. Measure and record the environmental, or non-living, features in the habitat.
3. Identify and name all the organisms in the habitat.
4. Collect samples of those organisms in the habitat that cannot be identified.
5. Estimate the number of each type of plant in the habitat.

Step 1: Map the habitat

Draw a simple map to show the main features of the habitat, e.g. walls, fences, ponds, large trees, hedges or paths. If possible, photograph the habitat.

Step 2: Measure environmental features

The environmental (non-living) features of a habitat are called abiotic factors. Some of the abiotic factors that you can measure and the equipment used are given in Table 8.1. You should measure and record as many of these factors as possible.

Table 8.1 **Measuring abiotic factors in a habitat**

Feature	Equipment
Temperature	Thermometer or data logger with a temperature probe
Light intensity	Light meter or data logger with a light intensity probe
Soil pH	pH meter or universal indicator paper, or a data logger with a pH probe
Wind direction	Ribbon and compass
Rainfall	Rain gauge

Measuring soil temperature

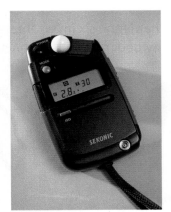
A light meter

A rain gauge

▲ Figure 8.3

Step 3: Identify the organisms

If possible, organisms in the habitat should be named and listed on site. Plants and animals should be removed from the habitat *only* if they cannot be identified there and then.

Organisms can be identified by comparing them to drawings or pictures in a book or by using a suitable key (see activity 8.1, over the page).

✐ Activity 8.1 How can we name (identify) plants and animals?

Compare the plant or animal to pictures or descriptions in field guides or use an **identification key**. A key contains a number of questions. By answering each question the name of the living thing can be discovered.

🧪 Equipment needed

Plant and animal guide books

Plant and animal keys

➡ Conducting the activity

Plant key Use the key below to name each of the four plants shown in Figure 8.4. Write your answers in the space provided in the Activity Book.

▲ **Figure 8.4** *Name the four plants using the key below*

1	Leaves have parallel veins	Plantain
	Veins are not parallel in the leaves	Go to 2
2	Edges of leaves not jagged	Daisy
	Leaves have jagged edges	Go to 3
3	Long leaves growing from a the base of the stem	Dandelion
	Leaves more rounded and growing along the length of the stem	Buttercup

Animal key The following key can be used to name the six invertebrate animals shown in Figure 8.5. Write your answers in the space provided in the Student Activity Book.

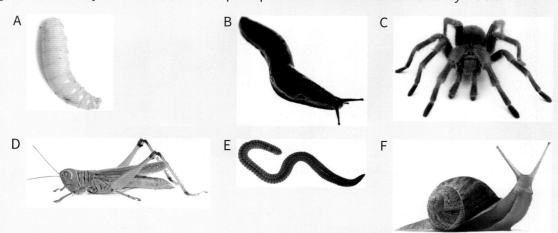

▲ **Figure 8.5** *Name the six animals using the key at the top of the opposite page*

1	Legs present	Go to 2
	Legs absent	Go to 3
2	Six legs present	Insect
	Eight legs present	Spider
3	Body divided into segments	Go to 4
	Body not divided into segments	Go to 5
4	Long body with many segments	Earthworm
	Shorter body with fewer segments	Maggot
5	Shell present	Snail
	No shell present	Slug

? Question

8.3 Figure 8.6 shows four different animals that were found in a habitat study.

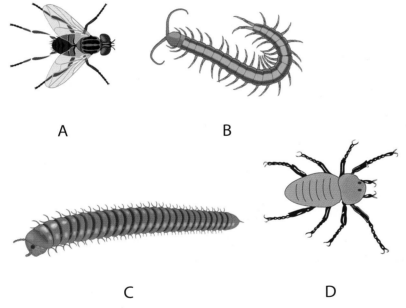

A B

C D

▲ Figure 8.6

(a) What identifies all four animals as invertebrates?

(b) Use the key below to name the four animals.

1	Wings present	Housefly
	Wings absent	Go to 2
2	More than 8 legs	Go to 3
	Not more than 8 legs	Spider
3	One pair of legs per segment	Centipede
	Two pairs of legs per segment	Millipede

Step 4: Collect organisms for identification in the laboratory

Plants are easy to collect as they do not move away. Slow or non-moving animals can be collected easily. Most animals will have to be trapped or collected using special devices.

Activity 8.2 How can we collect plants and animals in a habitat?

Equipment needed

Knife **Pitfall trap** **Beating tray**
Sweep net Small trowel **Pooter**
Tin or jar

Safety
- All equipment should be unbreakable so that it does not cause harm in the habitat.
- Suitable clothing and footwear should be worn.
- Care should be taken if the habitat is wet or rough.

Ethics

Ethics means the study of whether conduct is right or wrong. In this case:

- Is it right to enter someone's property?
- Is it right to remove plants and animals from a habitat?
- What can we do to reduce any damage to the habitat?

➡ Conducting the activity

Plants

Use a knife or small trowel to collect samples of plants and place them in labelled bags.

Remove only small sections of a plant. Remember to collect the leaves, twigs, flowers, seeds and fruits of each plant if they are present.

Use a suitable book or key to name each plant. In your Student Activity Book, make a list of the names of all the plants you found.

Animals

Some animals are collected easily. For example, use a tin or jar to collect slow-moving animals such as slugs, snails and earthworms. Sometimes you can find evidence (signs) of an animal, e.g. feathers, fur or hair attached to bushes, droppings, nests, burrows.

Special apparatus is needed to collect fast-moving animals. Examples of some of the methods used to collect animals are given in Figure 8.7.

Use a suitable book or key to name each animal. In your Student Activity Book, make a list of the names of all the animals (or evidence that they were present) that you found.

Name	Diagram	How used	Collects
Pooter	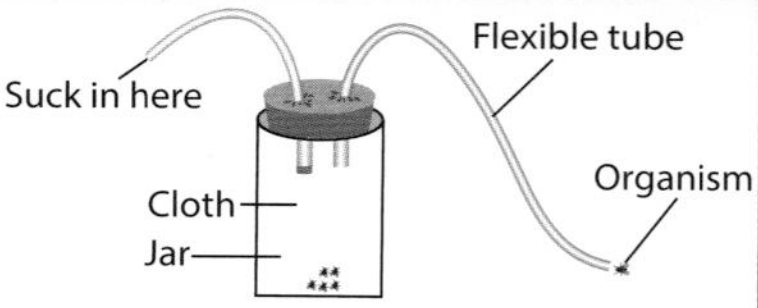 Suck in here · Flexible tube · Cloth · Jar · Organism	Place the flexible tube over the organism. Suck in on the other tube. The cloth stops you swallowing the organism.	Small flies, aphids, fruit flies, ants and other insects
Sweep net	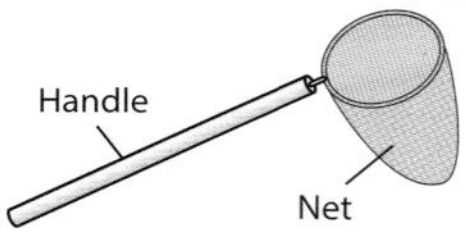 Handle · Net	Sweep it through long grass.	Ladybirds, flies, beetles, bees, wasps, spiders, moths, butterflies
Beating tray	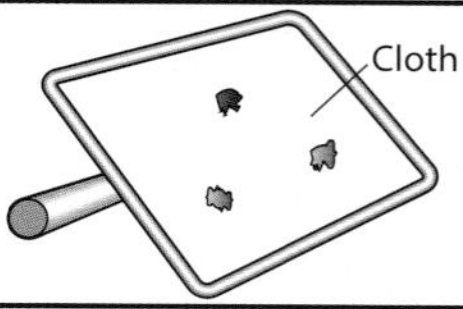 Cloth	Place it under a plant bush or a small tree. Shake the plant to dislodge animals.	Insects such as caterpillars, aphids, spiders
Pitfall trap	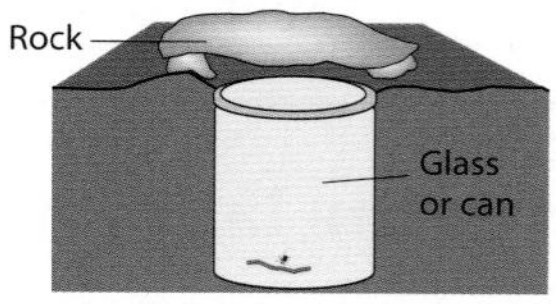 Rock · Glass or can	Place it in the soil and cover it to prevent rain entering.	Crawling animals, such as snails, slugs, spiders, beetles, wood lice

▲ **Figure 8.7** *Apparatus used to collect animals*

8.4 What observations did you make that suggest unseen animals were present in the habitat?

8.5 Why do you think it is important to replace animals that you collected in the same place as you found them?

▲ Figure 8.8 *A pitfall trap with a clear cover to prevent rain getting in*

Step 5: Estimate the number of plants

It is not normally possible to count all the plants in a habitat. Instead, the number of plants is calculated from samples taken at random in the habitat. We can then calculate how often a plant is likely to be found in the habitat (i.e. its frequency). The most common method of calculating plant numbers is to use a quadrat.

A **quadrat** is a square frame that is thrown at random in the habitat. Quadrats come in different sizes (e.g. their sides may measure 0.5 m or 0.25 m). They may be made of wood, metal or plastic, or they can be marked out using string or rope.

◄ Figure 8.9 *A student using a quadrat*

BIOLOGICAL WORLD

⏱ Activity 8.3 How can we estimate the number of plants in a habitat?

🧪 Equipment needed

- Ball or pen
- Quadrat
- Pen and notebook

➡ Conducting the activity

1. Throw a ball or pen carefully over your shoulder in the habitat. Ensure that you do not throw the ball or pen too far in case it should land beyond the habitat you are studying.

2. Place a quadrat on the ground wherever the ball or pen lands. This ensures that the quadrat is placed at random in the habitat. This will allow the samples to represent the habitat more accurately.

▲ Figure 8.10 *Using a quadrat in a rocky seashore habitat*

3. Record the names of the plants in your quadrat in the table provided in your Student Activity Book.

4. Repeat this ten times in different parts of the habitat.

5. Record the results in the table in your Student Activity Book, as shown in Figure 8.11.

6. Calculate the percentage frequency of each plant in the habitat. This is done by adding the number of quadrats in which the plant is found and expressing this as a percentage of the ten quadrats (e.g. buttercups were found in four out of ten quadrats, i.e. 40%).

7. The frequency of each type of plant can also be shown on a bar chart (as in Figure 8.12). Graph paper is provided in your Student Activity Book.

Name of plant	Quadrat number 1	2	3	4	5	6	7	8	9	10	Total	Percentage frequency
Grass	✓	✓	✓	✓	✓	✓	✓	✓	✓	✓	10	$^{10}/_{10}$ = 100%
Buttercup	✗	✓	✓	✗	✓	✗	✓	✗	✗	✗	4	$^{4}/_{10}$ = 40%
Daisy	✓	✓	✓	✓	✗	✗	✗	✓	✓	✓	7	$^{7}/_{10}$ = 70%
Clover	✗	✗	✗	✗	✗	✓	✓	✓	✗	✗	3	$^{3}/_{10}$ = 30%
Dandelion	✗	✓	✗	✓	✓	✗	✗	✓	✓	✗	5	$^{5}/_{10}$ = 50%
Thistle	✗	✗	✗	✗	✗	✗	✓	✗	✗	✗	1	$^{1}/_{10}$ = 10%

▲ Figure 8.11 *Recording the names of plants in a quadratic study*

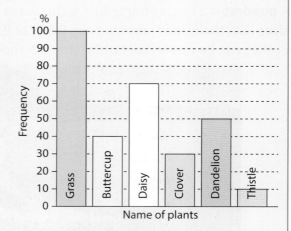

▲ Figure 8.12 *A bar chart showing the percentage frequency of plants in a habitat*

Competition also occurs between different types of plants and animals. For example:

- Grass and dandelions compete with each other for light
- Robins and blackbirds compete with each other for food.

▲ Figure 8.15 *Red deer competing for a mate*

▲ Figure 8.16 *Gulls compete for nesting space*

What is interdependence?

Interdependence means that all the organisms in a habitat depend on other organisms for their survival.

Examples of how plants and animals are interdependent include:

- Animals depend on plants, e.g. rabbits depend on grass for food
- Plants depend on animals, e.g. flowers depend on bees for pollination
- Plants depend on each other, e.g. plants depend on each other for shelter
- Animals depend on other animals, e.g. foxes depend on rabbits for food.

Other examples of interdependence include:

- Birds use twigs for nests
- Foxes hide in long grass
- Spiders use plants on which to build their webs
- Squirrels spread the seeds of trees
- Dead plants are decayed by decomposers such as bacteria and fungi to release minerals into the soil for new plants to absorb.

Food interdependence

One of the main ways in which living things depend on each other is for food. Organisms get their food in different ways, and can be categorised as:

- Producers
- Consumers
- Decomposers.

Producers

Producers are green plants that make their own food.

Examples of producers are:

- Grasses
- Buttercups
- Nettles.
- Dandelions
- Daisies

Consumers

Consumers are organisms that take in food.

Animals do not make their own food. Instead, they get their food by eating (or consuming) plants or other animals. For this reason, animals are called consumers. Depending on what they eat, consumers can be placed into three different groups:

● **Herbivores are animals that eat plants only**, e.g. rabbits, sheep, slugs and snails

● **Carnivores are animals that eat other animals**, e.g. foxes, hawks and ladybirds

● **Omnivores are animals that eat both plants and other animals**, e.g. badgers, thrushes, blackbirds and humans.

▲ Figure 8.17 *A slug is a herbivore*

▲ Figure 8.18 *A sparrowhawk is a carnivore*

▲ Figure 8.19 *Badgers are omnivores*

Decomposers

Decomposers are organisms that feed on and break down dead plants and animals.

Decomposers include a range of small animals (such as woodlice and earthworms) along with bacteria and fungi. Decomposers are of great value as they release chemicals back into the environment. This allows other organisms to use these chemicals. This means decomposers allow recycling.

> **? Question**
>
> 8.10 Barn owls (shown in Figure 8.20) feed on small animals, which they hunt at night. Their feathers are specially arranged so that they can fly silently.
>
> **(a)** Is this an example of adaptation, competition or interdependence?
>
> **(b)** What is the possible benefit to barn owls of being able to fly silently?

▲ Figure 8.20 *A barn owl in flight*

What is a food chain?

A food chain is a list of organisms in which each organism is eaten by the next one in the chain.

A food chain is a simple way of explaining how energy and nutrients pass from one living thing to another. The arrows in a food chain show the direction in which the energy and nutrients pass.

An example of a simple food chain is where grass is eaten by a rabbit and the rabbit is then eaten by a fox. This food chain is shown in Figure 8.21:

Grass *Rabbit* *Fox*

▲ **Figure 8.21** *A simple food chain*

This food chain has three feeding levels:

1. Grass: normally the first feeding level is a plant and a producer.
2. Rabbit: a herbivore and a consumer.
3. Fox: a carnivore and a consumer.

An example of another food chain is given in Figure 8.22.

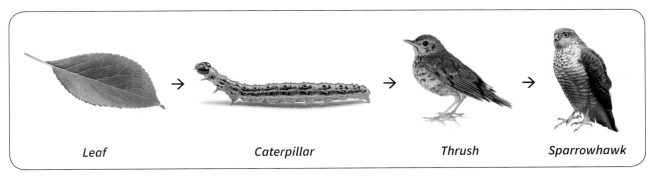

Leaf *Caterpillar* *Thrush* *Sparrowhawk*

▲ **Figure 8.22** *Food chain from a hedgerow*

Do food chains involve decomposers?

Another way to show a food chain is to refer to the decomposers. Decomposers act on dead plants and animals and on the waste products (such as urine and faeces) of animals. The food chain in Figure 8.23 shows the role of the decomposers.

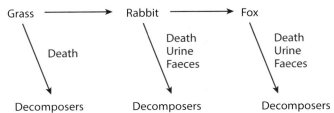

▲ **Figure 8.23** *The role of decomposers in the food chain*

What is a food web?

Food chains are a simple way to show how organisms feed in a habitat. For example, the simple food chain described earlier (grass → rabbit → fox) suggests that grass is eaten only by rabbits. It also suggests that rabbits are eaten only by foxes. Both of these are untrue.

A food web consists of a number of interlinked food chains.

A food web provides a more complete and realistic explanation of the way in which organisms in a habitat feed. In all food webs, the dead plants and animals are broken down by decomposers. Examples of food webs are given in Figures 8.24 and 8.25.

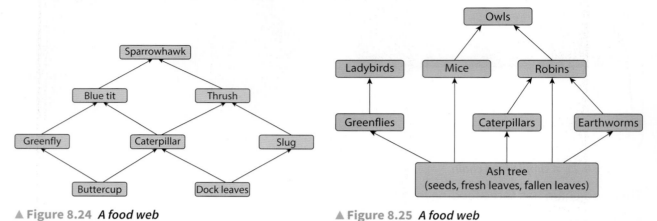

▲ **Figure 8.24** *A food web*   ▲ **Figure 8.25** *A food web*

⍰ Question

8.11 Answer the following questions in relation to the food web shown in Figure 8.25.

(a) Write out a food chain with four organisms in it.

(b) Name the producer in the web.

(c) Name two consumers in the web.

(d) Name a herbivore in the web.

(e) Name two carnivores in the web.

(f) Give one example of competition shown in this web.

(g) Give one example of how mice depend on the ash tree.

(h) Give one example of how the ash tree depends on mice.

(i) If all the robins died, what might happen to the number of:

    (i) Owls   **(ii)** Caterpillars?

(j) How many different types of organisms feed on the ash tree?

How does energy flow in an ecosystem?

Energy is the ability to do work. It can change from one form to another, which we will look at in more detail in chapters 10, 28 and 40.

The main source of energy for every ecosystem is the Sun (or solar energy). The Sun's energy is converted into food by photosynthesis (which we look at in chapter 10).

Energy flows along a food chain when each organism eats the previous one in the chain.

However, not all of the **energy flows** from each organism to the next one. Some of it is lost:

● The organisms lose heat to their environment

● The organisms may excrete waste such as urine and faeces (both contain energy)

- Some parts of organisms are not eaten (e.g. roots, bones, fur, teeth)

- Lots of energy is lost as heat when dead things decompose.

Only about 10% of the energy passes from organism to organism in a food chain. This means about 90% of the energy is lost at each step. As a result, food chains cannot be too long as there will be very little energy available at the end of a long food chain.

Energy is lost from ecosystems (mainly as heat). Energy is said to **flow** through an ecosystem.

| 10% of the energy | 10% of the energy |
| 90% of the energy | 90% of the energy |

Grass   Rabbit   Fox

▲ Figure 8.26 *Energy flow (and loss) in a food chain*

? Questions

8.12 Tests show that for every 100 kJ of food eaten by a cow it gains only 5 kJ in weight. Wastes (such as faeces, urine and gases) account for 60 kJ. The remaining energy is lost as heat in respiration.

(a) How much energy (expressed as a percentage) is lost as heat?

(b) How efficient (as a percentage) is a cow at transferring food into body weight?

8.13 In the following food chain the grass was calculated to contain 10 000 kJ of energy. Assuming a 90% energy loss at each step of the food chain, calculate how much energy would be available to the hawk.

grass → grasshopper → frog → hawk

How does matter flow in an ecosystem?

Matter is anything that occupies space (such as food, chemicals and elements or minerals such as calcium and carbon). We look at matter in some detail in chapter 13. Matter is absorbed by plants from their environment. For example:

- Calcium is absorbed by the roots from the soil

- Carbon is absorbed by the leaves from the air in the form of carbon dioxide.

Matter flows from one organism to another in a food chain as each organism is eaten, e.g.:

- Calcium passes from grass to rabbits to foxes

- Carbon (in the form of food) passes from grass to rabbits and from rabbits to foxes.

Calcium   Calcium
Carbon   Carbon
(as food)   (as food)

Grass   Rabbit   Fox

▲ Figure 8.27 *Calcium and carbon passing through a food chain*

Matter is not normally lost from an ecosystem (unless living things leave the ecosystem). Matter is said to be **cycled** in the ecosystem (you will look at nutrient cycling in chapter 39).

In a food chain, for example, any waste and the parts that are not eaten pass into the soil. Here it is broken down (by decomposers) and the elements are released into the soil. These elements may then be reabsorbed by plants, and the cycle starts all over again.

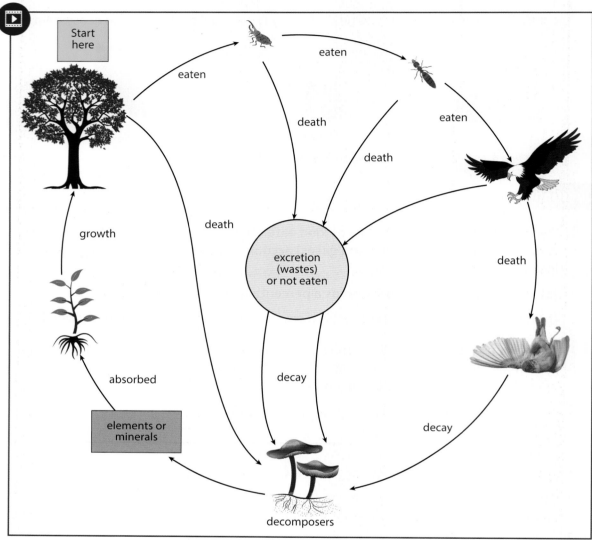

▲ **Figure 8.28** *Matter is cycled in an ecosystem*

In conclusion, it is said that:

● Energy flows through an ecosystem

● Matter is cycled in an ecosystem.

Summary questions

8.14 The pieces of apparatus shown in figure 8.29 can be used to collect organisms in a habitat.

(a) Name apparatus A.

(b) Describe how you might use apparatus A.

(c) Name two organisms that you might collect using apparatus A.

(d) Which tube, X or Y, should be flexible? Explain why.

(e) What is the function of structure Z?

(f) Name apparatus B.

(g) Name two organisms that you might collect using apparatus B.

(h) What is the function of structure K?

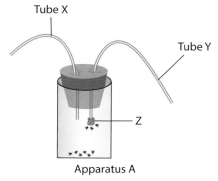

Apparatus A

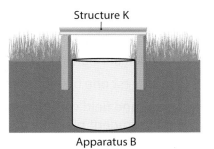

Apparatus B

▲ **Figure 8.29**

8.15 A food chain is shown below.

buttercup ⟶ greenfly ⟶ blue tit ⟶ hawk

▲ **Figure 8.30**

Based on this food chain, name:

(a) A carnivore

(b) A herbivore

(c) Two consumers.

(d) If the blue tits were to die of an infection, explain why:

　(i) The hawk numbers would fall

　(ii) The buttercup numbers would decrease.

8.16 **(a)** In your study of a habitat, name two pieces of equipment you used to measure environmental (abiotic) factors.

(b) In your habitat study you used a quadrat. What is a quadrat?

(c) The quadrat should be used in random positions in the habitat. How did you ensure that this was done?

(d) In using a quadrat a student found that dandelions were present in 6 out of 20 quadrats. Calculate the frequency of dandelions in the habitat.

(e) Why is a quadrat not used to study the number of frogs in a habitat?

Log on to **www.edcolearning.ie** for Additional Summary Questions

8.17 Rewrite the table below, matching up the titles with the correct definitions: **(15 marks)**

Title	Definition
Habitat	Living things struggling for a scarce resource
Competition	All the organisms in a particular area
Consumer	The place where an organism lives
Community	Takes in food by eating another organism

8.18 Figure 8.31 shows a kestrel feeding on a mouse. **(15 marks)**
The kestrel has a sharp beak and very strong talons (or claws).

(a) Which animal is acting as a carnivore in Figure 8.31?

(b) Is the sharp beak an example of an adaptation, competition or interdependence? Explain your answer.

(c) In Figure 8.31, energy passes from which animal to which animal?

(d) Suggest one benefit to the kestrel of having sharp talons.

▲ Figure 8.31

8.19 A grassland field was 80 metres long and 60 metres wide. A student placed a quadrat (1 metre × 1 metre) in an area of the field where dandelions were growing. The diagram on the right shows the dandelions in that quadrat. **(30 marks)**

Based on this one quadrat the student calculated that there were 38 400 dandelions in the field.

(a) How did the student calculate the number of dandelions in the field?

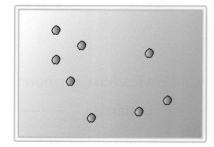
▲ Figure 8.32

(b) The student's estimate of the number of dandelions may not be accurate, as the dandelions are spread unevenly in the field. How could the student improve their method to get a more accurate estimate?

(c) The leaves of a dandelion spread out all around the centre of the plant to form what is called a rosette. However, the leaves stay very close to the ground.

(i) What chemical makes dandelion leaves green?

(ii) What process in the leaves produces glucose?

(iii) Suggest one reason why dandelions are adapted to have leaves so close to the ground.

(d) Dandelions growing in a grassy field are an example of competition.

(i) What two resources might dandelions and grass compete for?

(ii) Dandelions contain white, milky, bitter-tasting latex. This reduces the risk of them being eaten by insects. Is this latex an example of competition, interdependence or adaptation? Explain your answer.

 Log on to **www.edcolearning.ie** for Additional Assessment Questions

PowerPoint summary | Weblinks

FACTORS AFFECTING HUMAN HEALTH

LO: BW6

Learning intentions

At the end of this chapter you will be able to:

✓ Evaluate how inherited factors affect human health

✓ Evaluate how environmental factors and lifestyle choices (such as nutrition, smoking, exercise, drink, drugs, sleep and work/life balance) affect human health

✓ Examine the role of micro-organisms in human health.

Keywords

○— health
○— single-gene disorder
○— multi-gene disorder
○— balanced diet
○— food pyramid
○— energy value
○— micro-organisms
○— pathogens
○— viruses
○— parasites
○— antibodies
○— bacteria
○— antibiotics
○— fungi
○— immunisation
○— vaccination

What is health?

Health is a state of complete physical, mental and social well-being.

Health is not just the absence of disease or sickness. In general, it can be considered as:

● Physical (dealing with the body)

● Mental (dealing with the mind).

▲ Figure 9.1 *A stethoscope is used to listen to internal body sounds*

? Questions

9.1 Research and name three common physical illnesses. For one of the illnesses you named describe the main symptoms of the condition.

9.2 Research and name three common mental illnesses. For one of the illnesses you named describe the main symptoms of the condition.

What factors affect human health?

Human health is affected by a wide range of factors. Some of these are shown in Figure 9.2.

How do inherited factors affect our health?

In chapter 3 we saw that inherited features are controlled by genes. Normally there are two versions of each gene: the dominant and the recessive (non-dominant) version. The dominant version of a gene prevents the recessive version from working.

Are there single-gene disorders?

Cystic fibrosis

Cystic fibrosis (CF) is an inherited condition caused by a single gene (so it is known as a **single-gene disorder**). The dominant version of the gene (N) causes the formation of normal mucus in the breathing system.

However, the recessive version (n) causes the production of thick, sticky mucus, which leads to infections of the breathing system (it also affects the intestines). People can have three different genetic combinations with respect to CF:

- NN = normal mucus
- Nn = normal mucus
- nn = cystic fibrosis.

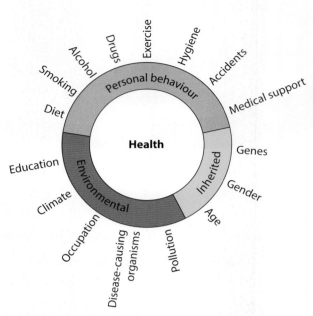

▲ **Figure 9.2** *Factors affecting human health*

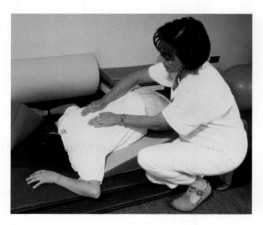

▶ **Figure 9.3** *People with cystic fibrosis often have massages to break up mucus in the lungs*

---

⑦ Questions

9.3 Suggest why a person who has the combination Nn does not have cystic fibrosis.

9.4 Suggest why most genetic diseases are caused when the person has two copies of the non-dominant or recessive gene.

9.5 In terms of mucus production, the dominant version of the gene (N) produces normal mucus. The recessive version of the gene produces abnormal mucus, which causes cystic fibrosis. Referring to chapter 3 if necessary, explain the following by showing the genetic crosses:

   (a) Why there is no possibility of children having cystic fibrosis if the parents are Nn and NN

   (b) Why two parents who do not have cystic fibrosis could have a child with cystic fibrosis.

Other single-gene disorders

Genes cause many other conditions. Some of these are:

- Sickle cell anaemia: in which red blood cells are wrongly shaped

- Coeliac disease: the inability to process gluten, which is found in wheat

- Huntington's: in which nerve cells die, which affects movement

- Haemophilia: the inability to form blood clots.

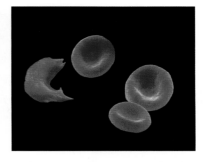

▲ Figure 9.4 *Three normal red blood cells and a sickle cell*

⑦ Questions

9.6 Work in groups and present your results to the class.

Choose one of the disorders listed above and research it under the headings:

Cause   Symptoms   Treatment

9.7 During your searching you probably came across some sites that you felt unsure were giving you information that you could trust. Select a site that you think provides reliable information and one that you suspect might not be reliable. Note the addresses of these sites and give reasons for your choice in each case.

Are there disorders caused by many genes?

Cancer

Cancer is the term given to a range of conditions (about 200) in which cells lose control of how fast they divide and for how long they divide. This causes the uncontrolled, rapid growth of cells. Cancer usually requires a number of genes to change (it is a **multi-gene disorder**). Some people are born with one or more of these alterations already in place. They are more likely to get cancer.

Other factors that speed up the risk of the alteration of genes are:

- Ultraviolet radiation (e.g. sunlight or sun beds) or excess X-rays

- Diet (e.g. too much red or processed meat and not enough fruit and vegetables)

- Being overweight   ● Viruses   ● Smoking   ● Lack of physical activity

- Problems with white blood cells that normally should prevent cancer.

Other multi-gene disorders

It is thought that there are many (altered) genes involved in:

- Heart disease   ● Arthritis

- High blood pressure   ● Diabetes

- Alzheimer's disease   ● Obesity.

In addition, some inherited disorders are caused by having an extra or a missing chromosome. An example of this type is Down syndrome (which results in altered mental and physical development).

▲ Figure 9.5 *Down syndrome is caused by an additional chromosome*

Did you know?

Down syndrome is named after a British doctor, John Langdon Down, who first described the condition in 1866. It was only in 1959 that it was discovered that the cause was an extra copy of chromosome 21.

? Questions

9.8 Work in groups and present your results to the class.

Choose one of the disorders listed as a multi-gene disorder on the previous page and research it under the headings:

Cause   Symptoms   Treatment

9.9 During your searching you probably came across some sites that you felt unsure were giving you information that you could trust. Select a site that you think provides reliable information. Write out the address of this site and give reasons why you find it a reliable site. Suggest reasons why some sites might not be reliable.

How does personal behaviour affect our health?

Many factors relating to personal behaviour affect our health (as outlined in Figure 9.2, see page 96). We will consider two of these factors: nutrition and lifestyle choices.

What are the effects of nutrition on health?

Nutrition is how an organism gets its food. All living things need food. Plants make their own food. Animals take in food when they eat plants or other animals.

Food is needed to:

- Supply living things with energy
- Allow them to grow and repair damaged body parts
- Prevent them from getting diseases.

Humans must ensure that they take in the correct types of food. These foods must also be eaten in the correct amounts. We do this by eating a **balanced diet**.

▲ Figure 9.6 *An example of a balanced diet*

What is a balanced diet?

A balanced diet contains the right amounts of each of the six different types (constituents) of food. The six constituents of a balanced diet, the functions of these constituents and the foods that contain them are given in Table 9.1.

Water is also essential for a balanced diet.

Table 9.1 **The functions and sources of the parts of a balanced diet**

Constituent	Function	Common source

Carbohydrates
  Sugars
  Starch
  Fibre
  (roughage)
	● Fast supply of energy
	● Slower supply of energy
	● Helps to move food through the intestines
		● Fruits, soft drinks, sweets, honey
		● Bread, potatoes, rice, pasta
		● Cereals, brown bread, fruit, vegetables

Fats	● Stored in the body ● Insulate the body	● Butter, cream, margarine, milk, oil, fried food
Proteins	● Form muscle, hair, nails, enzymes, antibodies	● Meat, fish, egg white, milk, cheese, nuts, peas, beans

Vitamins
There are
13 different
vitamins
	● Each vitamin has a different function, e.g. Vitamin C is used for the growth and repair of body cells	● Each vitamin has its own sources; generally found in:
		  ● fruits
		  ● vegetables
		  ● meat
		  ● milk
		  ● grains

Minerals
We need up to
20 different
minerals
	● Each mineral has a different function, e.g. Iron (F_e) is needed to make haemoglobin found in red blood cells	● Each mineral has its own sources; generally found in:
		  ● fruits
		  ● vegetables
		  ● meat
		  ● milk
		  ● grains

Water	● Cell reactions ● Transport ● Digestion ● Controlling temperature	● Drinks ● Fruit ● Vegetables

ⓘ **Question**

9.10 **Research one nutrient (a vitamin or a mineral) needed in our diet. For this nutrient:**

  (a) List three common sources

  (b) Explain its function

  (c) List the common symptoms of a deficiency (shortage).

Failure to eat a balanced diet results in a person being malnourished and unhealthy. For example:

● Too many high-energy foods may cause a person to be overweight or obese

● Not enough energy in a diet may cause a person to be tired and sluggish

● Lack of fibre may result in constipation (and may increase the risk of bowel cancer).

Food pyramid

The food we eat can be put into the following six food groups:

- Fruit and vegetables
- Cereals, bread, rice and potatoes
- Dairy products
- Meat and fish
- Fats and spreads
- Other types of food.

In order to maintain a balanced diet it is necessary to eat different amounts of each food group. The number of servings of each food group that we should eat each day is given in a **food pyramid** (see Figure 9.7).

Foods at the top of the food pyramid do not contain minerals or vitamins. They should be eaten rarely as they are high in fats and cause people to be overweight. They also lead to heart conditions and may cause diabetes.

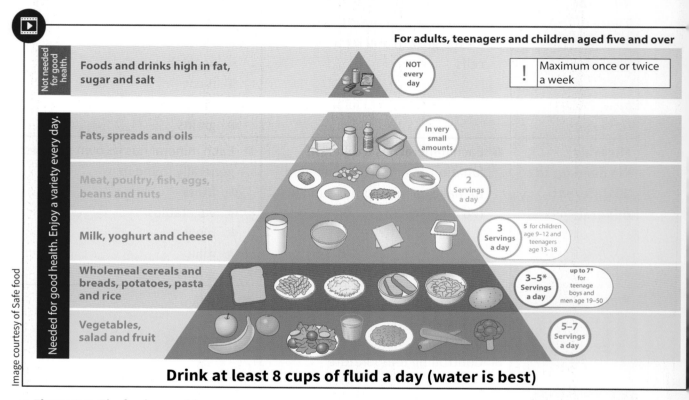

For adults, teenagers and children aged five and over

Not needed for good health.

Foods and drinks high in fat, sugar and salt — NOT every day — **!** Maximum once or twice a week

Needed for good health. Enjoy a variety every day.

Fats, spreads and oils — In very small amounts

Meat, poultry, fish, eggs, beans and nuts — 2 Servings a day

Milk, yoghurt and cheese — 3 Servings a day — 5 for children age 9–12 and teenagers age 13–18

Wholemeal cereals and breads, potatoes, pasta and rice — 3–5* Servings a day — up to 7* for teenage boys and men age 19–50

Vegetables, salad and fruit — 5–7 Servings a day

Drink at least 8 cups of fluid a day (water is best)

Image courtesy of Safe food

▲ Figure 9.7 *The food pyramid*

People need different amounts of food

The amount and type of food needed by each person varies according to factors such as:

- Age (younger people need more food than older people)
- Gender (males need more food than females)
- Activity levels (active people need more food than inactive people)
- Health (sick people need smaller portions and softer food)
- Occupation (active people need more food than inactive people).

9.11 Why, do you think, do each of the following groups need more food?

(a) Younger people versus older people

(b) Males versus females

(c) Active people versus inactive people

(d) Healthy people versus people who are sick

(e) Pregnant versus non-pregnant women

(f) A worker on a building site versus an office worker.

9.12 Suggest why a sportsperson needs more food when performing than when injured.

Energy values 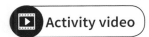 Activity video

Different foods contain different amounts of energy. The amount of energy in a food is known as its **energy value**.

Energy is measured in units called joules (J). However, the normal unit used for the energy value of a food is kilojoules per gram (kJ/g).

In general, carbohydrates and proteins have the same energy values, whereas fats have more than twice the energy value of the other two.

Although carbohydrates and proteins have the same energy values, the human body uses protein for energy only when it is close to starvation. This prevents the body from digesting its own body parts such as muscles and the heart.

Typical daily energy needs (kJ) for 12- to 15-year-olds are:

	Inactive	Active
Girl	10 000	11 000
Boy	12 000	15 000

The energy content of different foods is often given on nutrition information panels on the side of the food containers, as shown in Figure 9.8.

JAM Nutritional information Typical values per 100 g	
Energy	1127 kJ
Protein	0.1 g
Carbohydrate (of which sugars)	65.5 g 65.4 g
Fat (of which saturates)	0.0 g 0.0 g
Fibre	1.0 g

SOUP Nutritional information Typical values per 100 g	
Energy	205 kJ
Protein	1.0 g
Carbohydrate	4.0 g
Fat	3.3 g
Fibre	0.0 g

BEANS Nutritional information Typical values per 100 g	
Energy	326 kJ
Protein	4.3 g
Carbohydrate	13.8 g
Fat	0.5 g
Fibre	2.9 g

BISCUITS Nutritional information Typical values per 100 g	
Energy	1616 kJ
Protein	2.8 g
Carbohydrate	66.2 g
Fat	13.6 g
Fibre	0.4 g

▲ Figure 9.8 *Examples of nutrition information panels*

9.13 Answer these questions, based on the information on the labels in Figure 9.8.

(a) If an active girl eats 200 g of soup, what percentage of her daily energy needs is she getting?

(b) If an inactive boy eats 300 g of biscuits, how much of his daily energy needs is he getting?

(c) Which of the four foods do you consider is the unhealthiest? Give a reason for your answer.

(d) Which of the foods would you recommend for a person trying to build up muscle? Give a reason for your answer.

What happens if you eat too much food?

Eating too much food means that the surplus food is converted to fat and stored in the body. This leads to problems such as becoming overweight or obese (which means severely overweight). In turn this can lead to:

- Increased risk of heart disease
- High blood pressure
- Diabetes (high blood sugar concentration)
- Gallstones (which prevent bile reaching the small intestine)
- Breathing difficulties
- Some forms of cancer.

What happens if you eat too little food?

Eating less food than the body needs results in weight loss. In addition it causes:

- Mood swings
- Depression
- Inability to think clearly
- Heart and circulatory problems
- Low blood pressure
- Reproductive problems
- Weak bones.

What are the effects of lifestyle choices on health?

The main lifestyle choices that affect our health, and which we will look at in this chapter, are:

- Diet (which we have already studied)
- Smoking
- Exercise
- Drink and drugs
- Sleep
- Work/life balance.

Smoking

Smoking is bad for our health. This fact is indicated by the health warning printed on all packets of cigarettes. In addition, smoking is banned in an increasing number of locations and advertisements for cigarettes are strictly controlled.

Smoking has the following effects:

- Smoke clogs up the tiny hairs in the nose. This allows more dirt particles to enter the lungs.
- Smoke irritates the nose and bronchioles. This causes increased mucus to form, which leads to 'smoker's cough'.

- Smoking results in increased lung infections such as pneumonia and bronchitis.
- Smoking increases the risk of getting lung cancer and other cancers.
- Gases in cigarette smoke enter the blood. Some of these gases reduce the ability of the blood to carry oxygen. As a result the heart must pump harder and faster. This strains the heart and often leads to heart attacks.
- If a pregnant woman smokes, the chemicals in her blood will enter the baby's body. This can affect the development of the baby.

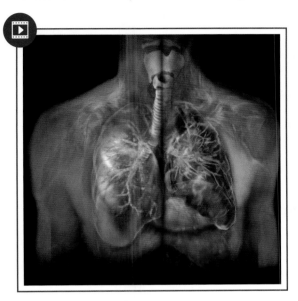

▲ Figure 9.9 *A normal, healthy lung (left) and a smoker's lung (right)*

Did you know?

There are over 7000 chemicals in cigarette smoke; several hundred of these chemicals can cause cancer.

? Questions

9.14 **In small groups discuss:**

(a) **Why young people start to smoke cigarettes**

(b) **The best ways to prevent young people from starting to smoke**

(c) **The advantages and disadvantages of vaping (using e-cigarettes).**

9.15 **Research and list the chemicals and products that are used to make up a cigarette.**

9.16 **Present your findings from question 9.15 to the class using suitable support methods (e.g. PowerPoint, charts, a mind map, summary notes).**

Exercise

Regular exercise has many benefits. This exercise might be organised, e.g. in terms of a sport or training or working out in a gym.

However, it can also be informal and carried out as part of our lifestyle. For example, walking or cycling to and from school and using the stairs instead of taking a lift are valid forms of exercise.

Suggested amount of exercise

- Adults need at least 30 minutes of moderate activity (such as fast walking or cycling) a day on at least 5 days a week.
- Children need at least 60 minutes of moderate to vigorous activity (such as jogging, running, fast cycling or very active sport) on 7 days a week.

Benefits of exercise

- Helps with weight loss if needed, and prevents weight gain.

- Reduces the risk of developing conditions such as stroke, heart attack, diabetes, depression, some cancers and arthritis.

- Increases energy. Regular exercise improves the efficiency of our lungs, heart and blood vessels, which gives us more energy.

- Improves mood. Physical activity stimulates many brain chemicals that cause us to be happier and more relaxed. It also improves our appearance, confidence and self-esteem.

- Improves sleep, by helping us fall asleep and stay asleep.

▲ Figure 9.10 *Exercise has many benefits*

Drink and drugs

Alcohol

It is illegal for anyone under the age of 18 in Ireland to purchase alcohol. What are the problems caused by alcohol?

- It is a depressant (it slows down the working of the brain). This can result in altering our emotions, perceptions, vision, hearing and movement.

- It is a toxic substance. This means that it causes us to feel sick, lose co-ordination, stagger, slur our speech and slow our reaction times.

- It changes our mood. Some people become more friendly and talkative, but some people become aggressive and angry.

- Large amounts of alcohol taken in a short period of time may result in alcohol poisoning. This may result in vomiting, extreme sleepiness, loss of consciousness and even death.

- It is addictive. Anyone who takes alcohol may become dependent on it.

Drugs

The effects of drugs depend on:

- The type of drug
- The amount of the drug
- The size of the person
- How often it is taken
- How fast it gets to the brain
- What other drugs, substances or food are taken at the same time.

Some drugs can have serious effects on our physical and mental health and are illegal.

? Question

9.17 Select and research one of the following common illegal drugs:

- Cannabis
- Cocaine
- Ecstasy
- Heroin.

Explain the effects and dangers of the selected drug.

Sleep

In general, young people need more sleep than adults. Most young people need about eight hours' sleep each night.

Sleep is vitally important to our health. It:

- Improves our concentration
- Makes us more alert
- Increases our energy levels
- Allows our body to recover and heal.

Work/life balance

An important lifestyle choice is to allow enough time for relaxation and play. We all need to have fun and a laugh. This is often best done in the company of good friends. We need to be aware of what makes us feel good and happy and to include this in our daily routine.

What are micro-organisms?

Micro-organisms are small living things.

Most micro-organisms are too small to be seen with the naked eye. They can be seen only using microscopes.

Micro-organisms are found in huge numbers almost everywhere. For example, they are present in the air, water and soil, on our skin, and inside plants, animals and humans.

There are three types of micro-organism:

- Viruses
- Bacteria
- Fungi.

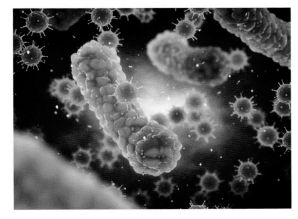

▲ **Figure 9.11** *Bacteria (green) and viruses (blue)*

Viruses and bacteria are too small to be seen by eye, but we can see some fungi.

Are all micro-organisms harmful?

Most micro-organisms are of benefit. For example, they are important as they play crucial roles in:

- Decomposition – which allows living things to be broken down and their minerals released so they can be recycled into new living things
- Food production – they are involved in making many foods, alcohol, baking
- Biotechnology – this is the use of living things, or parts of living things, to produce useful products such as drugs, flavourings, colourings, vitamins, artificial cloth and fuels
- Water treatment
- Digestive systems – bacteria in our intestines make vitamins, prevent the growth of disease-causing organisms and break down some foods.

What is the role of micro-organisms in human health?

Some micro-organisms (often called microbes or germs) are **pathogens**. This means they cause disease.

What diseases do micro-organisms cause?

Viruses

Viruses are the smallest micro-organisms. Up to one million viruses may fit across the thickness of a thumbnail (1 mm). Viruses cannot reproduce by themselves. For this reason, it can be argued that they are not living things.

Viruses increase in numbers by invading cells. They cause the invaded cells to form new viruses. For this reason, all viruses are said to be **parasites** (i.e. they live on or in another living thing).

Examples of human diseases caused by viruses include:

- Measles
- Mumps
- Chicken pox
- Polio
- Colds
- Flu (influenza)
- Cold sores
- AIDS (caused by HIV)
- Ebola.

Very few chemicals or medicines can kill viruses in our body. For example, antibiotics prevent bacterial infections but have no effect on viruses.

Our bodies fight off most virus infections when our white blood cells produce chemicals called **antibodies**.

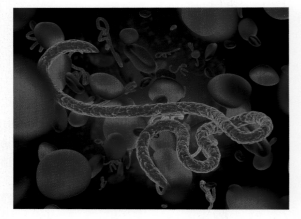

▲ Figure 9.12 *Ebola virus emerging from a cell*

Bacteria

Bacteria are larger than viruses. They are very simple organisms; for example, they do not have a proper nucleus.

In order to grow, bacteria need the following:

- Food
- Water
- A suitable temperature
- A suitable pH.

Under ideal conditions bacteria can reproduce very rapidly. They reproduce asexually. Many bacteria can double their numbers every 20 minutes.

Examples of human bacterial diseases are:

- Tetanus (lockjaw)
- Tuberculosis (TB)
- Pneumonia
- Sore throats
- Tooth and gum decay
- Food poisoning
- Cholera
- Anthrax.

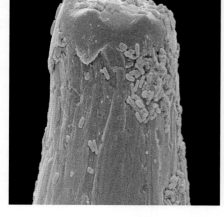

▲ Figure 9.13 *Bacteria on the sharp tip of a pin*

Antibiotics are chemicals made by bacteria and fungi, which kill or prevent the reproduction of other bacteria. Penicillin is an example of an antibiotic.

> ### ⑦ Questions
>
> **9.18** Why are antibiotics of no value in treating flu?
>
> **9.19** What is the difference between antibiotics and antibodies?
>
> **9.20** It is suggested that the misuse of antibiotics has resulted in the evolution of antibiotic-resistant bacteria.
>
> **(a)** Find out the name of two of the most common antibiotic-resistant bacteria in Ireland.
>
> **(b)** Research the ways in which antibiotics have been misused.
>
> **(c)** What is the main danger of misusing antibiotics?

Fungi

Fungi are simple organisms that do not contain chlorophyll. For this reason they are not green and cannot make their own food.

Examples of human fungal diseases are:

- Athlete's foot
- Ringworm.

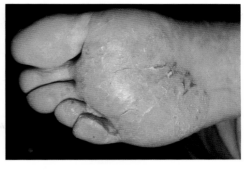
▲ Figure 9.14 *Athlete's foot infection*

How do we reduce the risk of infections?

Most pathogens spread through the air when we sneeze or cough. Some spread when we touch something, and a small number spread in body fluids such as sweat, saliva, blood or semen. In addition, some pathogens enter our body when we eat improperly cooked food.

The best ways to reduce infections are to:

- Wash our hands in soap and warm water for at least 15 seconds. This is important before eating or preparing food and after we cough, sneeze, use the toilet, touch animals, play outside or visit a sick person.

- Make sure we get all our **immunisations** (often called **vaccinations**). These introduce a small amount of the pathogen into the body, which allows our bodies to produce antibodies against the pathogen. This means we will have long-term resistance to the pathogen.

▲ Figure 9.15 *Some vaccinations are given to babies*

    As the pathogen cannot reproduce, the vaccination will not cause us to suffer all the symptoms of the infection.

- Cook food properly. High temperatures kill micro-organisms.
- Eat a proper diet, get regular exercise and get enough sleep, which all help our bodies to fight off pathogens.

? Questions

9.21 Research the most common diseases against which we can be immunised or vaccinated.

9.22 Explain why vaccinations give us long-lasting resistance to infection but antibiotics give only short-term resistance.

Did you know?

It is suggested that we wash our hands for the same length of time it takes us to sing one verse of the 'Happy Birthday' song.

Activity 9.1 How can we show that micro-organisms are present in different locations?

We will take samples from different locations and grow them on nutrient agar in petri dishes. Nutrient agar is a solid, jelly-like substance that contains food that micro-organisms need to grow.

🧪 Equipment needed

Nutrient agar

Petri dishes (also called plates)

Cotton wool buds

A beaker with boiled water

Masking tape

Pen or marker

Disinfectant

Basin

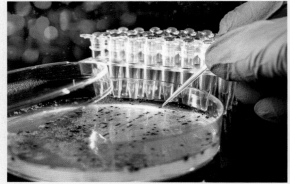

▲ Figure 9.16 *Micro-organisms growing on agar in a petri dish*

⚠ Safety

Micro-organisms can cause disease, so we have to reduce the risks by:
- Washing our hands before and after the activity
- Not putting anything dirty in or near our mouths
- Covering any cuts with a bandage or wearing plastic gloves
- Taping the dishes shut
- Killing any micro-organisms at the end of the activity by soaking the dishes in sterilising liquid or disinfectant.

➡ Conducting the activity

1. Dip a clean cotton wool bud in boiled water in a beaker. Rub the damp cotton wool bud over the surface to be tested. Sample surfaces are a door handle, a computer keyboard, a desk surface, a phone, the sink in a bathroom, a bin, the sole of your shoe, the inside of your mouth, under your finger nails, etc. Use a separate cotton wool bud in each location.

2. Open the lid of the plate slightly so that micro-organisms in the air do not enter. Rub the cotton wool bud gently over the surface of the agar in a petri dish.

   If you wish you could use half of each dish for two different samples, just remember which side has which sample. (You could also press your unwashed fingers gently on the surface of the agar in one dish and repeat this in a second dish after washing your hands.)

   Petri dish

   Nutrient ager

   Cotton wool bud

   ▲ Figure 9.17 *Rubbing a cotton wool bud over the surface of the agar in a petri dish*

3. Place the lid on the dish and seal it closed with tape.

4. Place a piece of (masking) tape across the base of the dish and use it to label the source of the sample(s) and your name.

5. Tape a petri dish shut without opening it. This dish will act as a control or comparison for the other dish(es).

6. Leave the dishes in a warm place (between 20°C and 30°C) to allow micro-organisms to grow.

7. Leave the dishes upside down to prevent water from dripping onto any micro-organisms that grow.

8. Leave the dishes for 4 to 7 days.

9. Examine the dishes, but do not open them.

▲ Figure 9.18 *Tape the lid shut and turn the dish upside down*

10. Take a note of which locations had:

    (a) The greatest and least numbers of different types of micro-organisms

    (b) The greatest and least amounts of overall growth of micro-organisms.

11. Record your results in the copy of the table below provided in your Student Activity Book. Do not forget to include the control dish.

Observation	Location
Greatest number of different types of micro-organisms	
Least number of different types of micro-organisms	
The dish(es) with the most overall growth	
Dish(es) with no visible growth	

12. When you are finished, the dishes should be soaked in sterilising liquid or disinfectant before being placed in a bin (unless your teacher instructs you otherwise).

⑦ Questions

9.23 Why did you use nutrient agar?

9.24 Why is it better to use a damp cotton wool bud rather than a dry one?

9.25 What problem might arise if the petri dishes were left in a cold place?

9.26 Why were the petri dishes left lying on their lids?

9.27 Name two types of micro-organisms that might grow on the agar.

9.28 You are asked to compare how effective two liquid hand sterilisers are in killing micro-organisms. Work in groups to plan how you might carry out this investigation.

Each group should present their findings to the class and then change their plan if necessary to respond to any good ideas they took from other groups in the class.

Summary questions

9.29 **(a)** What is meant by the term 'health'?

   (b) What is the difference between physical and mental health?

   (c) Name four factors that affect human health.

9.30 **(a)** Name two disorders caused by inherited factors.

   (b) Name two lifestyle choices that affect our health.

   (c) Our diet should contain carbohydrates, proteins and fats.

   (i)   Name one carbohydrate that we often eat.

   (ii)   Why do we need carbohydrates?

   (iii)   Why must we eat proteins?

   (iv)   Give one benefit of fat in our body.

9.31 Copy out the chart shown below and fill it in for 7 days to record what you have eaten.

For every portion of a particular type of food you eat, place a tick (✓) opposite that food type in the chart. Answer the questions on page 59 of the Student Activity Book

Food groups	Mon	Tues	Wed	Thurs	Fri	Sat	Sun
Fats, oils, cakes, biscuits, crisps, sugar, sweets							
Meat, fish, peas, beans							
Milk, cheese, yoghurt							
Fruit, vegetables							
Cereals, bread, rice, potatoes							

9.32 **(a)** What are micro-organisms?

   (b) Name three types of micro-organism.

   (c) Copy out the table below and include each of the following diseases in the correct column: ringworm, influenza, mumps, TB, cholera, athlete's foot, polio, common cold, pneumonia, cold sores.

Virus	Bacterium	Fungus

Log on to **www.edcolearning.ie** for **Additional Summary Questions**

Assessment question

9.33   **Question from Junior Cycle Science exam paper**   **(30 marks)**

Write the answers in your science copy book.

Read the article below, adapted from an Irish newspaper, and answer the questions that follow.

UCC Study: High fibre foods ease stress effects

Interest has been growing in recent years in the link between gut bacteria and stress-related disorders. Researchers at University College Cork (UCC) have shown that micro-organisms in the gut (intestines) are really important for our brain health.

▲ Figure 9.19

Bacteria in the gut produce fatty acids which are a source of nutrition for cells in this part of the body. Foods such as grains and vegetables contain high levels of fibre and will stimulate gut bacteria to produce these fatty acids.

The UCC study involved feeding mice the fatty acids normally produced by gut bacteria and then subjecting them to stress. Using behavioural tests, the mice were assessed for anxiety and depressive-like behaviour. The researchers found that there was a decreased level of this type of behaviour when fatty acids were consumed. These results provide new insights into mechanisms related to the impact of the gut bacteria on our brains and behaviour.

Irish Examiner

(a) Name a type of food that is high in fibre.

(b) The study involved feeding mice fatty acids and then subjecting them to stress. Describe a control experiment which the scientists could have used in this investigation.

(c) What observation did the scientists note about the behaviour of the mice after they had been fed fatty acids?

(d) Do you agree or disagree with the use of animals (such as mice) in scientific research? Explain your answer.

(e) Human health is affected by environmental factors such as stress. Name another environmental factor which has an effect on human health.

(f) This article highlights a beneficial role of micro-organisms in human health. State another example of how bacteria could have an effect on human health.

(g) Figure 9.20 shows bacterial cells dividing in order to reproduce. This is an example of asexual reproduction. Describe one difference between sexual and asexual reproduction.

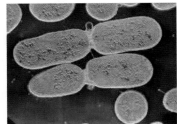

(h) Over time a bacterial population can evolve. Outline the theory of evolution by natural selection.

▲ Figure 9.20

 Log on to **www.edcolearning.ie** for **Additional Assessment Questions**

BIOLOGICAL WORLD

CHAPTER 10
RESPIRATION AND PHOTOSYNTHESIS

LO: BW7

Biochemical processes

A biochemical process is a chemical reaction (or a series of chemical reactions) that takes place in a living thing.

Respiration and photosynthesis are biochemical processes. They both involve energy conversions:

- In respiration, energy is released from food
- In photosynthesis energy is used to make food.

What is respiration?

High-energy drinks give us an extra burst of energy when we are getting tired. Have you ever wondered how energy in food ends up as energy in the body that keeps us moving?

Respiration is the release of energy from food.

- If this process needs oxygen, it is called **aerobic respiration**.

- If oxygen is not needed, the process is called **anaerobic respiration**.

Respiration is summarised by the equation:

$$\text{food} \xrightarrow{\text{respiration}} \text{energy}$$

What is aerobic respiration?

Living things need energy to allow them to move, grow, stay warm and repair damaged parts. They get their energy from food in a process called respiration. Respiration for the majority of living things is aerobic.

Aerobic respiration can be summarised by the word equation:

$$\text{glucose} + \text{oxygen} \longrightarrow \text{carbon dioxide} + \text{water} + \text{energy}$$

> **? Question**
>
> **10.1** Respiration is vital to life.
>
>   **(a)** Why do all living things need respiration?
>
>   **(b)** Why do humans normally have higher rates of respiration by day than they do by night?
>
>   **(c)** What are the end products of aerobic respiration?

To allow aerobic respiration to take place, cells need a supply of glucose and oxygen. In humans:

● Glucose is carried by blood plasma from the small intestine to all the cells of the body

● Oxygen is carried by haemoglobin in red blood cells from the lungs to all the cells of the body.

In all living cells glucose combines with oxygen to release energy and the waste products (end products) carbon dioxide and water (vapour). Some of the energy is used by the cells, while some is lost as heat.

The waste products are carried by blood plasma to the lungs, where they pass out of (are excreted from) the body.

As well as taking place in all the living cells in the human body, aerobic respiration also takes place in most animal and plant cells.

Aerobic respiration starts in the cytoplasm of a cell but finishes (and releases most of the energy) in the mitochondria.

> **? Questions**
>
> **10.2** What do we use energy for?
>
> **10.3** When we take in more energy than we need, what happens to the surplus energy?
>
> **10.4** Active people need larger amounts of food than inactive people. Explain why this is the case.
>
> **10.5** Suggest two reasons why we breathe faster when we exercise.
>
> **10.6** Oxygen gas is held in the atmosphere by the force of gravity. This prevents it from escaping from Earth. Suggest why people who live at high altitudes have greater concentrations of red blood cells than those who live at sea level.

▲ Figure 10.1 *Activity uses energy*

▲ Figure 10.2 *Much less energy is needed while resting*

What factors affect respiration?

The main factors affecting respiration are:

● Temperature

● Oxygen

● Water.

Temperature

Respiration is a process that occurs in living things. This means it is a biological process. Most biological reactions are controlled by **enzymes**. These are proteins that speed up reactions without being used up in the reaction.

Above a certain temperature enzymes change shape, which means they do not work so well. This means that the rate of the reaction slows down. These changes are shown in the graph in Figure 10.3.

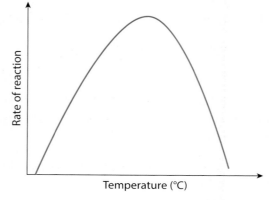

▲ Figure 10.3 *Rate of enzyme reaction at different temperatures*

Human enzymes have their maximum rate of reaction at 37°C, while plant enzymes work best between 20°C and 30°C. This means the rate of respiration is highest at these temperatures in humans or in plants.

Oxygen

Oxygen is essential for aerobic respiration. When we exercise we breathe faster and deeper to take in more oxygen and release more energy and carbon dioxide.

If there is a shortage of oxygen (e.g. when we exercise vigorously, or if a plant's roots are in waterlogged soil) the rate of respiration may not supply enough energy.

In cases such as those mentioned above, cells can respire anaerobically; this means they break down glucose in the absence of oxygen. This supplies a small amount of extra energy to the cells. However, it also produces harmful waste products. In humans, anaerobic respiration produces **lactic acid** and some energy, as shown in the equation below:

$$\text{glucose} \longrightarrow \text{lactic acid} + \text{a small amount of energy}$$

Lactic acid causes muscles to cramp, which forces us to stop the exercise.

In yeast cells anaerobic respiration produces alcohol, carbon dioxide and some energy:

glucose ⟶ alcohol + carbon dioxide + a small amount of energy

Did you know?

Yeast is a fungus and is used to make alcohol (beers and wine) and can also be used in baking (the carbon dioxide causes dough to rise).

▲ Figure 10.4 *Cramp can often occur when we play sports, which forces us to stop exercising*

Water

Water is essential to allow enzymes to work. This means a lack of water in cells will slow down the rate of respiration. This is why we must ensure that we drink enough water, especially when we lose water as sweat (e.g. in hot weather or during exercise).

Did you know?

Lactic acid forming in our chest muscles causes a stitch: if it forms in our heart muscles it causes pain in the chest before a person experiences a heart attack.

What are the products of respiration?

We have seen that the products of respiration are:

● **Energy:** This is why all living things carry out respiration. The more active an organism is, the more respiration it needs to carry out.

● **Carbon dioxide:** This is a waste product of respiration.

  ■ Animals release carbon dioxide into the air.

  ■ Plants may use some of the carbon dioxide they produce for photosynthesis; any carbon dioxide not used in photosynthesis is released into the air.

● **Water (vapour):** This is another waste product of respiration. Both plants and animals release water vapour into the air.

✐ Activity 10.1 Can we investigate a factor that affects respiration?

Yeast respires to produce carbon dioxide. The carbon dioxide produces foam at the top of the solution. The volume of the foam produced indicates the rate of respiration.

🧪 Equipment needed

Glucose

Weighing scales

5 beakers

Stirring rod

Yeast

4 graduated cylinders

1 (or preferably 4) thermometer(s)

Water

➡ Conducting the activity

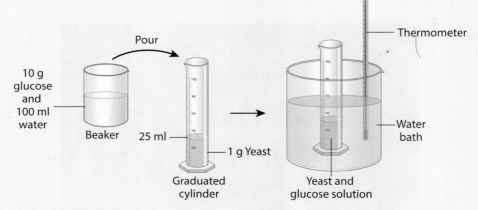

▲ Figure 10.5

1. Add 10 g of glucose to 100 ml of water in a beaker. Stir to dissolve the glucose in the water.
2. Add 1 g of yeast to a large graduated cylinder.
3. Add 25 ml of the glucose solution to the graduated cylinder.
4. Place the graduated cylinder in a water bath at 10°C.
5. After 10 minutes measure the volume of foam produced.
6. Repeat steps 2–5 in water baths at 20°C, 30°C and 40°C.
7. Record the results in the copy of the following table in your Student Activity Book.

Temperature (°C)	10	20	30	40
Volume of foam produced (ml)				

⑦ Question

10.7 A student carried out activity 10.1 as outlined above. The top of the foam was at the 60 ml line in the graduated cylinder at the end of the activity. The student recorded the volume of foam as 35 ml.

(a) Was this the correct volume of foam produced?

(b) Explain your answer to (a).

(c) They repeated the activity at a temperature of 80°C and found that no foam was produced. Why was no foam produced?

(d) Suggest a suitable control for activity 10.1.

(e) What volume of foam do you predict will be found in your control?

Activity 10.2   Can we show that a gas is produced by respiration in yeast?

Yeast breaks down sugars to form alcohol and carbon dioxide. If we carry out this reaction in a plastic bottle covered by a balloon, the gas formed may cause the balloon to inflate.

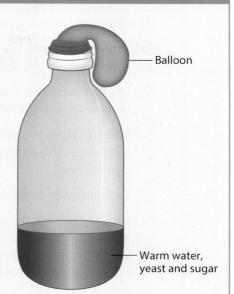
Balloon

Warm water, yeast and sugar

▲ **Figure 10.6** *To show that gas is produced by respiration in yeast*

Equipment needed

Small, clear plastic drinks bottle   Sugar

Balloon   Warm water

Yeast

➡ Conducting the activity

1. Blow the balloon up and let it deflate a few times to stretch and loosen it.

2. Pour warm water into the bottle to a depth of about 3 cm.

3. Add a teaspoonful of dried yeast and swirl it around a few times to dissolve it.

4. Add a teaspoonful of sugar to the yeast solution and swirl it to ensure it is dissolved.

5. Place the balloon over the neck of the bottle to seal it.

6. Leave it in a warm place and observe what happens over the next 30 minutes (or longer).

7. As a control, set up a second bottle in the same way but leave out the sugar.

8. Record the results in the copy of the following table provided in your Student Activity Book.

Contents of bottle	Amount of expansion of balloon (e.g. none / some / most)
Water, yeast, sugar	
Water, yeast (no sugar)	

? Questions

10.8   Apart from respiration, what other factor might cause either balloon to expand?

10.9   The balloon with the yeast and sugar will stop expanding after some time. Suggest why this happens.

10.10   Why is it better to use warm water than cold water?

10.11   Suggest how you might adapt this activity to investigate the effects of carrying out respiration at different temperatures.

10.12 The equipment in Figure 10.7 was set up to investigate gas exchange in animals.

(a) After some time the drop of coloured liquid was seen to move. In which direction do you think it will move?

(b) Explain why the drop moved in the direction you stated.

(c) Will the concentration of carbon dioxide in the container change over time?

(d) Explain your answer to part (c).

(e) If the test tube were placed in a water bath at 10°C and later at 20°C, would this affect the speed at which the drop of liquid moves?

(f) Explain your answer to part (e).

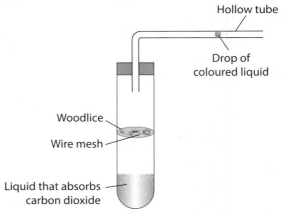

▲ Figure 10.7 *Investigating gas exchange in respiration*

What is photosynthesis?

The Sun is the source of most of the energy on Earth. It provides heat to keep our planet warm. It also provides energy in the form of light (**solar energy**).

Plants use solar energy to make food in a process called photosynthesis. In this way, they convert energy from one form (light) to another form (the chemical energy in food):

10.13 What term is used to describe organisms that make their own food?

10.14 What term is used to describe organisms that cannot make their own food?

$$\text{light energy} \xrightarrow{\text{photosynthesis}} \text{chemical energy}$$

One of the main differences between plants and animals is that plants can make their own food, while animals cannot.

What is the word equation for photosynthesis?

Photosynthesis can be summarised by the word equation:

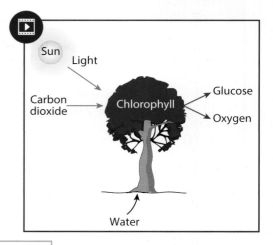

▲ Figure 10.8 *Summary of photosynthesis*

$$\text{carbon dioxide} + \text{water} \xrightarrow[\text{chlorophyll}]{\text{light}} \text{glucose} + \text{oxygen}$$

10.15 Photosynthesis has many benefits.

(a) What is the main benefit of photosynthesis to plants?

(b) Photosynthesis has two main benefits for animals. What are they?

What are the factors that affect photosynthesis?

Photosynthesis is affected by the following factors:

● Light   ● Water   ● Temperature.

● Carbon dioxide   ● Chlorophyll

Light

Plants get light from the Sun.

● Sunlight is absorbed by leaves

● Leaves have large flat surfaces to allow them to absorb as much light as possible

● Light provides the energy needed to form food (or glucose).

The effects of increasing light intensity (brightness) on the rate of photosynthesis are shown by the graph in Figure 10.9.

● At low light intensities, increasing the light intensity will increase the rate of photosynthesis (as shown in part A of the graph).

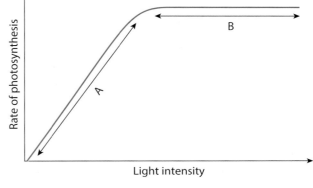

▲ **Figure 10.9** *The effects of increasing light intensity on the rate of photosynthesis*

● Above a certain light intensity, the rate of photosynthesis remains constant (as shown in part B of the graph). This is because the plant cannot get enough of a necessary factor, e.g. carbon dioxide.

❓ **Question**

10.16 Why do many leaves have large, flat surfaces?

Carbon dioxide

Plants get carbon dioxide from the air or from respiration in the plant.

● Carbon dioxide passes from the air into leaves through tiny openings called **stomata**.

● Stomata are mainly found on the lower surface of a leaf.

The effect of increasing carbon dioxide concentrations on the rate of photosynthesis is shown by the graph in Figure 10.10.

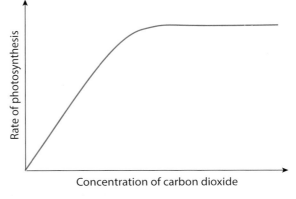

▲ **Figure 10.10** *The effect of increasing carbon dioxide concentration on the rate of photosynthesis*

- If plants are short of carbon dioxide the rate of photosynthesis will slow down.
- Increasing the concentration of carbon dioxide increases the rate of photosynthesis.
- Above a certain concentration of carbon dioxide the rate of photosynthesis remains constant. This is because the plant cannot get enough of another factor, such as light.

Water

Plants get water from the soil. Water from the soil enters the roots and then passes from the roots up through the stem to the leaves.

Water is needed to allow glucose to be made, and it allows enzymes to work so that photosynthesis can take place.

Chlorophyll

Plants make chlorophyll. Chlorophyll is a green dye or pigment that is mostly found in chloroplasts in the leaves (and other green parts) of a plant. It absorbs light and allows photosynthesis to take place.

Chlorophyll is not used up in the process of photosynthesis. In this way it acts as a catalyst (a catalyst speeds up a reaction without being used up in the reaction).

Plants lacking chlorophyll are often yellow(ish) and have reduced rates of photosynthesis.

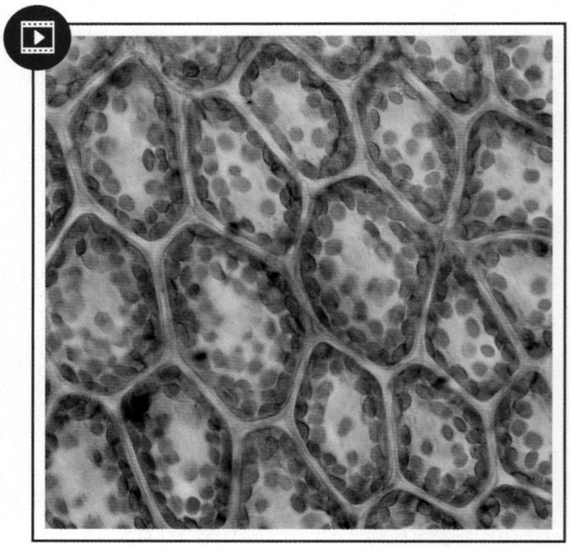

▲ **Figure 10.11** *Chloroplasts in plant cells*

Temperature

Photosynthesis is an enzyme-controlled reaction. This means it is affected by temperature. The ideal temperature for photosynthesis in most plants is between 20°C and 30°C.

Other factors

Other factors that affect photosynthesis are:

- The surface area of the leaves
- The number of leaves
- The distribution of leaves (i.e. whether they are blocking light from each other)
- The number of tiny openings (called stomata) on the leaves.

Questions

10.17 **Suggest two reasons why the rate of photosynthesis is greater in summer than in winter.**

10.18 **In a sealed glasshouse the concentration of carbon dioxide was measured over 24 hours. The concentration was found to be at its minimum around the middle of the day and reached a maximum just before dawn.**

(a) Give reasons for these two observations.

(b) Suggest why small gas flames are sometimes left alight for a period of time in glasshouses.

Activity 10.3 **Can we investigate a factor that affects photosynthesis?**

 **Activity video**

Plants produce glucose in photosynthesis. They then convert the glucose to starch, which they store. We can use starch to indicate whether photosynthesis takes place or not.

Equipment needed

Potted plant (e.g. Busy Lizzie)
Aluminium foil (tinfoil)
2 beakers
Forceps (or tweezers)
Boiling water
Alcohol (methylated spirits)

Water bath
Bunsen burner
Tripod
White tile
Iodine solution
Test tube

➡ Conducting the activity

1. Place the plant in darkness overnight. This will remove starch from the leaves.
2. Immediately after taking the plant out of the light cover some of the leaves (front and back) with aluminium foil (tinfoil).
3. Leave the plant in bright light for several hours.
4. Take one covered and one uncovered leaf and test them for starch.

Leaves covered in aluminium foil

Leaves exposed to light

▲ **Figure 10.12** *Plant showing some leaves covered by aluminium foil*

How can we test leaves for starch?

1. Put the leaf in boiling water for a few minutes to soften it.
2. Put the leaf into a test tube of alcohol.
3. Place the test tube with the leaf and alcohol into a water bath with boiling hot water. This will warm the alcohol. Warm alcohol removes chlorophyll from the leaf (but it also makes the leaf brittle).
4. Take the leaf out of the test tube with the tweezers and rinse it in warm water. This re-softens the leaf.

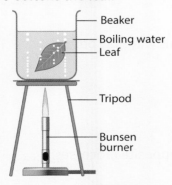

Beaker
Boiling water
Leaf
Tripod
Bunsen burner

▲ **Figure 10.13** *Softening a leaf*

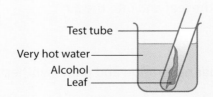

Test tube
Very hot water
Alcohol
Leaf

▲ **Figure 10.14** *Removing chlorophyll from a leaf*

5. Place the leaf on a white tile and add iodine solution (which is red/yellow).
6. If starch is present the leaf turns blue-black. If no starch is present the leaf remains red/yellow. Record the results in the table provided in your Student Activity Book.

Final colour of the leaf	Leaf in the light	Leaf in the dark

? Question

10.19 Answer the following questions with reference to activity 10.3.

(a) Why was the plant placed in the dark?

(b) What was the function of the aluminium foil?

(c) Why was the plant left in bright light?

(d) Which leaf would you predict would contain starch? What final colour would you expect in this leaf?

(e) Michelle adapted this activity to produce her initial on a leaf by cutting its shape into the aluminium foil. Her original leaf is shown.

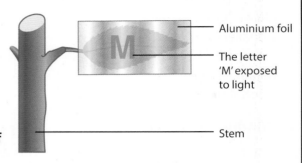

▲ Figure 10.15 *Michelle's leaf*

After exposure to light the aluminium foil was removed and the leaf was tested for starch. What colour(s) would you expect:

 (i) The letter 'M' to be?

(ii) The rest of the leaf outside of the letter 'M' to be?

What are the products of photosynthesis?

Glucose

The food made by a plant is called glucose. Glucose made in a leaf may be used:

● To provide energy in respiration
● To form starch in different parts of the plant
● To form new cells and allow for growth.

Oxygen

The gas made by photosynthesis is oxygen. The oxygen made in this way may be:

● Used for aerobic respiration, to provide energy in the leaf
● Released out of the leaf and into the air.

Summary

Table 10.1 shows that respiration and photosynthesis are largely opposite processes.

Table 10.1 **Comparison of respiration and photosynthesis**

	Respiration	**Photosynthesis**
Gases required	Oxygen	Carbon dioxide
Gases produced	Carbon dioxide and water (vapour)	Oxygen
Energy required or released	Released	Required
When it takes place	Daylight and darkness	Daylight
Where it occurs	Plants and animals	Plants

Summary questions

10.20 Copy out the following table and insert the word 'Respiration' or 'Photosynthesis' into column B to match each of the statements in column A.

Column A	Column B
Breaks down glucose	
Needs light	
Releases carbon dioxide	
Takes place in all living things	
Makes glucose	
May be aerobic or anaerobic	
Requires chlorophyll	

10.21 **(a)** What is meant by the term 'biochemical process'?

(b) Name two biochemical processes.

(c) Which biochemical process takes place in:

   (i) Chloroplasts

   (ii) Mitochondria?

10.22 Name two factors that affect:

(a) Respiration

(b) Photosynthesis.

10.23 **(a)** Name a gas needed for respiration.

(b) Name a gas produced by respiration.

(c) What is the benefit to a plant of respiration?

10.24 **(a)** Name a gas needed for photosynthesis.

(b) Name a gas produced by photosynthesis.

(c) What is the benefit to a plant of photosynthesis?

(d) Photosynthesis has two main benefits for animals. What are these benefits?

10.25 Write out the word equations for:

(a) Respiration

(b) Photosynthesis.

10.26 Pondweed is a green plant that lives under water. When exposed to light it carries out photosynthesis and releases a gas. The gas can be collected as shown in Figure 10.16.

(a) Name the gas produced.

(b) Name two factors that would increase the volume of the gas produced.

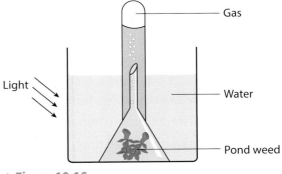

▲ Figure 10.16

Assessment question

10.27 Question from SEC Junior Cycle Science sample paper (30 marks)

Write all answers in your science copy book.

A group of students carried out a habitat study.

(a) Use words from the list to name the pieces of equipment shown below, which can be used in a habitat study.

Beating tray   Pooter   Net   Pitfall trap

Picture	Name

(b) The students also used a quadrat during their habitat study.

What shape is a quadrat? Describe how the students might have used the quadrat. In one part of the habitat, the students used the quadrat 30 times and found that a certain species was present on 18 occasions. Calculate the percentage frequency of that species.

The students were given permission to remove some green plants from the habitat to take back to their school laboratory. They did this in order to investigate factors that affect photosynthesis.

(c) Imagine that you are one of the students. You have been asked to carry out an experiment to investigate how any one factor affects photosynthesis.

Name one factor which could affect photosynthesis and which you might investigate.

List two factors which you would keep constant (fixed) during the experiment to ensure that it is a fair test.

(d) Write a suitable hypothesis for this experiment.

(e) Draw a labelled diagram of the setup of your experiment.

 Log on to **www.edcolearning.ie** for Additional Assessment Questions

 PowerPoint summary   **Weblinks**

Learning intentions

At the end of this chapter you will be able to:

✓ Describe the structure and functions of the male and female reproductive systems

✓ Explain what happens in a menstrual cycle

✓ Explain how pregnancy occurs and develops

✓ Discuss some medical, ethical and societal issues associated with sexual reproduction.

Keywords

- gametes
- testis
- sperm
- puberty
- penis
- scrotum
- ovaries
- fallopian tube
- uterus
- cervix
- vagina
- birth
- menstrual cycle
- pregnancy
- menstruation
- ovulation
- fertile period
- intercourse
- fertilisation
- implantation
- amnion
- amniotic fluid
- placenta
- umbilical cord
- contraception
- IVF
- stem cells

What is reproduction?

Reproduction is the production of new individuals.

As outlined in chapter 3, reproduction can be asexual or sexual.

Asexual reproduction is the production of offspring from one parent only. Examples of asexual reproduction are given in chapter 3.

Sexual reproduction is the production of offspring from two parents. Humans reproduce sexually. Sexual reproduction involves two parents. Each parent produces sex cells (also called **gametes**). The male gametes are the sperm. The female gametes are the eggs.

? Question

11.1 Figure 11.1 shows a zorse. This is the result of crossing a male zebra with a female horse.

(a) Name the male and female gametes that form a zorse.

(b) What structures in the gametes cause the zorse to have features of a horse and of a zebra?

(c) While zorses are produced by sexual reproduction, they cannot reproduce (i.e. they are sterile). Research two other examples of sterile animals produced by crossing two different species.

▲ Figure 11.1 *A male zebra and a female horse produce a zorse*

The male reproductive system

What are the functions of the parts of the male reproductive system?

Testis

The testis (plural testes) makes sperm. The testes start to make sperm between the ages of 12 and 14. This is the age of sexual maturity (**puberty**) in boys.

Along with making sperm, other changes take place in a boy's body at puberty. These include:

- Enlargement of the **penis** and testes
- A rapid growth spurt
- Enlargement of the voice box (larynx, or Adam's apple), causing the voice to deepen
- Growth of hair on the body.

Each sperm cell is tiny and they are produced in huge numbers by the testes.

Scrotum

The scrotum is a sac in which the testes are held. The scrotum holds the testes outside the body, allowing them to be kept at a temperature just lower than body temperature. This allows sperm to be made successfully.

Sperm ducts

Two sperm ducts carry sperm from the testes to the penis.

A number of glands are located beside the sperm ducts. These glands produce a liquid called seminal fluid. The mixture of sperm and seminal fluid is called semen.

Penis

The sperm ducts join a tube called the urethra. Sperm pass through this tube, which is located in the centre of the penis.

The penis allows semen to pass out of the male body and into the body of the female.

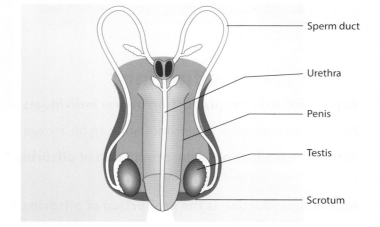

Sperm duct

Urethra

Penis

Testis

Scrotum

▲ Figure 11.2 *The male reproductive system*

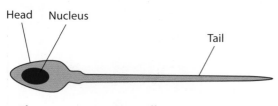

Head   Nucleus

Tail

▲ Figure 11.3 *A sperm cell*

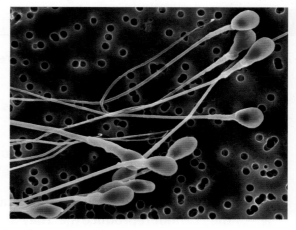

▲ Figure 11.4 *Sperm cells*

⑦ Questions

11.2 Rewrite the words below in the correct order to describe the path taken by sperm cells:

Sperm duct   Penis   Testis

11.3 Name the structure in males responsible for each of the following:

(a) Making sperm

(b) Controlling the temperature at which sperm are produced

(c) Transferring sperm to the female

(d) Carrying sperm from the testes to the penis.

The female reproductive system

What are the functions of the parts of the female reproductive system?

Ovary

The ovaries produce eggs. They start to make eggs at puberty. This occurs between the ages of 10 and 13 years in girls. Other changes taking place in the girl's body at puberty include:

- Growth of the pelvis, breasts, vagina and uterus
- Growth of hair on parts of the body.

Eggs are the female gametes. Each egg is much larger than a sperm cell.

Normally, one egg is formed each month in the female body. Egg production starts at puberty. Beyond the age of 35 the number of eggs in each ovary falls dramatically.

Egg production usually stops between 45 and 55 years of age. This stage, when the ovaries have run out of eggs, is called the menopause (also known as the 'change of life').

Fallopian tube

The fallopian tube collects an egg from the ovary and carries it to the uterus.

If sperm are present, one of them may join (or fuse) with the egg in the fallopian tube. If there are no sperm present, the egg dies within 2 days.

Uterus

The uterus, or womb, is the place in which a baby (or embryo) will develop.

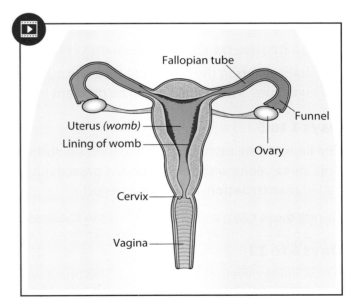

▲ Figure 11.5 *The female reproductive system*

Cervix

The cervix is the opening or neck of the uterus.
Sperm pass through the cervix in order to reach an egg.

Vagina

The vagina is a muscular tube into which the penis releases sperm. It forms the **birth** canal when the baby passes down the vagina during childbirth.

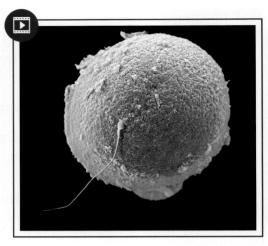

▲ Figure 11.6 *A sperm cell fertilising an egg*

? Questions

11.4 Name the structures in males and females that produce gametes.

11.5 Outline the differences between sperm and eggs in terms of:

(a) Size (b) Numbers formed (c) Structure.

11.6 In order to prevent pregnancy some women have their fallopian tubes closed by surgery. How does this prevent pregnancy?

11.7 Research the name given to a similar procedure to that in question 11.6 for males, in which the sperm ducts are cut or sealed.

What is the menstrual cycle?

The menstrual cycle is a series of changes that take place in females about every 28 days between puberty and the menopause.

The menstrual cycle does not take place during **pregnancy** (i.e. when a baby is developing in the uterus).

What happens during a menstrual cycle?

The main events in the menstrual cycle are outlined below. The times given in this account are average times. These timings can be different in different females and during different months.

Days 1 to 5

The lining of the uterus (which had built up during the previous menstrual cycle) breaks down. This lining, along with some blood, is passed out of the body through the vagina. This process is called **menstruation**, or having a period.

During these days, a new egg matures in the ovary.

Days 6 to 13

A new lining develops in the uterus. This lining will be needed to nourish a developing baby if the female becomes pregnant. The egg continues to develop in the ovary.

Day 14

The egg is released from the ovary. This is called **ovulation**. The egg can survive for 2 days in the fallopian tube.

Days 15 to 28

The lining of the uterus remains in place. It will break down on the first day of the next menstrual cycle.

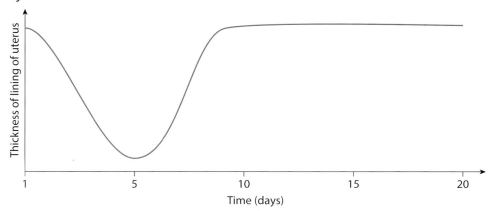

▲ Figure 11.7 *The changes in thickness of the lining of the uterus over part of the menstrual cycle*

? Question

11.8 Figure 11.7 shows what happened to the thickness of the uterus lining over part of a menstrual cycle. Refer to this figure to answer the following questions.

(a) What is menstruation?

(b) On what day did menstruation finish?

(c) Why does the lining of the uterus thicken?

(d) On what day would you expect the lining to decrease in thickness again as it did on day 1?

(e) What is ovulation?

(f) On what day in a normal menstrual cycle does ovulation occur?

The fertile period

The **fertile period** is the time during the menstrual cycle when a female is most likely to become pregnant if she has sexual intercourse.

- Sperm can survive in the female reproductive system for 5 to 7 days. They survive for such a long time because the female system nourishes the sperm.

- The egg can stay alive for 2 days.

- The fertile period is the time in the menstrual cycle when pregnancy is most likely to take place. For a 28-day cycle this is normally from day 9 to day 16.

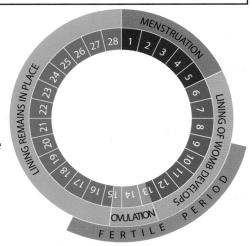

▲ Figure 11.8 *The menstrual cycle and the fertile period*

- The fertile period may be different in every female or in every month because menstrual cycles are not always 28 days long. In some females the fertile period could start before day 9 and last beyond day 16.

Did you know?

There is effectively no time within the menstrual cycle during which a female cannot get pregnant if she has sexual intercourse.

What is sexual intercourse?

Sexual intercourse (which is also called copulation) takes place when the erect penis of the male is placed in the vagina of the female.

The movement of the penis in the vagina causes semen to be released from the penis.

What happens to sperm in the vagina?

Normally, millions of sperm are released into the vagina. The sperm move through the cervix and into the uterus. They then move from the uterus towards a fallopian tube.

After ovulation, the egg is pushed along the fallopian tube by tiny hairs. Many sperm are attracted by a chemical released from the egg. The sperm swarm around the egg in the fallopian tube. Soon the head of one of the sperm will enter the egg.

If there is no egg present in the fallopian tube, the sperm die, normally within five days.

? Question

11.9   How do the sperm know which ovary has released the egg?

What is fertilisation?

Fertilisation takes place when the nucleus of a sperm joins or fuses with the nucleus of an egg.

Fertilisation normally takes place in the fallopian tube. The fertilised egg forms a single cell called a zygote.

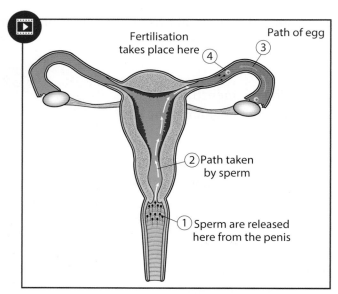

▲ **Figure 11.9** *Path of sperm and egg leading to fertilisation*

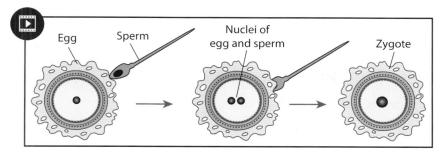

▲ Figure 11.10 *The process of fertilisation*

⑦ Questions

11.10 Figure 11.11 represents sexual reproduction in humans.

   (a) Name the structures represented by the letters A and C.

   (b) Name the cells represented by B and D.

   (c) Name the process E.

   (d) Name the cell F.

   (e) In what part of the female reproductive system does process E normally occur?

11.11 Research how identical twins are formed.

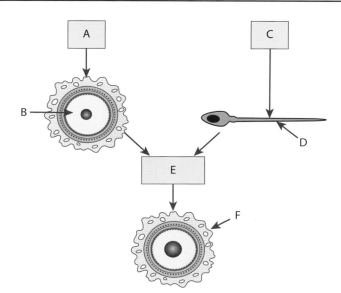

▲ Figure 11.11 *Representation of sexual reproduction in humans*

11.12 In what way is the formation of non-identical twins different to the formation of identical twins?

Pregnancy

Once the zygote has formed it goes through many cell divisions to form a ball of cells. These cells then form an embryo.

Within a few days of fertilisation, the embryo becomes attached to the lining of the uterus. **This attachment is called implantation.**

Soon after this, the embryo becomes surrounded by a membrane called the **amnion**. This membrane fills up with a liquid called

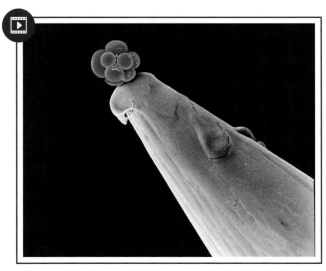

▲ Figure 11.12 *A 3-day-old embryo on the tip of a pin*

amniotic fluid. Amniotic fluid acts as a shock absorber to protect the embryo (or baby) during pregnancy.

After 8 weeks, the embryo can be recognised as a human. At this stage, it is called a foetus.

Pregnancy normally lasts from implantation until birth. A normal pregnancy lasts around 40 weeks (about 9 months).

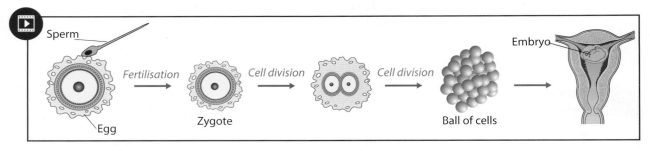

▲ Figure 11.13 *Sexual reproduction*

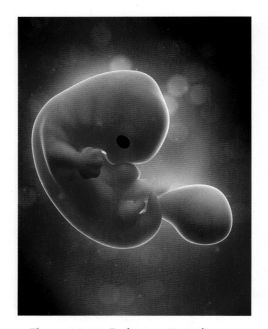

▲ Figure 11.14 *Embryo at 7 weeks*

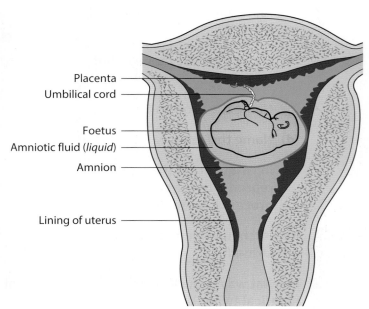

▲ Figure 11.15 *Foetus in uterus*

? Question

11.13 Rewrite the following in the order in which they normally take place:

Implantation	Gamete formation	Amnion formation	Fertilisation
Intercourse	Embryo formation	Zygote formation	

What is the placenta?

A structure called the **placenta** forms early in pregnancy. The baby's blood passes through the umbilical cord **to and from the placenta**. The placenta attaches to the lining of the uterus.

The umbilical cord attaches to the baby at the navel (belly button).

The function of the placenta

The function of the placenta is to allow materials to pass between the mother and the baby in the uterus. These materials pass by diffusion.

- **Food and oxygen** pass from the mother's blood into the baby's blood

- **Waste products** (such as carbon dioxide and salts) pass from the baby to the mother

- Along with these useful functions, the placenta also allows **harmful substances**, e.g. alcohol, smoke and drugs, to pass into the baby.

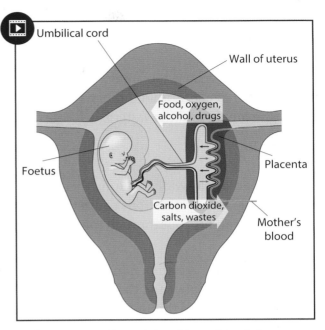

▲ **Figure 11.16** *Essential and harmful substances can pass between mother and foetus*

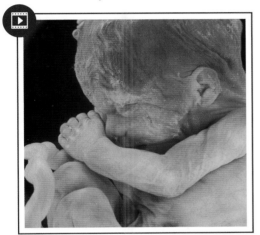

▲ **Figure 11.17** *Foetus at 12 to 15 weeks*

? Question

11.14 Figure 11.18 represents the links between a mother and her foetus during pregnancy.

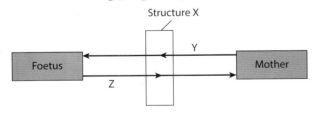

▲ **Figure 11.18** *Representation of pregnancy*

(a) Name the structure shown as X.

(b) Name a gas that passes in the direction of arrow Y.

(c) Why does the foetus need the gas named in part (b)?

(d) Name a gas that passes in the direction of arrow Z.

(e) From what organ does the gas named in part (d) pass out of the mother's body?

(f) Why can a foetus in the uterus not breathe through its mouth?

What happens at birth?

Stage 1

Towards the end of pregnancy, muscles in the uterus begin to contract. These contractions are called labour.

The contractions cause the amnion to burst. The release of the amniotic fluid through the vagina is called 'the breaking of the waters'.

Stage 2

The cervix gradually widens during these contractions. The contractions cause the baby to be pushed head first out through the cervix and the vagina.

The umbilical cord is clamped (to prevent loss of blood from the baby) and then cut. The baby soon starts to breathe through its lungs for the first time.

Stage 3

The uterus continues to contract after the baby is born. These contractions push the placenta and the remains of the umbilical cord out of the vagina. These materials are called the afterbirth.

The remains of the umbilical cord fall away from the baby's navel after about 7 days.

Growth of the baby

The baby may feed on breast milk produced by the mother. The main benefits of breastfeeding are:

● Breast milk is full of the ideal nutrients that a young baby needs

● Breast milk contains antibodies, which help to protect the baby from infections.

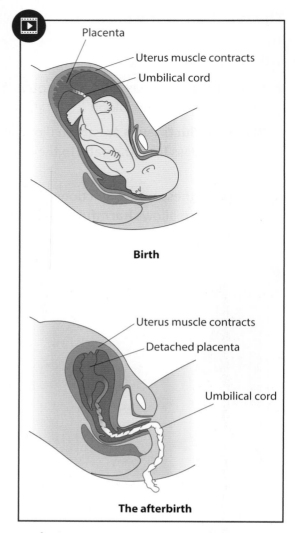

Birth

The afterbirth

▲ Figure 11.19 *Representation of childbirth*

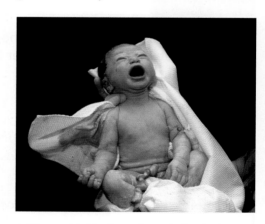

▲ Figure 11.20 *A newborn baby, before the umbilical cord is cut*

⑦ Question

11.15 Rewrite the following in the order in which they occur:

Amniotic fluid passes out of uterus / The baby's feet emerge from the vagina / The amnion breaks / The cervix expands / The baby's head emerges from the vagina / The placenta is expelled from the uterus / Contractions of the uterus begin

What are the main medical, ethical and societal issues surrounding sexual reproduction?

The area of sexual reproduction presents many issues for debate in terms of topics:

- Relating to our health
- That test our beliefs
- That relate to the society we live in.

Some of these topics are discussed in the following sections. Other topics can be researched and discussed in class groups.

Contraception

Medical issues

Contraception is the deliberate use of artificial methods to prevent pregnancy.

Some couples want to control the number of children they have or to control how soon after each other their children are born. Others wish to have sexual intercourse without the female becoming pregnant.

These couples may use contraception as a method of birth control, or family planning, in order to prevent unwanted pregnancies.

There are two main types of contraception:

- Preventing fertilisation
- Preventing implantation.

Preventing fertilisation

Natural methods

Natural methods of preventing the sperm from reaching the egg are based around avoiding intercourse during the female's fertile period. These methods aim to predict or detect the time of ovulation.

Artificial methods

Artificial methods of contraception include stopping the female from producing eggs. This can be achieved by the female taking the contraceptive pill.

Other artificial methods involve preventing the sperm from reaching the egg. These methods include:

- The use of a condom, which covers the top of the penis
- A cap, which covers the cervix
- Chemical creams or foams, which kill sperm
- Medical operations in which the sperm ducts or fallopian tubes are cut and sealed.

Preventing implantation

- Some pills prevent pregnancy by stopping the embryo from attaching (or implanting) in the uterus.
- A T-shaped device inserted by a doctor in the uterus also acts in this way.

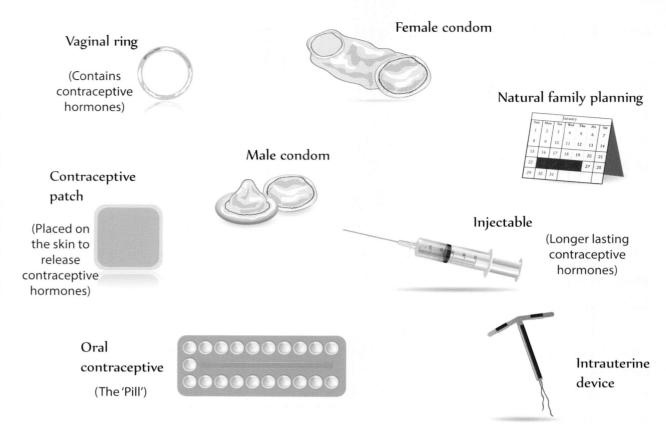

▲ Figure 11.21 *Contraceptive methods*

Ethical issues

Ethics means whether conduct is right or wrong.

Some couples may decide that a number of contraceptive methods are not acceptable to them. This may be because they are not reliable enough or that they do not agree with them, i.e. ethically, or because of their religious belief system.

Societal issues

Different societies have different views on contraception. These views are often reflected by the laws in a country or state.

In vitro fertilisation

Medical issues

Infertility is the inability to have offspring. Slightly more than one in six Irish couples are infertile. Some of these couples may use in vitro fertilisation (**IVF**) treatment in order to have a child.

IVF involves taking eggs from the female and taking sperm from the male and allowing them to fertilise outside of the body (i.e. in a container such as a petri dish).

If fertilisation is successful, one (or more) of the embryos is placed into the uterus of the female. The hope is that the embryo(s) will implant and develop in the uterus just as in a normal pregnancy.

The process is called in vitro fertilisation because the sperm and the egg join together outside the body of the female.

Did you know?

In vitro means 'in glass'.

Advantages of IVF

● IVF allows a couple who are unable to achieve fertilisation naturally to have a child.

● The child develops normally in the uterus.

Disadvantages of IVF

● There is a small risk of more than one embryo developing (and multiple pregnancies increase the risk of premature births or low birth weight). Some people consider multiple births an advantage.

● There may be some side effects of the drugs that are taken to allow IVF.

● There is a slightly higher risk of the baby being born with a birth defect.

● It is a costly process that often does not result in pregnancy.

Ethical issues

Some people feel that IVF is wrong for one or more of the following reasons:

● It is not a natural process

● Not all of the embryos are used, and those that are not used are destroyed or used for stem cell research (see next page)

● There is an increased risk of birth defects.

Societal issues

Different societies have different views on IVF. These views are often reflected by the laws in a country or state.

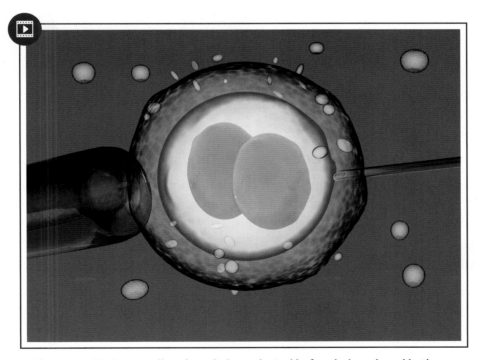

▲ **Figure 11.22** *A two cell embryo being selected before being placed in the uterus*

Stem cells

Medical issues

Stem cells are cells that can develop into any type of body cell. They are often used to learn how structures in the body are formed and to test the effect of new drugs.

It is hoped that stem cells will provide treatments for problems such as spinal cord injuries, heart diseases, strokes, Parkinson's disease, and many other disorders. In addition, they may be used to form new healthy structures for use in transplants.

Stem cells can be obtained from 3- to 5-day-old embryos, from umbilical cords and from adult sources such as bone marrow, fat and nose cells.

Ethical issues

Embryonic stem cells are often obtained from embryos left over after IVF treatment. Some people believe that using stem cells from embryos is wrong as it destroys a potential life.

Others feel that the possible benefits outweigh this issue.

Societal issues

Different societies have different views on the use of stem cells. The basic problem is the conflict of two sets of values:

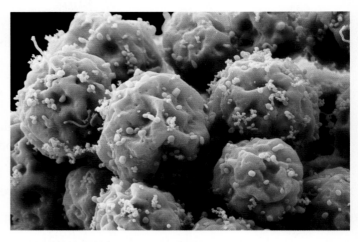

▲ Figure 11.23 *Embryonic stem cells*

▲ Figure 11.24 *A bladder grown from stem cells for transplant*

- The duty to prevent or reduce suffering
- The duty to respect the value of human life.

In some countries or states the use of all stem cells is banned by law. In others the use of all stem cells is legal. In yet other countries the use of non-embryonic stem cells is legal. Some countries do not have any clear guidelines on stem cells, as it is a relatively new issue.

? Question

11.16 **The class should vote on which of the following proposals they will discuss:**

- Contraception is a good thing and should be available to those over 18 years old.
- IVF is of more harm than benefit to society.
- Stem cell research should be illegal.

Work in groups to research and discuss the proposal selected. Each group should elect a person to explain the group's views to the class.

Summary questions

11.17 Figure 11.25 shows human gametes joining.

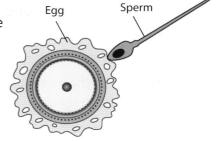

▲ Figure 11.25

  (a) Which of the following is the correct term for the female sex cell?

     Ovary   Egg   Testis   Sperm

  (b) In which of the following is the human male sex cell formed?

     Penis   Cervix   Scrotum   Testis

  (c) Which of the following is the name given to the cell that forms when an egg and a sperm unite?

     Gamete   Zygote   Foetus   Placenta

  (d) Where in the female reproductive system does fertilisation normally take place?

  (e) Name one method a couple could use to prevent fertilisation after sexual intercourse.

11.18 Figure 11.26 shows the human female reproductive system.

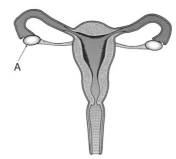

▲ Figure 11.26

  (a) Name the part labelled A.

  (b) Name the female gamete (sex cell) that is made in part A.

  (c) Make a copy of this diagram and indicate on your diagram with the letter F the location where fertilisation normally takes place.

  (d) Indicate on your diagram with the letter P the location where the placenta would be located if the female were pregnant.

  (e) How long does pregnancy normally last?

11.19 Figure 11.27 shows how the lining of the uterus changes over the course of the menstrual cycle.

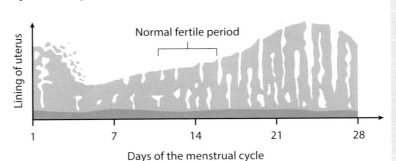

▲ Figure 11.27

  (a) What process begins on day 1 of the menstrual cycle?

  (b) On what day of a normal menstrual cycle is an egg released from an ovary?

  (c) What is meant by the 'fertile period' of the menstrual cycle?

  (d) Why does the lining of the uterus build up in the second half of the menstrual cycle?

  (e) What happens to an egg during fertilisation?

 Log on to **www.edcolearning.ie** for Additional Summary Questions

Assessment questions

11.20 Question from SEC Junior Cycle Science sample paper   (15 marks)

Write your answers in your science copy book.

Figure 11.28 shows a human female sex cell surrounded by human male sex cells.

(a) What is the human female sex cell called?

Sperm   Egg   Vagina   Penis

(b) What is the human male sex cell called?

Sperm   Egg   Vagina   Penis

(c) Where in the female reproductive system is the female sex cell produced?

Womb   Testes   Vagina   Ovary

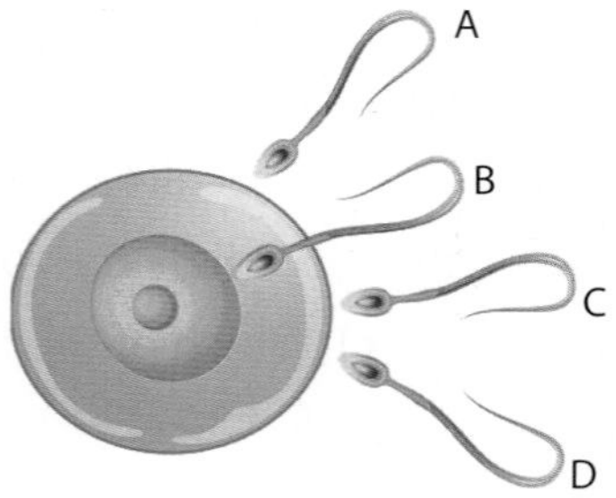

▲ Figure 11.28

(d) In Figure 11.28, which male sex cell A–D is fertilising the female sex cell?

(e) State one way of reducing the chance that sexual intercourse could result in fertilisation.

11.21 **Mothers are advised** to breastfeed their babies rather than feed them on formula milk.   (30 marks)

(a) Give two advantages of breastfeeding.

(b) The table below compares the composition of breast milk and formula milk.

Composition	Breast milk	Formula milk
Lactose (milk sugar)	74 g/dm³	75 g/dm³
Protein	13 g/dm³	9 g/dm³
Lipid (fat)	38 g/dm³	39 g/dm³
Volume of milk taken	450 ml/day	750 ml/day
Energy content	670 kJ/dm³	680 kJ/dm³

(i) Give one similarity between the breast milk and the formula milk.

(ii) Give one difference between the breast milk and the formula milk.

(iii) Babies fed on formula milk put on more fat than breastfed babies. Based on the information given above, suggest why this might happen.

Log on to **www.edcolearning.ie** for **Additional Assessment Questions**

PowerPoint summary   Weblinks

MAINTAINING BIODIVERSITY, BENEFITS OF ECOSYSTEMS AND GLOBAL FOOD PRODUCTION

CHAPTER 12

LO: BW10

Learning intentions

At the end of this chapter you will be able to:

✓ Evaluate how humans can conserve ecological biodiversity

✓ Appreciate the benefits that people obtain from ecosystems

✓ Evaluate how humans can contribute to global food production.

Keywords

- conservation
- biodiversity
- pollution
- waste management
- reduce
- reuse
- recycle
- ecosystem
- global food production
- food gap
- extinct
- critically endangered
- endangered
- habitat fragmentation
- invasive species

What is conservation?

Conservation is the protection of plants, animals and natural areas from the damaging effects of human activity.

If we look after our wildlife and their habitats we can prevent them from being wiped out (becoming **extinct**).

Failure to conserve can result in the death of organisms in their habitats. In some cases the entire species or type of organism may become extinct.

For example, birds called corncrakes are in danger of being wiped out in Ireland due to the loss of hay meadows in which they breed.

Some orchids are also threatened with extinction because their habitats are being destroyed.

Biodiversity means the variety of living things. The word is a contraction of the words 'biological diversity'. Any decrease in the number or types of plants and animals means there is a decrease in biodiversity. To prevent the loss of habitats and biodiversity it is necessary to look after our environment. Examples of good conservation practice are given on page 146.

▲ Figure 12.1 *The corncrake's habitat is being destroyed*

▲ Figure 12.2 *Some orchids are under threat as they lose their habitat*

12.1 Work in groups to discover the names of two plants in Ireland from each of the following categories:

(a) **Extinct**

(b) **Critically endangered** (i.e. in danger of becoming extinct)

(c) **Endangered** (i.e. whose numbers are declining).

12.2 Select one of the plants you listed in question 12.1 and:

(a) Find an image (drawing or photograph) of it

(b) Explain why it is in danger

(c) Present your results to the class and vote on the best presentation.

12.3 Work in groups to research what is meant by a 'protected species' in Ireland.

12.4 Name two animals in Ireland that are protected species.

12.5 Select one of the animals you have listed in question 12.4 and:

(a) Find an image (drawing or photograph) of it

(b) Explain why it is protected

(c) Present your results to the class and vote on the best presentation.

Why do we need conservation?

Conservation is necessary for the following reasons:

- To prevent organisms from becoming extinct; at present, many organisms are facing this threat
- To maintain the balance of nature; the loss of any one type of organism can cause dramatic results for other types of organism
- Future generations have the right to the same natural resources as are found at present, e.g. the world would be a poorer place if elephants, tigers, corncrakes, orchids or any other animal or plant became extinct
- Plants are the source of many medicines; as plants become extinct, we lose the ability to test them for new medications
- If our natural resources are not protected there is a danger that human lifestyles (and even our survival) would be at risk.

? Questions

12.6 Give three examples of how the loss of named living things might cause problems for other named living things? (Hint: how is the reduction in honey bees affecting plants?)

12.7 Why would it be a tragedy if elephants (or any animal or plant) became extinct?

What can we do to support conservation?

The only species on Earth that threatens conservation is humans. It is up to us, both as a species and as individuals, to support conservation measures. Humans can support conservation by:

- Making themselves aware of the issues
- Joining conservation groups
- Supporting groups in society that encourage proper conservation
- Refusing to join in any activity that threatens conservation
- Refusing to buy products that have been sourced unethically.

? Questions

12.8 Sinéad wants to support conservation in Ireland.

(a) Find out the names of three groups that she could join to achieve her aim.

(b) Explain the role of one of these groups in more detail.

12.9 Work in groups to research two chemicals or medicines that we get from plants. Explain the benefit of these substances.

12.10 Work in groups to discover the five most threatened big animals (i.e. larger than a cat) on Earth.

12.11 Discuss why the animals you named in your answer to question 12.10 should be conserved and agree on the three most important reasons.

▲ Figure 12.3 *Killarney National Park: a centre for conservation and biodiversity*

What are the main causes of loss of biodiversity?

Some of the factors that are responsible for organisms being killed off (resulting in a loss of biodiversity) are:

- Habitat loss or fragmentation
- Pollution
- **Invasive species** (organisms that are introduced to an area and which cause harm)
- Climate change (see chapter 41)
- Over-exploitation (the overuse of wildlife by people)
- Human population numbers.

We will now look at habitat loss and pollution in more detail.

Habitat loss or fragmentation

Habitats are being destroyed on a huge scale. For example:

● We cut down forests and woodlands for timber or to clear land for housing and agriculture

● Boglands are being drained for farming

● Grassland is being built on for roads, housing and factories

● Lakes are being destroyed by pollution.

Destruction of habitats destroys the organisms in that habitat. Sometimes the remaining habitat is too small to support any surviving organisms, or the remaining habitats are too far apart to allow organisms to move between them.

The breakup of a large habitat into smaller, unconnected areas is called **habitat fragmentation**.

Pollution

Pollution is caused mainly when humans add unwanted material to the environment.

Pollutants are the materials that cause pollution.

There are three main environments that get polluted: air, water, soil.

Air pollution

The main sources of air pollution are:

● Greenhouse gases

● Acid rain

● CFCs

● Dirt particles

● Smog.

Water pollution

The main causes of water pollution are:

● Badly treated sewage (toilet) waste

● Oil spills

● The dumping of household, farming and industrial wastes.

▲ Figure 12.4 *The habitat for this orangutan has been destroyed*

> **? Question**
>
> 12.12 Work in groups to find out what habitats were wiped out in the area around your school. For example, what was there before your school was built, before local houses were built, before any local factories or shopping areas were built?

> **? Question**
>
> 12.13 Work in groups to research the sources of air pollution listed.
>
> (a) Explain the source of each pollutant and the effect it has on the environment.
>
> (b) Present your findings to the class in a suitable manner (i.e. a talk, poster, slide presentation, etc.).

▲ Figure 12.5 *Air pollution*

Soil pollution

Soil pollution is mainly caused by:

- Acid rain (see chapter 41)

- Overuse of fertilisers and slurry (which is animal waste, such as faeces and urine in a liquid form) on the land

- Improper dumping of wastes.

? Questions

12.14 One area we can all contribute to is minimising household waste.

    (a) Make a list of the main wastes that your family produces each week.

    (b) What steps does your family already take to reduce the amount or effect of wastes produced?

    (c) What other steps could you take to reduce the amount of wastes produced by your family?

12.15 Work in groups to research one of the following causes of loss of biodiversity:

    - Invasive species

    - Climate change

    - Over-exploitation

    - Human population numbers.

12.16 Prepare a poster to outline your findings from question 12.15.

12.17 When nutrients enter a water supply (such as a stream, river, pond or lake) they allow more simple plants called algae to grow in the water. This happens because the nutrients are rich in minerals such as phosphates. The extra minerals may result in an overgrowth of algae, called an algal bloom (see Figure 12.6).

When the algae die, bacteria cause them to decompose. The bacteria use up all the oxygen in the water as they grow. This results in the death of all the animals and plants in the water (see Figure 12.7).

Nutrients are present in wastes such as animal manure (slurry), fertilisers that are washed off the soil, dumped milk, sewage and washing detergents.

    (a) What chemical element is mainly responsible for the death of animals, as described above?

    (b) When algae grow in water they carry out photosynthesis. What gas do they add to the water?

    (c) The gas you named in part (b) has benefits for fish and other water-based animals. In what way do animals benefit from this gas?

    (d) Why are farmers advised not to apply fertilisers when there is heavy rain?

    (e) Untreated sewage or waste water from kitchen sinks can be examples of poor conservation practice. Explain why this is so.

▲ Figure 12.6 *An algal bloom caused by excess fertiliser* ▲ Figure 12.7 *Fish killed by lack of oxygen in the water*

How can we conserve ecological biodiversity?

To conserve organisms we must control the factors listed earlier (habitat loss and fragmentation, pollution, invasive species, climate change, over-exploitation and human population numbers). Some of the ways these factors can be controlled are considered below.

Preventing habitat loss and fragmentation

Habitats can be preserved by:

- Reducing pollution (which may destroy plant and animal life)
- Planting native vegetation (i.e. plants that would naturally grow in that area), which will support native animals
- Controlling or limiting building to preserve habitats
- Preventing the entry and growth of invasive (or non-native) species
- Developing national parks and special areas of conservation where wildlife is protected by law.

Controlling pollution

Pollution can be controlled by proper **waste management.**

Waste management

The large numbers of humans and the modern style of life produce huge amounts of waste materials. These wastes include dirty water, urine, faeces, plastics and packaging, along with agricultural and industrial wastes.

These wastes can be managed by using the 3Rs (see also chapter 23). These are:

- **Reduce** the use of unnecessary goods and packaging (e.g. plastic bags)
- **Reuse** as many materials (e.g. shopping bags, water bottles or second-hand furniture) as possible
- **Recycle** as much waste as possible (e.g. paper, glass, metals and plastics).

> **⑦ Questions**
>
> **12.18** List three ways in which you or your family use, or could use, the 3Rs.
>
> **12.19** A good example of recycling is composting (see page 267).
>
>   **(a)** Find out what is meant by 'composting'.
>
>   **(b)** What substances can be composted?

(c) List two advantages and two disadvantages of composting.

(d) Investigate the possibility of your school or class making your own compost.

Check out the Green-Schools Ireland website for details and advice.

▲ Figure 12.8 *Garden and kitchen waste in a compost heap*

12.20 At present most Irish household waste is disposed of by <u>landfill</u>. However, there are problems associated with this method. Some people suggest that <u>incinerators</u> would be a better way to dispose of household waste.

Research the words underlined and answer the following questions.

(a) What is meant by 'landfill'?

(b) What are the main problems associated with landfill?

(c) What are incinerators?

(d) What are the main benefits of incinerators?

(e) Why might you not like to live close to an incinerator?

▲ Figure 12.9 *A waste incinerator*

▲ Figure 12.10 *Waste being burned in an incinerator*

▲ Figure 12.11 *A landfill site*

? Question

12.21 Giant hogweed and the grey squirrel are two invasive species in Ireland. Research both of these and explain:

(a) How or why they are thought to have entered Ireland

(b) The problems they are causing

(c) What can be done to control or prevent them from spreading.

What benefits do people obtain from ecosystems?

An ecosystem is a large area containing similar types of environments and living things (e.g. a woodland, a grassland or a seashore). We obtain many benefits from ecosystems. These benefits can be grouped into four main types:

● Supporting   ● Products   ● Controlling   ● Cultural.

Supporting benefits

Supporting benefits allow the other three types of benefits to exist. Ecosystems support:

- Biodiversity (i.e. ecosystems contain many types of living things)
- Soil formation
- Photosynthesis (which absorbs carbon dioxide and helps reduce global warming)
- Nutrient recycling (dead materials rot to release valuable elements needed for new growth to occur); you will look at this in more detail in chapter 39
- Water recycling (water is absorbed by plant roots and released back into the air as water vapour); see chapter 39.

Products benefits

Ecosystems produce valuable substances or products such as:

- Wood
- Fuel (turf/peat or firewood)
- Food (including seafood and wild animals)
- Fresh water
- Medicines
- Useful chemicals.

▲ Figure 12.12 *A wood pile*

Controlling benefits

Ecosystems help to control features such as:

- Air quality (the plants take in carbon dioxide and give out oxygen)
- Water quality (water is purified as it goes down through the soil)
- Pollination (by supporting insects)
- Soil erosion (roots stabilise soil)
- Flood damage (water is absorbed or diverted)
- Pest control (pests are reduced by being eaten or weakened by parasites).

▲ Figure 12.13 *A turf pile*

Cultural benefits

The social or non-material benefits of ecosystems include:

- Recreation (in parks, mountains and by the sea)
- Sports (swimming, climbing, walking)
- The use of nature in arts (pictures, paintings, films)
- Education (trips to parks, seashore, mountains)
- Scientific (research on habitats and wildlife).

▲ Figure 12.14 *Field trips are educational*

> ### ⑦ Question
>
> **12.22** Research national parks in Ireland.
>
>   **(a)** Name a national park in Ireland.
>
>   **(b)** What are the five main benefits of this park to Irish society?
>
>   **(c)** Suggest why there are more plant and animal species in national parks than in land outside the parks.

✍ Activity 12.1 Can we purify water?

Our drinking water is purified in five steps.

1. Oxygen is added to the water and unwanted gases are removed (this is called aeration).
2. Small dissolved dirt particles are made to clump together (this is called flocculation).
3. It is allowed to settle so that large particles sink to the bottom (sedimentation).
4. It is filtered to remove tiny particles from the water (filtration).
5. Chemicals are added to kill micro-organisms (disinfection).

We will carry out the first four steps. Disinfectants are dangerous, so we will not use them in the classroom. As a result, the water we purify is not safe to drink.

🧪 Equipment needed

About 1 litre of muddy water (or 1 litre of water with two cups of soil mixed into it)	250 ml beaker
	Fine sand
Empty 2 litre plastic soft drinks bottle with its cap	Coarse sand
Empty 2 litre plastic bottle cut about halfway down	Small pebbles
Two large beakers	Filter paper
Filter funnel	Rubber band
Alum (aluminium potassium sulfate) solution	Stirring rod or spoon
Small graduated cylinder	Stopwatch or timer

Safety
- Take care when cutting the plastic bottle – make sure your knife (or scissors) does not slip.
- Remember, the filtered water is **not** safe to drink.

➡ Conducting the activity

1. Pour half of the dirty water into a beaker and leave it aside. This acts as a control.
2. Pour the other half of the dirty water into the empty bottle. Close the lid and shake vigorously for 30 seconds.
3. Pour the water into a large empty beaker and back into the bottle 10 times. (Steps 2 and 3 aerate the water and remove any smelly gases.)
4. Pour the water into the base of the bottle with the top cut off.
5. Add 30 ml of alum solution to the water and slowly stir it for 5 minutes. What do you notice about the water as you stir it? (What you are seeing is called flocculation.)
6. Let the water sit without stirring it or moving it for 20 minutes. Observe it every 5 minutes. What do you notice is happening in the water? (What you are seeing is called sedimentation.)

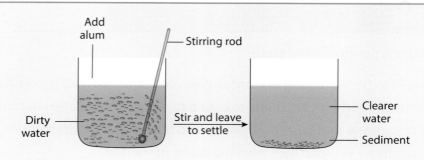

Add alum — Stirring rod

Dirty water — Stir and leave to settle → Clearer water — Sediment

▲ Figure 12.15

7. Place the filter paper over the mouth of the bottle with the bottom cut off and secure it firmly in place using the rubber band. Place it upside down in the beaker.

8. Pour a 250 ml beaker of pebbles into the bottle. Then pour a 250 ml beaker of coarse sand on top of the pebbles. Then pour two 250 ml beakers of fine sand on top of the coarse sand.

9. Pour about 2 litres of clean tap water onto the sand in the upturned bottle. Be careful not to disturb the sand too much. Pour away the water that passes through the filter paper. (This step cleans the filter materials, i.e. the sand and pebbles.)

10. Pour about two-thirds of the dirty water through the filter system. Do not pour any of the sediment into the filter bottle.

11. When all the water has filtered through, compare the filtrate to the original dirty water. What do you notice? How different are the two water samples? Write up your observations in the table in your Student Activity Book.

12. Note that the filtrate is not safe to drink. It may contain micro-organisms that are harmful.

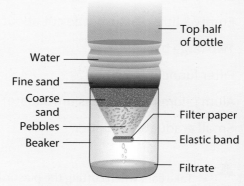

Top half of bottle
Water
Fine sand
Coarse sand — Filter paper
Pebbles
Beaker — Elastic band
Filtrate

▲ Figure 12.16

ⓘ Questions

12.23 How is water aerated naturally?

12.24 How is water naturally filtered?

12.25 Find out what chemicals are added to our drinking water to disinfect it.

12.26 Why is rainwater that is collected in a barrel not safe to drink but water in a well (or spring water) is safe to drink?

How can humans contribute to global food production?

At present there are slightly over 7 billion people on Earth. It is predicted that the number of humans in 2050 will be between 9 and 10 billion. As the numbers rise it will be necessary to increase **global food production**. This need for more food is not a new problem.

In the late 1950s and the 1960s the human population was increasing faster than it is now. However, the 'green revolution' at that time resulted in huge increases in the production of food worldwide. As a result, food production matched the rise in human numbers.

The green revolution resulted in some problems, too. For example:

- The number of crops grown fell dramatically as the new 'super-crops' were planted widely

- The new crops needed large amounts of fertilisers and had to be sprayed with pesticides to kill off insect pests

- The new crops also used much more fresh water and needed a higher level of farm technology (tractors, sprayers, etc.)

- Natural land that contained many species of plants and animals was converted to growing single crops (such as rice, wheat or oil palm). These single crops are called monocultures and result in huge loss of biodiversity.

There are two possible ways to produce more food:

- Convert more land to growing crops

- Increase the yield of crops grown on present farm land.

▲ Figure 12.17 *A wheat field at sunset*

▲ Figure 12.18 *An oil palm plantation. Note there is only one type of plant growing*

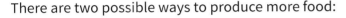

? Question

12.27 Research the role played by Norman Borlaug in increasing global food production.

Animated Scientist Biography

Watch an Exploring Science animation to find out more about Borlaug and his ideas.

▶ Figure 12.19 *Norman Borlaug*

Can we increase the amount of farmland worldwide?

At present only about 10% of the world's surface is used for growing crops (66% of Earth's surface is water, some land is too dry or too hot or too cold, or the soil is too poor to grow crops).

If we use more land for crops it will mean we have to destroy habitats. This will result in loss of biodiversity. For this reason, this option is not the best one.

Can we increase the yield of crops?

A huge amount of research is going on worldwide to increase the yield of crops. Some of this involves using older crops that were preserved as seeds (in seed banks).

Much of the research is attempting to develop new strains of crops by adding genes to existing plant crops. It is hoped that the new crops will be able to produce increased yields, resist higher global temperatures, use less fresh water, resist pests and diseases, have improved taste and contain more nutrients.

In addition, attempts are being made to allow plants to produce more than one crop each year. This could potentially increase food production hugely.

? Questions

12.28 The photograph in Figure 12.20 shows the entrance to the Svalbard Global Seed Bank. This is a project sponsored by Bill Gates and a number of multinational companies to store seeds from every plant on Earth in a huge underground vault.

Research this project and find out:

(a) Who Bill Gates is

(b) Where the project is located

(c) The aim of the project

(d) Why some people question this project.

▲ **Figure 12.20** *The Svalbard Global Seed Bank*

12.29 Most of the world's food is produced by a small number of plants.

(a) Research and list the top five food plants grown worldwide.

(b) Which of the plants named in part (a) can grow in Ireland?

How can we reduce the food gap?

The food gap refers to the difference between the amount of food produced and the amount of food needed worldwide. This gap can be reduced in a number of ways.

▲ **Figure 12.21** *Feeding fish on a fish farm – this is one type of aquaculture*

- Reduce the loss or waste of food – at present it is estimated that up to 33% of food produced for human use is not eaten

- Adjust our diets – it takes far more land to produce meat (especially beef) than it does to produce the same energy content in plants; the world's population is increasingly demanding more meat in its diet, which may not be sustainable

- Increase our use of poor-quality land

- Improve how we use our existing land and water resources

- Control human population increases

- Increase our use of water-based food production (aquaculture).

? Questions

12.30 Research food wastage.

(a) Find out how we waste up to one-third of our food.

(b) How much of this waste is avoidable?

Summary questions

12.31 **(a)** What is meant by the term 'conservation'?

(b) Give three reasons why conservation is necessary.

(c) A person has a very large garden. They decide to cut the lawn in only a small area very close to the house. They allow the grass and vegetation to grow uncut in a large area of the garden farther away from the house.

   (i) Is this a good example of conservation?

  (ii) In which part of the garden would you expect to find more plants growing?

 (iii) In which part of the garden would you expect to find more animals living?

  (iv) Explain how the uncut part of the garden would have a richer biodiversity than the part of the garden that was cut.

12.32 Conservation is very important if we wish to protect the environment for future generations.

(a) What is meant by 'the environment'?

(b) Give two examples of how human activity can have a negative effect on the environment.

(c) Explain how any one of the activities you have named has a negative effect.

(d) Name two ways that humans can help protect our natural resources.

12.33 Humans produce vast amounts of waste. Some of the methods used to manage our waste include landfill, composting, recycling and incineration.

(a) Select one of these methods and state how it works.

(b) Select a second of these methods and describe how it works.

(c) Select any one of the four methods and give (i) an advantage and (ii) a disadvantage of the method chosen.

12.34 Ecosystems provide many benefits. These benefits can be categorised as supporting life, forming products, controlling the environment and cultural benefits to humans. Copy out the table below and place each of the 12 benefits listed below in the correct column.

Supporting life	Forming products	Controlling the environment	Cultural benefits to humans

List of benefits: Educational trips, Food production, Improving air quality, Recycling minerals, Allows biodiversity, Sporting use, Firewood, Helps prevent flood damage, Walkways in forest parks, Supplies some medicines, Makes good-quality soil, Purifies water.

 Log on to **www.edcolearning.ie** for Additional Summary Questions

BIOLOGICAL WORLD

Assessment questions

12.35 Aphids are flies that harm crops such as lettuce **(30 marks)** and potatoes. Ladybirds eat aphids and can be used to limit the number of aphids in a habitat. This is called biological control, which is the use of one living thing to reduce the number of a second living thing. Biological control is more environmentally friendly than the use of pesticide sprays to kill insect pests.

▲ **Figure 12.22** *A ladybird eating aphids*

   (a) What is meant by 'biological control'?

   (b) What are pesticides?

   (c) Suggest why biological control is better than using pesticides.

   (d) Construct a food chain based on the biological control of aphids.

   (e) Why, do you think, is biological control not more popular?

   (f) A lettuce crop is being badly damaged by aphids. How would the introduction of ladybirds affect the yield of lettuce?

   (g) Ladybirds are rarely eaten by any other animals. This is because they contain a foul-smelling chemical that is released from their legs. To advertise this, they have a brightly coloured outer skeleton, which deters predators.

   Is the bright colour an example of interdependence, adaptation or competition?

12.36 Question from SEC Junior Cycle Science sample paper **(15 marks)**

Read the following article and answer the questions that follow. Write your answers in your science copy book.

Space invaders: the alien species that are costing us millions

In 1847 the Japanese knotweed was a medal-winning plant with strong growth and pretty white flowers. Things are very different today, with British house buyers being denied mortgages if this plant is found on a property.

▲ **Figure 12.23**

It has also taken hold in Ireland. Japanese knotweed can grow through the smallest crack and grow up to 2 cm a day, extending 7 m horizontally and 3 m deep. It is one of a number of unwanted and sometimes dangerous invasive species that have taken a foothold in Ireland.

   (a) Name one invasive species found in Ireland.

   (b) Describe one way an invasive species could get to Ireland.

   (c) In the comments section below this article, an online reader comments that "all species are invasive – that's nature, that's evolution".

   Do you agree or disagree with this comment? Explain your answer.

 Log on to **www.edcolearning.ie** for Additional Assessment Questions

 **PowerPoint summary**  **Weblinks**

CHEMICAL WORLD

UNIT 3

CHAPTER 13

THE PARTICLE THEORY

LO: CW2, CW4

Learning intentions

At the end of this chapter you will be able to:

✓ Describe matter

✓ Recognise the three states of matter

✓ Classify materials as solid, liquid or gas

✓ Describe how particles are arranged in each state of matter

✓ State the properties of solids, liquids and gases

✓ Explain changes of states of matter.

Keywords

- matter
- atoms
- volume
- melting
- boiling
- condensation
- freezing
- evaporation
- diffusion

What is matter?

Matter is anything that occupies space and has mass. Everything – *everything*: a cat, a leaf, a book, a raindrop, a flea, a pencil, even you! – on Earth is made up of matter.

Did you know?

Nothing is the only thing that is not matter.

Matter has three forms, which are known as the three states of matter:

- Solid
- Liquid
- Gas.

? Question

13.1 Identify the solids, liquids and gases you see in this serving of hot food.

Arrangement of particles

One thing that is common between solids, liquids and gases is particles (atoms or molecules). The particles in a substance stay the same whether it is a solid, liquid or gas; what changes is the arrangement of the particles and their energy. These particles are like small balls and they behave differently in each state of matter.

Properties of the states of matter

The phrase 'properties of a substance' is just a way of defining how the substance behaves – how it looks, how it feels and how it acts.

Properties of solids

The particles in a solid are closely packed together. They can vibrate but do not move from their position. As a result, solids keep their shape and **volume**. As the particles are in fixed places, solids cannot flow and cannot be compressed (squashed).

Properties of liquid

The particles in liquids are close to each other but are free to move past each other. They do tend to stick together, however. Liquids do have a definite volume, but will take the shape of whatever container they are placed in. They cannot easily be compressed or squashed.

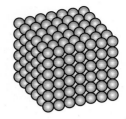

▲ **Figure 13.1** *Solids have a definite volume*

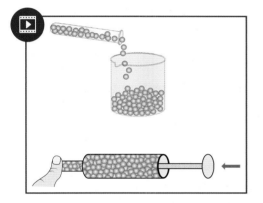

▲ **Figure 13.2** *Liquids are not easily squashed*

▲ **Figure 13.3** *Liquids have no definite shape and always take the shape of the container they are poured into*

Properties of gases

In gases the particles are free to move in all directions. They don't keep a definite shape or volume and always fill the container they are placed in. As the particles are very spread out it is easy to compress them into a smaller volume.

▲ **Figure 13.4** *Gas particles are free to move in all directions but can be compressed*

▲ **Figure 13.5** *Gases can be compressed*

Table 13.1 Summary of the states of matter

	Solid	Liquid	Gas
Definite shape	✓	✗	✗
Definite volume	✓	✓	✗
Can be compressed	✗	✗	✓
Can flow	✗	✓	✓
Arrangement of particles	▲ Figure 13.6	▲ Figure 13.7	▲ Figure 13.8

⑦ Questions

13.2 You have all three states of matter as part of you! Identify a solid, liquid and a gas that is part of you.

Properties of states of matter

13.3 Within your group, imagine each person is a particle. Move into position to demonstrate the arrangement of the particles in:

(a) Solids   **(b)** Liquids   **(c)** Gases.

13.4 Explain which arrangement has the most energy: solid, liquid or gas.

Different states – different jobs

13.5 Look at what makes up a car. In your group, discuss each state of matter – where it may be used in the car and why.

13.6 Natural gas from the North Sea is piped into some homes. It is invisible. What has been added to the gas to enable leaks to be detected?

13.7 Temperature is measured with mercury or alcohol thermometers. Do you think water is suitable as a liquid in thermometers? Explain.

Properties of states of matter

13.8 Coal, petrol and butane are three common fuels.

▲ Figure 13.9 *Coal*

▲ Figure 13.10 *Petrol*

▲ Figure 13.11 *Butane*

(a) Divide your class into five groups. Each group answers a question from the list below relating to the different fuels.

Group A – What is the state of matter for each fuel?

Group B – Can each fuel move/flow?

Group C – Can each fuel change shape?

Group D – Is it possible for each fuel to change volume?

Group E – Which fuel(s) can be compressed?

(b) Come back together as a class and discuss your answers.

(c) Together, write out the properties of each state of matter.

Change of state

This is where material can change from one state of matter to another. There is no change in mass and no new substance is formed.

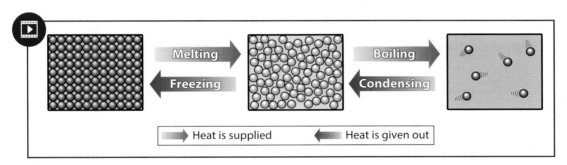

▲ **Figure 13.12** *Change of state*

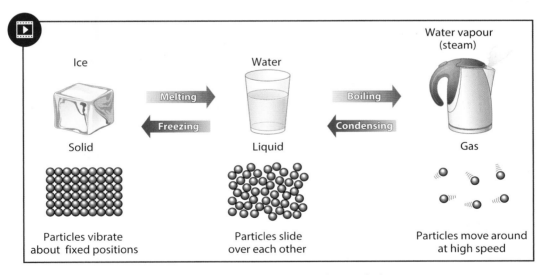

▲ **Figure 13.13** *Substances change state when heated or cooled*

Melting

Melting takes place when a solid is heated (gains energy) and it changes into a liquid.

? Question

13.9 Can you figure out what is happening to the particles in the solid when they are heated? Write down what you think is happening.

Boiling

Boiling takes place when a liquid is heated and it turns into a gas.

? Questions

13.10 Explain what is happening to the particles when they change from a liquid to a gas.

13.11 Do the particles in a gas require more energy than the particles in a solid?

Condensation

Condensation is where cooling a gas (removing energy) causes it to change into a liquid.

? Question

13.12 Explain what effect the removal of energy may have on the particles and why a gas changes into a liquid.

Freezing

Freezing happens when a liquid is cooled and changes into a solid.

? Question

13.13 What, do you think, is happening to the particles in a liquid that causes them to stop moving and form a solid?

Boiling point of a liquid

The boiling point is the temperature at which a liquid changes into a gas throughout the liquid. The temperature at which this occurs in water is 100°C, and in ethanol it happens at 78°C.

Did you know?

When water boils, water vapour (steam) is released. The steam is not the white cloud produced – that is tiny droplets of water. Steam is an invisible gas next to the surface of the water.

? Question

13.14 Puddles disappear quickly when the sun comes out. This is where the water changes from a liquid to water vapour by **evaporation**. Investigate how evaporation differs from boiling and why we don't see anything happening during evaporation.

Diffusion

Imagine the smell of a stink bomb! When the bomb is opened (broken) the small particles move from where there are lots of them, to where there are fewer of them. This is how the smell spreads. This is called **diffusion**.

Diffusion is the movement of particles from an area of high concentration to an area of lower concentration. Diffusion occurs mainly in liquids and gases.

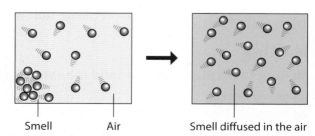

Smell   Air   Smell diffused in the air

▲ **Figure 13.14** *Particles in a gas spread evenly by diffusing*

✏ Activity 13.1 How does matter change state?

⚗ Equipment needed

Beaker	Bunsen burner
Ice	Tripod
Clock glass	Wire gauze

> ⚠ **Safety**
> • Make sure the equipment has cooled down before moving it.

➡ Conducting the activity

1. Heat cubes of ice in a beaker.
   (a) Explain your observations.
2. Continue heating the liquid in the beaker.
   (b) Did the particles lose or gain energy?
   (c) Name the change of state.
3. Place a clock glass over the beaker.
   (d) Explain what you see.
   (e) Name the change of state.
4. Place the beaker in a freezer for a few hours.
   (f) Record your result in the space provided in your Student Activity Book.
   (g) Describe what happened to the particles.
5. Discuss and evaluate your results and explanations as a whole class.

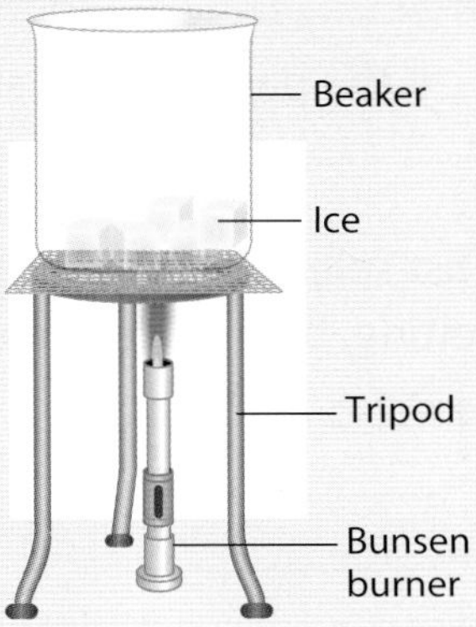

▲ Figure 13.15

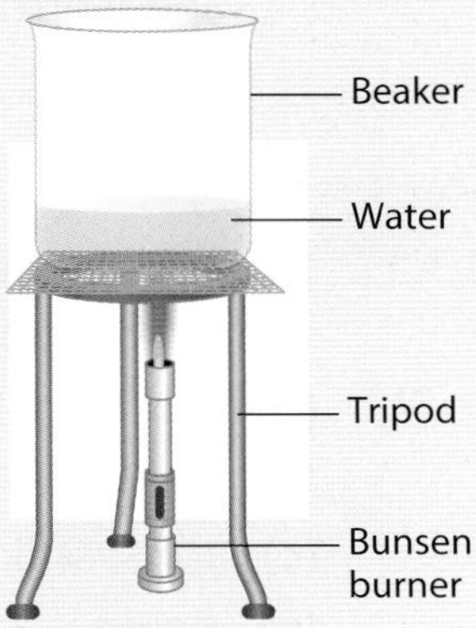

Beaker
Ice
Tripod
Bunsen burner

▲ Figure 13.16

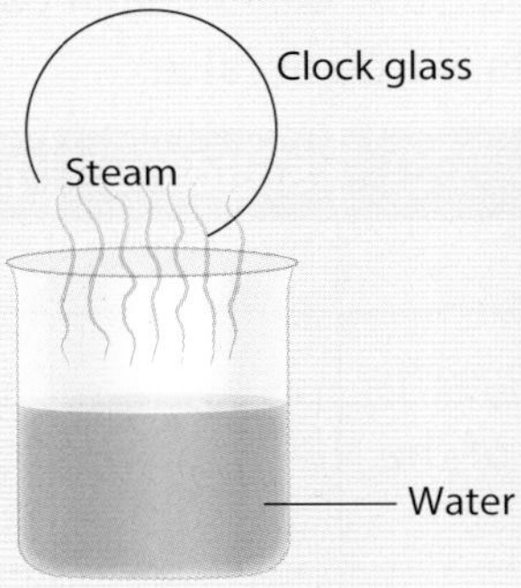

Beaker
Water
Tripod
Bunsen burner

▲ Figure 13.17

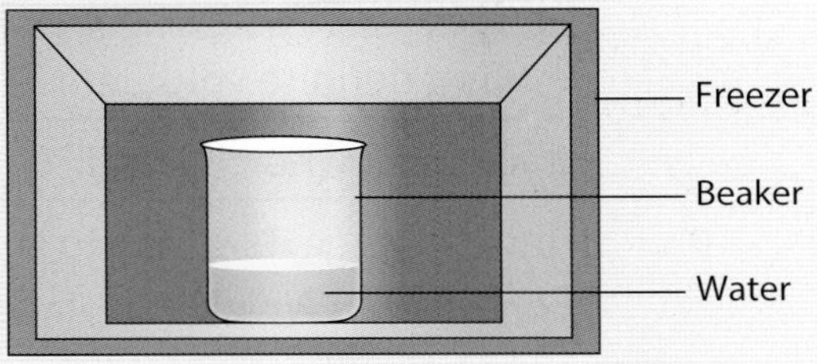

Clock glass
Steam
Water

▲ Figure 13.18

Freezer
Beaker
Water

Fourth state of matter

Plasma is the fourth state of matter. It is very similar to a gas – in fact, plasma is a gas that can carry an electrical charge. Plasma particles spread out and move around randomly, but unlike gas, plasma has the ability to conduct electricity.

⍰ Question

13.15 Research plasma to find the answers to the following questions:

(a) Where is plasma found on Earth?

(b) What is the most common form of plasma?

(c) What percentage of the universe is plasma?

(d) Where is plasma used in industry?

Summary questions

● 13.16 Write out and complete the following:

(a) Matter is anything that occupies _____ and has _____. There are three states of matter: _____, _____ and _____.

(b) In a solid the particles are packed _____ together. Therefore, solids have a _____ shape. In a gas, particles move around very _____ and there are large _____ between them.

In a _____, the particles can slide past each other. As a result, they have no _____ _____.

● 13.17 From the following list select the correct word to complete the changes of states of matter: freezing, melting, boiling, condensation.

(a) solid ⟶ liquid = _____

(b) liquid ⟶ gas = _____

(c) gas ⟶ liquid = _____

(d) liquid ⟶ solid = _____

● 13.18 The temperature at which a solid turns into a liquid is called its _____ point.

● 13.19 The temperature at which a liquid turns into a gas is called its _____ point.

● 13.20 Copy the following table and place a ✓ or ✗ in each column to indicate whether each of the following statements is true or false.

Statement	Solids	Liquids	Gases
It has a definite volume.			
It expands when heated.			
It will change its shape to that of the container in which it is placed.			
Its particles will spread out to fill the container in which it is placed.			

● 13.21 There are three states of matter: solid, liquid and gas.

(a) Identify one property that liquids and gases have in common.

(b) identify one property in which liquids and gases differ.

● 13.22 Explain the following statements in terms of particles:

(a) A balloon will deflate slightly over time.

(b) You can smell the dinner cooking in the kitchen from upstairs.

(c) On a cold wet day the windows of a car get 'steamed up'.

Log on to **www.edcolearning.ie** for Additional Summary Questions

Assessment questions

13.23 Substances can change from one state of matter to another. **(15 marks)**

Copy word equations (a), (b) and (c) and above each arrow write the correct word to explain the change from the following list: Condensing, Evaporating, Freezing, Melting.

(a) Solid ——————→ Liquid

(b) Liquid ——————→ Gas

(c) Gas ——————→ Liquid

13.24 Coal, petrol and butane are three common fuels used in everyday modern living. **(30 marks)**

(a) Copy and complete the table below, identifying the state of matter for each fuel.

Fuel	State of matter
Coal	
Petrol	
Butane	

(b) Draw diagrams of the fuels, showing the arrangement of the particles for each state of matter.

(c) State which of these fuels can be compressed.

13.25 When a substance goes from one state of matter to another state of matter, this process is called a change in state. **(45 marks)**

(a) Describe how to investigate the heating of 10 g of ice to observe changes in state. As part of your description, name each piece of equipment you would use (a labelled diagram may help your answer).

(b) A heating curve such as the one shown in Figure 13.19 shows the changes as the substance is heated.

Draw diagrams showing the arrangement of particles in each state of matter.

(c) Identify the changes of state at points A and B on the heating curve. Explain in terms of particles what happens as the substance is heated.

(d) As the ice changes from one state of matter to another, is there a change in mass and a new substance formed?

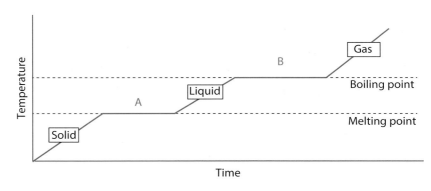

▲ **Figure 13.19**

Log on to **www.edcolearning.ie** for Additional Assessment Questions

PowerPoint summary   Weblinks

CHAPTER 14

OBSERVING CHANGE

LO: CW1, CW2

In science there are many changes, but can they always be reversed?

Physical change

Our study of chemistry leads us to a better understanding of our world and the processes by which materials can change and be changed. We know from chapter 13 that matter exists in three states (see Figure 14.1 for a recap).

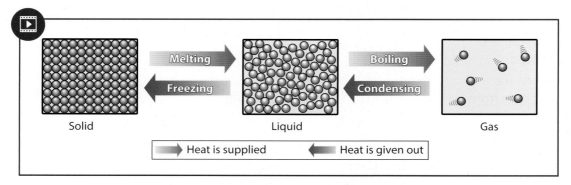

▲ **Figure 14.1** *Physical changes in matter*

The changes shown in Figure 14.1 are reversible and no new substance is formed; there is just a change of state. This is called a **physical change**. **It describes a situation in which there is no change in particles, just the particle arrangement and energy.**

? Questions

14.1 Look at the following pictures and discuss in groups why these may be physical changes.

For each of them, discuss the questions:

(a) Are any new substances made?

(b) Can you reverse the changes (that is, go back to what it looked like at the start)?

Blowing up a balloon   *Melting chocolate*   *Melting ice*   *Sharpening a pencil*

▲ **Figure 14.2** *Different matter undergoing physical changes*

14.2 Now consider what might happen when a match is ignited and burning.

Discuss these questions:

(a) What changes occur to the match when it has been lit? List them.

(b) Is energy produced?

(c) What forms of energy have been produced?

(d) Can you reverse this change?

(e) Is this a physical change?

▲ **Figure 14.3** *A burning match*

Chemical change

A burning match is an example of a **chemical change, in which a chemical reaction takes place and a new substance is formed. During a chemical change energy may be released or absorbed. This means chemical changes are usually very difficult to reverse.**

▲ **Figure 14.4** *Iron reacts with oxygen and water to form iron oxide (rust)*

▲ **Figure 14.5** *When you add a dissolvable tablet to water you may get bubbles*

Chemical reactions

Many useful materials are produced from chemical changes (also known as chemical reactions). These include plastics, which are made from reactions with oil.

The chemicals that react together are called reactants and the substances formed are called products. Chemical reactions are represented using equations (word equations and chemical equations).

Word equation: **carbon + oxygen → carbon dioxide**

                          reactants   product

Chemical equation: $C + O_2 \rightarrow CO_2$

Observing change

During a chemical reaction the atoms rearrange to form a new substance. There are some signs that indicate this has occurred:

- Colour changes
- Temperature changes
- Light is emitted
- Bubbles of gas are produced.

▲ Figure 14.7 *When you add a dissolvable tablet to water and you get bubbles then a chemical change occurs*

▲ Figure 14.8 *A chemical reaction takes place when a firework is lit*

Did you know?

Have you ever smelled a rotten egg? It smells completely different from fresh eggs. A chemical change during spoilage of eggs causes this odour.

Activity 14.1 What changes are taking place in chemical reactions?

Equipment needed

4 test tubes
Test tube rack
Spatula
Iron nail
Thermometer
Sodium hydroxide (0.1 M)
Sulfuric acid (0.1 M)
Vinegar
Baking soda
Copper oxide
Water
Universal indicator

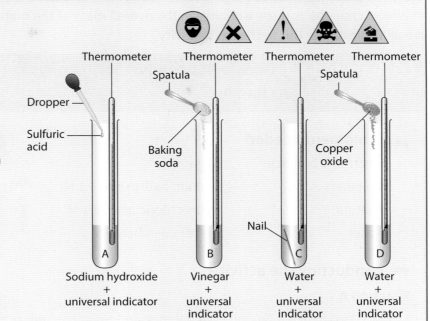

▲ Figure 14.9 *Investigating changes*

Conducting the activity

You are going to add substances to four different test tubes. For each test tube, record:

(a) Any change in temperature
(b) Any change in colour
(c) Any noticeable odour
(d) If there is formation of bubbles.

1. **Test tube A** Place 3 cm³ of sodium hydroxide into the test tube. Add a few drops of universal indicator. Measure the temperature of the solution. Add 3 cm³ of sulfuric acid. Measure the temperature again. Note any changes.

2. **Test tube B** Place 3 cm³ of vinegar into a test tube. Add a few drops of universal indicator. Measure the temperature. Add half a spatula of baking soda. Measure the temperature again. Note any changes.

3. **Test tube C** Place 3 cm³ of water and a few drops of universal indicator into a test tube. Measure the temperature. Add an iron nail. Measure the temperature again. Note any changes.

4. **Test tube D** Place 3 cm³ of water into a test tube and add a few drops of universal indicator. Add half a spatula of copper oxide. Measure the temperature again. Note any changes.

Results

Record your results for each test tube in the space provided in your Student Activity Book and answer the following questions:

(a) In which test tubes did a physical change take place, and in which did a chemical change take place?

(b) Write down the properties that tell you if there has been a chemical reaction (chemical change).

Conservation of mass

We know that matter can be changed from one form into another, but during physical and chemical changes, is there a change in the overall mass of the matter, or does it remain constant? We will investigate this in the next activity.

Activity 14.2 Does mass change during physical changes and chemical changes?

Equipment needed

Electronic balance	Sugar
4 beakers	Sodium hydroxide (0.1 M)
Spatula	Hydrochloric acid (0.1 M)
Water	Universal indicator

Safety
- Always wear safety goggles.
- Handle acid with care.

➡ Conducting the activity

Reaction A

1. Place two beakers (50 ml) on a balance and press the zero button.
2. Place 10 cm³ of water in one beaker and add a few drops of universal indicator.
3. Place one spatula of sugar into the other beaker.

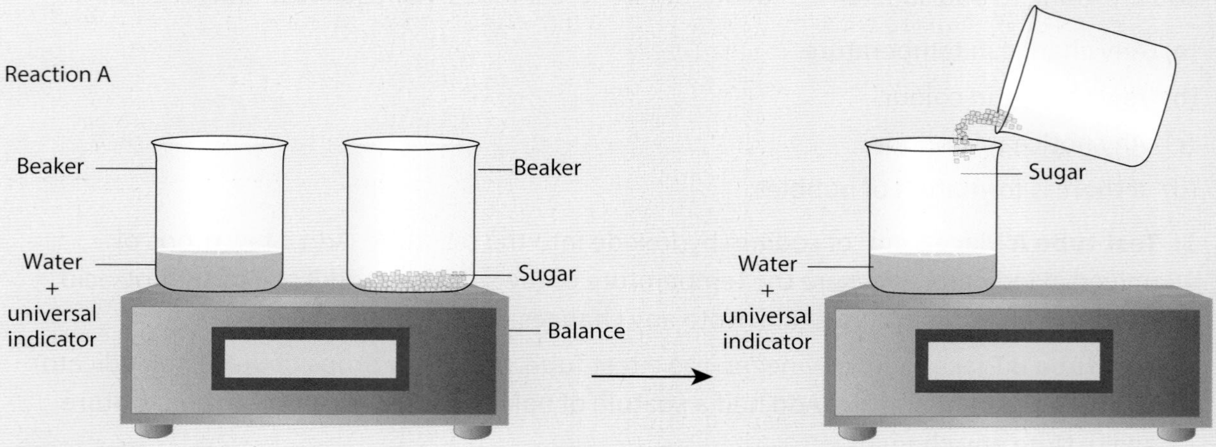

Reaction A

▲ **Figure 14.10**

4. Record the total mass on the balance.
5. Add the sugar to the water and replace the empty beaker on the balance.
6. Record the total mass.

Reaction B

1. Place two beakers (50 ml) on a balance and press the zero button.
2. Add 10 cm³ of sodium hydroxide into one beaker and add a few drops of universal indicator.
3. Add 10 cm³ of hydrochloric acid into a second beaker on the balance.
4. Record the total mass on the balance.

5. Add the hydrochloric acid solution to the sodium hydroxide solution and replace the empty beaker on the balance.

6. Record the total mass.

Reaction B

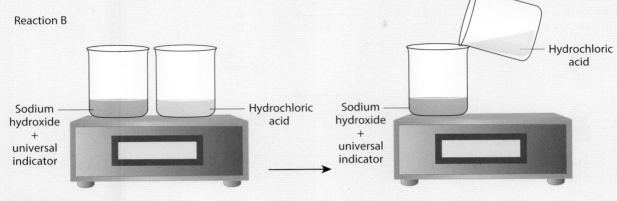

Sodium hydroxide + universal indicator

Hydrochloric acid

Sodium hydroxide + universal indicator

Hydrochloric acid

▲ Figure 14.11

? Questions

Divide into groups. Within your group, analyse your results and answer the following questions.

14.4 Did you notice any changes during reaction A and reaction B? Which reaction, A or B, showed a chemical reaction? What evidence do you have to support this?

14.5 Was the initial mass the same as the final mass for each reaction?

14.6 During a physical or chemical change is there a change in the overall mass?

Law of conservation of mass

Antoine Lavoisier, a French chemist in the 18th century, discovered the law of the **conservation** of mass. He discovered that the mass of a substance cannot be created or destroyed, so during a physical and chemical change there is no change in the overall mass.

▲ Figure 14.12 *Antoine Lavoisier*

> total mass of reactants = total mass of products

carbon + oxygen → carbon dioxide
  2 g   2 g   4 g
mass of reactants = 4 g   mass of products = 4 g

? Question

14.7 If 0.16 g of copper is reacted with 0.04 g of oxygen, how many grams of copper oxide will be produced?

Particle model diagrams

A particle model diagram shows how particles (atoms) rearrange to form a new substance during a chemical reaction. Figure 14.13 and Figure 14.14 are examples of these diagrams.

Particle model diagrams

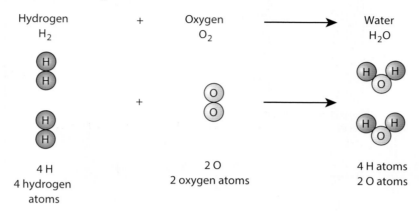

▲ Figure 14.13 *Particle model diagrams*

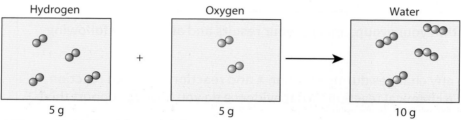

▲ Figure 14.14 *Particle model diagrams*

The reactants and the products have the same number of each type of atom, so this explains why there is no change in overall mass.

? Questions

14.8   Draw a particle model diagram for Figure 14.15.

> copper + oxygen → copper oxide

▲ Figure 14.15

14.9   According to the law of the conservation of mass, how much zinc was produced? See Figure 14.16.

> calcium + zinc carbonate → calcium carbonate + zinc
>
> 68 g   192 g   152 g   x g

▲ Figure 14.16

14.10   If 50 grams of sodium reacts with chlorine to form 128 grams of salt, how many grams of chlorine reacted? See Figure 14.17.

> sodium + chlorine → sodium chloride (salt)
>
> 50 g   x g   128 g

▲ Figure 14.17

Summary questions

14.11   List two differences between physical change and chemical change.

14.12   State which of the following changes are physical changes and which are chemical changes:

Burning wood

Making toast

Dissolving sugar in tea

Dicing potatoes

14.13   Look at the candle in Figure 14.18. Identify which label (A or B) shows a physical change and which shows a chemical change. Explain your answer.

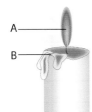

◀ Figure 14.18

14.14   Copy the following table. Consider the changes and put a ✓ or a ✗ in your table to show whether it is chemical or physical.

Change	Physical	Chemical
Drying clothes		
Iron rusting		
Perfume evaporating		
Milk turning sour		
Burning magnesium		
An apple rotting		

14.15   Explain what is meant by the term 'chemical reaction'.

14.16   Explain the terms 'reactants' and 'products' of a chemical reaction.

14.17   In a chemical reaction, the chemicals that react together are called _____ and the substances formed are called the _____.

14.18   Explain the law of conservation of mass.

14.19   State which of the following are chemical changes. Explain why.

   (a) A plant absorbing energy from the Sun and producing food by photosynthesis.

   (b) A cup falling from a table and shattering on the ground.

   (c) Baking a birthday cake for your best friend.

14.20   If four hydrogen atoms react with two oxygen atoms, how may atoms will there be in the product?

Assessment questions

14.21 Copy and complete the table below for the following changes. State whether they are physical or chemical changes. One has been done for you. **(15 marks)**

A candle burning	
Freezing food	Physical
Milk going sour	
Inflating a balloon	
Dicing potatoes	
Wax melting	

14.22 Question 4 from Junior Cycle Science exam paper **(15 marks)**

Write all answers in your science copy book.

(a) Name the reactants and products in the following chemical reactions.

Chemical reaction	Reactants	Products
Copper + Oxygen → Copper oxide		
Sodium + Chlorine → Sodium chloride		
Hydrogen + Oxygen → Water		
Carbon + Oxygen → Carbon dioxide		
Iron + Sulfur→ Iron Sulfide		

(b) Natural gas contains methane (CH_4). Methane is a fuel. Methane burns in oxygen to produce carbon dioxide and water. Figure 14.19 represents the reaction.

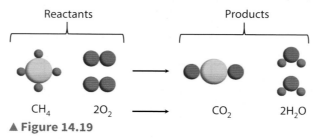

Reactants   Products

CH_4 $2O_2$ CO_2 $2H_2O$

▲ **Figure 14.19**

i Count the number of each type of atom in the products to complete the table below.

Element	Type of atom	Number of atoms in reactants	Number of atoms in products
Carbon		1	
Hydrogen		4	
Oxygen		4	

ii Mass is conserved during this reaction. What evidence is there for this?

iii The burning of methane is an example of a chemical change. Describe one difference between a physical change and a chemical change.

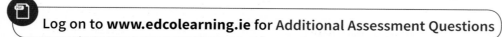

Log on to **www.edcolearning.ie** for Additional Assessment Questions

PowerPoint summary   Weblinks

Learning intentions

At the end of this chapter you will be able to:

✓ Distinguish between solute, solvent and solution

✓ Outline how different mixtures may be separated.

Keywords

- 🔑 solution
- 🔑 insoluble
- 🔑 dissolve
- 🔑 filtration
- 🔑 solute
- 🔑 distillation
- 🔑 solvent
- 🔑 chromatography
- 🔑 soluble

What are solutions?

When we think about **solutions** we usually think of them as a solid **dissolved** in a liquid, e.g. seawater contains salt dissolved in water. However, solutions can be very different to this. For example, oxygen dissolves in water to form a solution that allows fish to breathe.

Dissolving

When a substance dissolves in a liquid its particles slip into the gaps between the particles of the liquid and they become completely mixed up together.

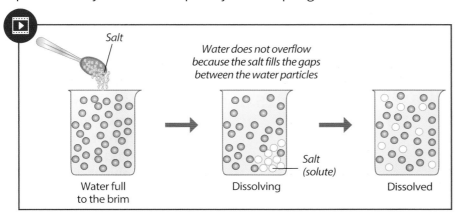

Salt

Water does not overflow because the salt fills the gaps between the water particles

Salt (solute)

Water full to the brim — Dissolving — Dissolved

▲ **Figure 15.1** *Salt dissolving in water*

A solution is made whenever two substances mix completely through each other.

The substance which dissolves is called the solute.

The substance which does the dissolving is called the solvent.

Did you know?

If you pour a handful of salt into a full glass of water, the water level will actually go down rather than overflowing the glass. Why do you think this is?

15.1 Look at Figure 15.2. There are certain words we need to know.

Explain each of the following words:

(a) Solvent

(b) Solute

(c) Solution.

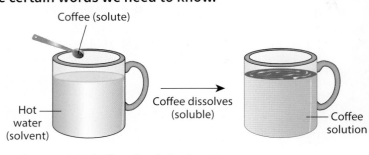

▲ **Figure 15.2** *Coffee dissolving in water*

Concentrated and dilute solutions

Have you ever tried tasting fruit squash without adding water first? It tastes unbearably sweet. **These types of drinks are concentrated solutions. This means there is a lot of solute dissolved in the solvent.**

? **Question**

15.2 What is the solute in the concentrated solution of squash?

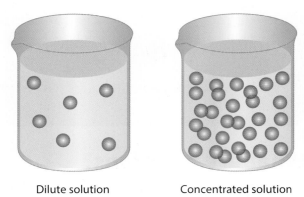

Dilute solution   Concentrated solution

▲ **Figure 15.3** *Dilute and concentrated solutions*

By adding water to the concentrated solution of squash, you are making the solution more dilute and nicer to taste. If you add too much water, the drink may taste too weak (dilute).

Did you know?

There is about ½ lb, or 250 g, of salt (NaCl) in the average human body.

? **Question**

15.3 Divide into groups. Within your group outline how you could investigate if there is a change in the overall mass when a solid dissolves in a solvent.

Soluble/insoluble

Solids that dissolve in a liquid are said to be soluble and solids that do not dissolve are said to be insoluble. There is a limit to the amount of solute dissolved in a solvent at a certain temperature. A solution that contains as much solute as possible at that temperature is called a saturated solution.

Questions

15.4 Make a list of five solids that are soluble in water and five solids that are insoluble in water.

15.5 In a salt solution you cannot tell if there is any solute present. Draw a particle diagram for a salt solution and one for pure water.

15.6 Find out:

(a) What name is given to two liquids that mix, e.g. alcohol and water

(b) What name is given to two liquids that do not mix, e.g. oil and water.

Solubility

How many spoons of sugar will dissolve in a cup of tea? **The solubility of the substance is the number of grams of the solute that dissolves in 100 g of the solvent at a particular temperature**.

✐ Activity 15.1   How does temperature affect the solubility of a solute?

🧪 Equipment needed

2 beakers	Thermometer	Water
Graduated cylinder	Mass balance	Salt
Hotplate	Spatula	Sugar

➡ Conducting the activity

1. Place 100 cm³ of water in a beaker and note its temperature.
2. Slowly, and with constant stirring, add 10 g of sugar to the water. Add sugar continually until no more sugar will dissolve but instead settles to the bottom (saturated solution).
3. In a table record the mass of sugar added. Copy the table below for your results.
4. Heat the beaker to 40°C and note what happens to the undissolved sugar.
5. Add more sugar (10 g at a time) until no more will dissolve. Record the total mass of sugar added in the table.
6. Repeat step 5 at 60°C, 80°C and 100°C, recording the total mass of sugar added at each temperature.
7. Repeat steps 1–6 using salt (10 g) and record all results in the table.

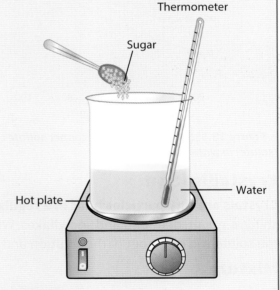

▲ Figure 15.4

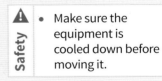

Safety
- Make sure the equipment is cooled down before moving it.

Results

Record your findings in the table in your Student Activity Book.

? Question

15.7 Draw a graph showing how the solubility of sugar and salt varies with temperature.

Referring to your results, answer the following questions in your Student Activity Book:

(a) How did temperature effect the solubility of sugar and salt?

(b) What is the solubility of sugar at 55°C?

(c) At what temperature will 30 g of salt dissolve in 100 cm³ of water?

A solubility curve plots the mass of solute dissolved in a saturated solution at different temperatures.

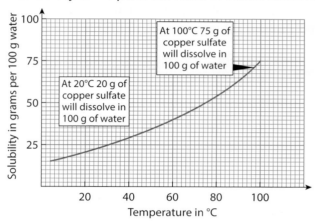

At 100°C 75 g of copper sulfate will dissolve in 100 g of water

At 20°C 20 g of copper sulfate will dissolve in 100 g of water

▲ **Figure 15.5** *Solubility curve for copper sulfate (solute) in water (solvent)*

? Question

15.8 The solubility of solutes usually increases with temperature but there is one notable exception: oxygen dissolved in water. As water is heated, less and less oxygen can dissolve in it.

(a) Suggest why this happens.

(b) Global warming is causing the Earth's water to heat up. How might this affect the fish life?

Crystallisation

Crystals are tiny particles built in a regular pattern. They have a definite shape and are usually shiny, e.g. salt, diamond and snowflakes. When a hot, saturated solution is cooled down, some of the solute will come out of the solution and form crystals. This is known as crystallisation.

Mixture

A mixture consists of two or more substances mingled together but not chemically combined.
Many everyday substances are mixtures. For example:

● Seawater is a mixture of water, salt and lots of other substances dissolved in it

● Air is a mixture of gases.

? Question

15.9 Research why water is such a good solvent and why certain substances will dissolve in water and why other substances will not.

Separation of mixtures

The different substances in mixtures can be separated easily by physical methods. The method depends on the type of mixture. There are four separation methods:

1. Filtration   **2.** Evaporation   **3.** Distillation   **4.** Chromatography.

Filtration

Filtration is used to separate an insoluble solid from a liquid, for example soil and water.
Filtration involves the use of a sieve or filter paper. Filter paper contains tiny pores which allow tiny particles through but block large ones.

Activity 15.2 How do you separate an insoluble solid and a liquid?

Equipment needed

Conical flask
Filter funnel
Filter paper
Test tube or beaker
Water
Soil sample

Safety
• Handle the glassware with care.

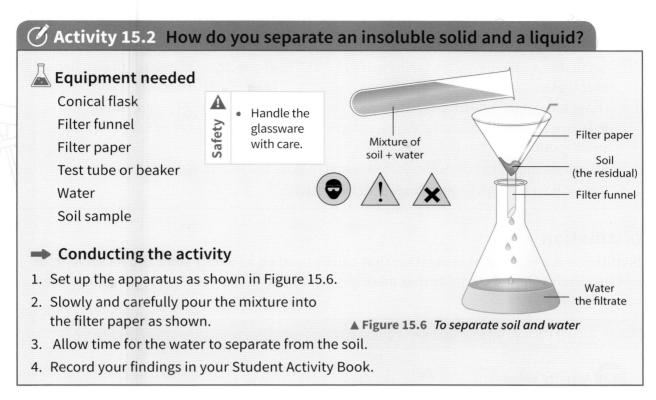

▲ Figure 15.6 *To separate soil and water*

Conducting the activity

1. Set up the apparatus as shown in Figure 15.6.
2. Slowly and carefully pour the mixture into the filter paper as shown.
3. Allow time for the water to separate from the soil.
4. Record your findings in your Student Activity Book.

Evaporation

Evaporation is used to separate a soluble solid and a liquid, e.g. salt and water. It involves heating the solution until the solvent (liquid) evaporates, leaving the solute (solid) behind.

Activity 15.3 How do you separate a soluble solid and a liquid?

▶ Activity video

Safety
• Use tongs for moving the evaporating dish off the tripod.
• Wait for the equipment to cool before removing the salt.

Equipment needed

Evaporating basin   Tripod   Bunsen burner
Beaker   Wire gauze   Solution of salt water
Tongs   Water

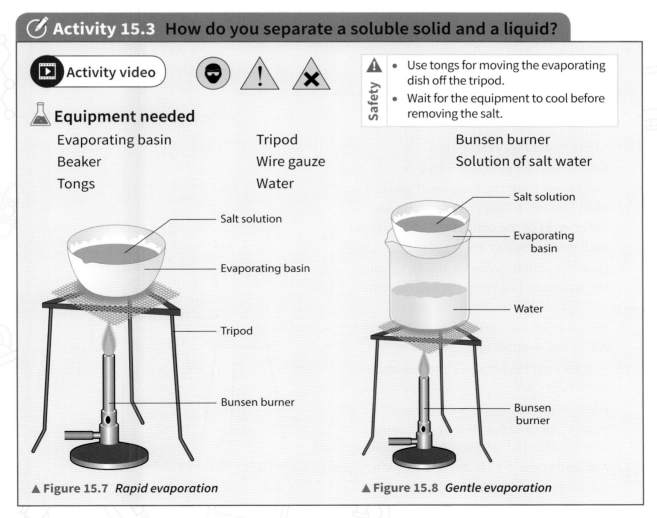

▲ Figure 15.7 *Rapid evaporation*

▲ Figure 15.8 *Gentle evaporation*

➡ Conducting the activity

1. Set up the apparatus as shown in Figure 15.7 and heat directly until most of the water has evaporated.

2. Using tongs, carefully transfer the evaporating dish onto a beaker of boiling water as in Figure 15.8. (This heats the evaporating dish more gently and prevents the salt from spitting out of the dish.)

3. Evaporate the rest of the water (solvent) and remove the salt from the dish when cooled.

4. Record your findings in your Student Activity Book.

Distillation

Distillation is a method of separation that can be used on a soluble solid and its solvent, or on two miscible liquids (liquids that mix). It is used when the two substances to be separated have different boiling points.

🖉 Activity 15.4 How do you separate two substances by distillation?

 **Activity video**

Safety
- Use retort stands for holding the round-bottomed flask and the Liebig condenser.

🧪 Equipment needed

Bunsen burner
Tripod
Wire gauze
Round-bottomed flask beaker

Thermometer
Quickfit distillation apparatus (Liebig condenser)
Salt/water mixture, or water/alcohol mixture

➡ Conducting the activity

1. Set up the apparatus as shown in Figure 15.9 and heat directly until most of the water has evaporated.

2. Ensure that water flows into the condenser from the lower end and out of the top end. This ensures that the outer layer of the condenser is fully filled with moving water and kept cool.

3. Heat the round-bottomed flask to boil the solution. The temperature remains at 100°C as the water distils across.

4. Remove the Bunsen burner when all the water has evaporated.

5. Record your findings in your Student Activity Book.

   Note: Miscible liquids with different boiling points can be separated by distillation. The liquid with the lower boiling point will boil first and come across as the distillate, leaving the other liquid behind as the residue.

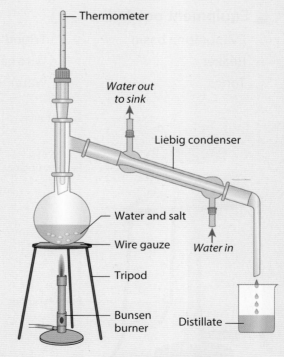

▲ **Figure 15.9** *Simple distillation*

Labels: Thermometer; Water out to sink; Liebig condenser; Water and salt; Wire gauze; Water in; Tripod; Bunsen burner; Distillate

Question

15.10 Outline one advantage of using distillation over evaporation.

Chromatography

Paper chromatography can be used to separate mixtures of substances that are in solution. The different substances move through the paper at different rates or speeds. They are carried by a suitable solvent. Chromatography is an ideal separation method for separating the dyes found in inks and for identifying blood samples.

 **Activity 15.5 How do you separate colours in a sample of ink?**

▶ **Activity video**

Safety
- Take care when cutting paper with scissors.

🧪 **Equipment needed**

Chromatography paper	Glass rod
Scissors	Capillary tubes
Gas jar	Samples of inks, markers or food dyes
Paper clip	Solvent

➡ **Conducting the activity**

1. Cut a strip of chromatography paper to fit inside the gas jar as shown in Figure 15.10.
2. Remove the paper and draw a horizontal line 2–3 cm from the bottom of the paper.
3. Using the capillary tube, place a small concentrated spot of the ink/colour to be separated on the centre of the line.
4. Pour a suitable solvent into the gas jar, ensuring that the level of the solvent is below the level of the ink.
5. Place the chromatography paper back in the jar and suspend it from the glass rod. Use a paper clip to ensure that the paper does not fall into the solvent.
6. Allow time for the solvent to soak up to near the top (10–15 minutes).
7. Record your findings in your Student Activity Book.

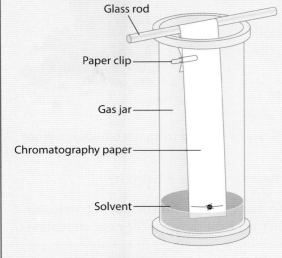

▲ **Figure 15.10** *Initial stage*

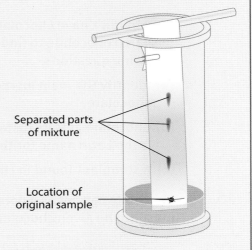

▲ **Figure 15.11** *End stage*

CHEMICAL WORLD

15.11 Divide into groups. Discuss the following mixtures within your group and write down what activities you would do to separate each mixture.

Mixture 1: Bag of coloured sweets – sorting out the sweets into the different colours

Mixture 2: Broken glass sugar bowl – separating pieces of glass from sugar

Mixture 3: Drinking water – getting pure water from salt water

Mixture 4: Metal and salt – separating a mixture of aluminium foil, paper clips and salt

Mixture 5: Orange sweet – finding out what colours an orange food colour is made from

15.12 **Investigation:** In your group, read the following and determine if you can solve the problem using separation methods. Brand A crisps states that it has less salt than Brand B crisps. Design and carry out an investigation to test and analyse the crisps to see if this is true. Write up your investigation and the results in your Student Activity Book.

15.13 Research which foods contain large amounts of salt.

15.14 What problems can arise from excess salt in your diet?

15.15 Research the solutes in a fizzy soda drink.

15.16 Water is the most important solvent as it dissolves very many solutes. Make a list of all the different jobs that water is used for around the home. Note how it is being used as a solvent in each job.

Were you surprised at how much we use water?

15.17 Can you resist the mixture we know as chocolate? Chocolate is a mixture of around 300 different substances. Some of these are chemicals that can act like drugs and affect the way your brain works. They are present in chocolate only in small quantities, but this may explain our liking for the confection.

We wouldn't have chocolate without science! Research chocolate to find the answers to the following questions:

(a) Identify the main ingredients in a bar of chocolate.

(b) Chocolate gets its taste from the chemicals extracted from cocoa beans. What is the Latin name for the cocoa tree?

(c) A stimulant found in chocolate is also found in coffee. What is it?

15.18 Chocolate can act as a poison to some animals. Which domestic pet in particular must not be given chocolate, and what will they experience if they eat chocolate?

CHEMICAL WORLD

Summary questions

15.19 Write out and complete the following:

Most solutions are made up of a substance called the _____, which dissolves in the liquid called the _____. Substances that dissolve are said to be _____, while those that don't are _____. A cup of coffee is a _____, the hot water is the _____ and the coffee granules are the _____.

15.20 Briefly explain the difference between a dilute solution and a concentrated solution.

15.21 If you make your glass of squash too dilute, what could you do to make it more concentrated again?

15.22 Name a solvent other than water and a substance that dissolves in it.

15.23 Give an everyday example of:

(a) A gas dissolved in a liquid

(b) A solid dissolved in a liquid

(c) A gas dissolved in a solid.

15.24 Explain the terms:

(a) Solution

(b) Saturated solution.

15.25 A student investigated the effect of temperature on the solubility of a salt, sodium chloride, in water. She determined the maximum mass (grams) of the salt that would dissolve in 100 g of water at various temperatures. The data of her results is given in the following table:

Solubility g/100 g water	29	37	46	56	65	77
Temperature (°C)	0	20	40	60	80	100

(a) Plot a graph of solubility against temperature.

(b) What conclusion about the solubility of sodium chloride can be drawn from this graph?

(c) Use the graph to estimate the solubility of sodium chloride at 50°C.

15.26 Choose from the list below the most suitable method for each of the separations (a) to (d).

Chromatography   Distillation   Evaporation   Filtration

(a) To obtain salt from salt water

(b) To separate a mixture of different coloured inks

(c) To obtain a sample of pure water from tap water

(d) To purify whiskey.

Assessment questions

15.27 Mixtures can be easily separated by physical methods. **(15 marks)**
Select the correct term from the box below to complete the sentences.

Distillation	Condenser	Chromatography	Separated	Soluble
Insoluble	Chromatography paper			

To separate an ink into its various dyes we use a method called _____.
Some dyes are carried further up the _____ _____ than others.
As a result the dyes are _____. The dyes that are most _____ in
the solvent are carried furthest up the _____.

15.28 Question from Junior Cycle Science exam paper **(30 marks)**

Sodium chloride (table salt) is a white crystalline solid.
Water is a solvent with a boiling point of 100°C. Sodium
chloride can dissolve in water.

A student was asked to investigate what effect adding salt
has on the boiling point of water.

(a) Write a suitable hypothesis for this investigation.

(b) What is meant by the boiling point of a substance?

▲ Figure 15.12

(c) The laboratory instrument used to measure the mass
of the salt is shown in Figure 15.13.
Identify this instrument.

(d) Draw a labelled diagram of the arrangement of the
apparatus used to determine the boiling point of
water.

The student collected the following data for the boiling
point of the solutions made when various masses of salt
were dissolved in 60 cm³ of water.

▲ Figure 15.13

Mass of salt (g)	Boiling point (°C)					Average boiling point (°C)
0	100	101	100	100	102	100.6
2	101	104	101	100	103	101.8
4	103	105	104	106	107	
6	106	108	107	107	108	107.2
8	108	110	109	111	110	109.6

(e) Calculate the average boiling point when 4 g of salt was dissolved in 60 cm³ of water.

(f) Suggest a reason why the student repeated the investigation five times for each
mass of salt used.

(g) Does the data support the hypothesis you wrote in part (a)? Explain your answer

Log on to www.edcolearning.ie for Additional Assessment Questions

BUILDING BLOCKS

CHAPTER 16

LO: CW3, CW4

Learning intentions

At the end of this chapter you will be able to:

✓ Describe an atom

✓ Distinguish between elements, compounds and molecules

✓ Construct a model for any molecule.

Keywords

- atom
- element
- symbol
- molecule
- compound
- proton
- neutron
- electron

What are atoms?

Atoms are the basic building blocks of all materials. The word 'atom' comes from a Greek word describing something that cannot be divided. When atoms were discovered, scientists thought of them as solid balls, like snooker balls, which could not be split into anything smaller.

Element

An element is a substance made up of only one type of atom. If you burn a piece of wood, you will get a black solid. That solid is called carbon. Carbon is an element because it is made up of only carbon atoms and cannot be broken down into anything simpler.

▲ Figure 16.1 *When atoms were discovered, they were thought to be solid, like this snooker ball*

▲ Figure 16.2 *The burned log is carbon, and only carbon*

Did you know?

Hydrogen is the most abundant element in the universe.

The periodic table shows a list of all the elements.

1 H Hydrogen																	2 He Helium
3 Li Lithium	4 Be Beryllium											5 B Boron	6 C Carbon	7 N Nitrogen	8 O Oxygen	9 F Fluorine	10 Ne Neon
11 Na Sodium	12 Mg Magnesium											13 Al Aluminium	14 Si Silicon	15 P Phosphorus	16 S Sulfur	17 Cl Chlorine	18 Ar Argon
19 K Potassium	20 Ca Calcium	21 Sc Scandium	22 Ti Titanium	23 V Vanadium	24 Cr Chromium	25 Mn Manganese	26 Fe Iron	27 Co Cobalt	28 Ni Nickel	29 Cu Copper	30 Zn Zinc	31 Ga Gallium	32 Ge Germanium	33 As Arsenic	34 Se Selenium	35 Br Bromine	36 Kr Krypton
37 Rb Rubidium	38 Sr Strontium	39 Y Yttrium	40 Zr Zirconium	41 Nb Niobium	42 Mo Molybdenum	43 Tc Technetium	44 Ru Ruthenium	45 Rh Rhodium	46 Pd Palladium	47 Ag Silver	48 Cd Cadmium	49 In Indium	50 Sn Tin	51 Sb Antimony	52 Te Tellurium	53 I Iodine	54 Xe Xenon
55 Cs Cesium	56 Ba Barium	57 La* Lanthanum	72 Hf Hafnium	73 Ta Tantalum	74 W Tungsten	75 Re Rhenium	76 Os Osmium	77 Ir Iridium	78 Pt Platinum	79 Au Gold	80 Hg Mercury	81 Tl Thallium	82 Pb Lead	83 Bi Bismuth	84 Po Polonium	85 At Astatine	86 Rn Radon
87 Fr Francium	88 Ra Radium	89 Ac** Actinium	104 Rf Rutherfordium	105 Db Dubnium	106 Sg Seaborgium	107 Bh Bohrium	108 Hs Hassium	109 Mt Meitnerium	110 Ds Darmstadtium	111 Rg Roentgenium	112 Cn Copernicium	113 Uut Ununtrium	114 Uuq Ununquadium	115 Uup Ununpentium	116 Uuh Ununhexium	117 Uus Ununseptium	118 Uuo Ununoctium

*	58 Ce Cerium	59 Pr Praseodymium	60 Nd Neodymium	61 Pm Promethium	62 Sm Samarium	63 Eu Europium	64 Gd Gadolinium	65 Tb Terbium	66 Dy Dysprosium	67 Ho Holmium	68 Er Erbium	69 Tm Thulium	70 Yb Ytterbium	71 Lu Lutetium
**	90 Th Thorium	91 Pa Protactinium	92 U Uranium	93 Np Neptunium	94 Pu Plutonium	95 Am Americium	96 Cm Curium	97 Bk Berkelium	98 Cf Californium	99 Es Einsteinium	100 Fm Fermium	101 Md Mendelevium	102 No Nobelium	103 Lr Lawrencium

▲ **Figure 16.3** *Periodic table*

Symbol

Each element has a symbol (see some examples in Table 16.1). H is the symbol for hydrogen. Fe is the symbol for iron, which comes from the Latin name *ferrum*.

Table 16.1 Some elements and their symbols

Element	Symbol
Oxygen	O
Carbon	C
Potassium	K
Nitrogen	N

Question

16.1 **Look at the periodic table in Figure 16.3. List the names of all the elements whose symbols start with the letter C.**

? Questions

16.2 Your teacher will divide the class into five groups and give each group four different elements to research. In your group for each element, find out:

(a) Its symbol

(b) Its state of matter at room temperature

(c) Whether it is a metal, a non-metal or a semi-metal

(d) Its appearance

(e) Where it may be used.

16.3 Which of the elements in Figure 16.4 are used in:

(a) Jewellery

(b) Thermometers

(c) Plumbing?

> **Did you know?**
> The element helium was discovered on the Sun before it was found on Earth.

Bromine

Mercury

Carbon

Silver

Copper

Zinc

▲ **Figure 16.4** *Elements*

Molecules

A molecule is formed when two or more atoms join (bond) together chemically.

Compounds

When a molecule is made up of two or more different types of elements chemically combined, we call it a compound. All compounds are molecules, but not all molecules are compounds.

Hydrogen gas (H_2) and oxygen gas (O_2) are not compounds because each is composed of one element. Water (H_2O) and carbon dioxide (CO_2) are compounds because each is made up of more than one type of element. **All compounds are non-elements.**

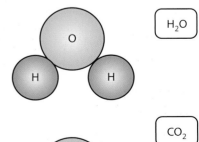

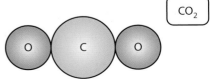

▲ **Figure 16.5** *Molecules*

⑦ Questions

16.4 State two differences between a mixture and a compound.

16.5 Look at the structures in Figure 16.6 and state whether each is an element or a compound.

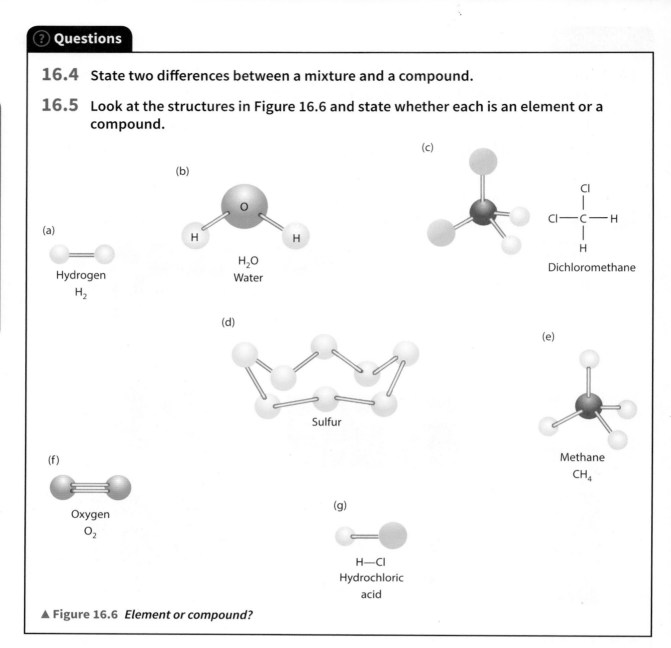

▲ **Figure 16.6** *Element or compound?*

Making models

You can use models to show how atoms bond (join) to each other. Model kits have different coloured balls for each element and sticks to join one ball to another.

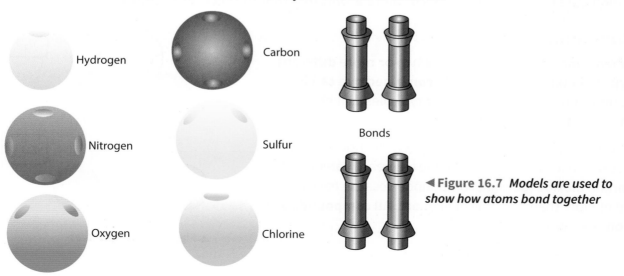

◄ **Figure 16.7** *Models are used to show how atoms bond together*

Questions

16.6 Make your own model.

(a) Using a model kit, design your own model of an element or compound.

Remember to use the colours for each element as shown in Figure 16.7.

(b) Compare your model with those of others in your group. Do the other students know the name of the atoms in your model of an element or compound?

(c) Was the model you made an element or a compound?

(d) Draw diagrams of the molecules everyone in your group made.

16.7 Look at the boxes in Figure 16.8. Which box contains:

(a) A pure compound

(b) Only one element

(c) A mixture of elements and a compound

(d) A mixture of elements?

A   B   C   D

▲ Figure 16.8

Structure of the atom

The atom is made up of smaller particles called sub-atomic particles.

These are:

● **Protons**   ● **Neutrons**   ● **Electrons**.

The three particles in the atom are quite different from each other.

▲ Figure 16.9 *Computer image of the atomic structure*

Table 16.2 **The properties of protons, neutrons and electrons**

Particle	Charge	Mass	Location
Proton	+1	1	Nucleus
Neutron	0	1	Nucleus
Electron	−1	Negligible	Shells

All the particles are extremely small. Electrons are so small it would take almost 2000 of them to have the same mass as a single proton or neutron.

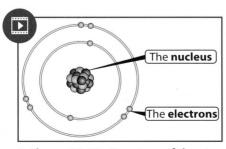

▲ Figure 16.10 *Structure of the atom*

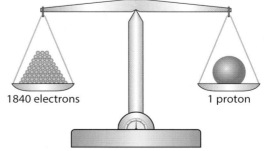

1840 electrons   1 proton

▲ Figure 16.11 *It takes almost 2000 electrons to have the same mass as a single proton (or neutron)*

CHEMICAL WORLD

Atomic and mass numbers

Atoms of different elements differ from each other by the number of protons, neutrons and electrons they have.

Every element has its own atomic number. **The atomic number tells you how many protons (which is the same as the number of electrons) there are in one atom of the element.**

There is also the mass number. **The mass number tells you how many protons and neutrons there are in the atom.** Examples are given in Figure 16.12 and Figure 16.13.

▲ **Figure 16.12**
Atomic and mass numbers of aluminium

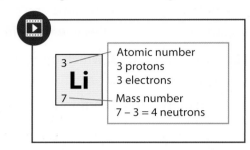

▲ **Figure 16.13** *Atomic and mass numbers of lithium*

How electrons are arranged

Electrons whizz around the nucleus in energy levels called shells, or orbits. The first shell can hold only two electrons; the second and third shells can each hold up to eight electrons.

Electrons fill up the shells one by one, starting with the first shell. When a shell is full, they start a new one. All atoms would 'like' to have full electron shells, but in most atoms the outer shell is not full, and this makes the atom 'want' to react to fill it.

Bohr model

A Danish scientist called Niels Bohr was the first person to suggest the idea of electron shells containing electrons orbiting the nucleus. The way these electrons are arranged is called the electron configuration. The way they are explained is called the Bohr model.

Figures 16.15, 16.16 and 16.17 show some examples of atoms of elements using Bohr models.

? Question

16.8 Would an atom with full electron shells be more or less likely to react chemically with another material?

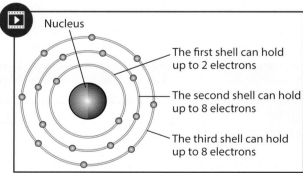

▲ **Figure 16.14** *The arrangement of electrons in an atom*

▲ **Figure 16.15** *Helium*

 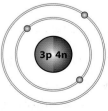

▲ **Figure 16.16** *Lithium*

 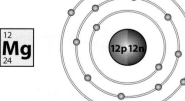

▲ **Figure 16.17** *Magnesium*

16.9 Give the number of protons, electrons and neutrons in the atoms in Figure 16.18.

(a) | 10 | Ne | 20
(b) | 9 | F | 19
(c) | 27 | Co | 60
(d) | 92 | U | 235
(e) | 7 | N | 14
(f) | 19 | K | 39

▲ Figure 16.18

16.10 Draw fully labelled diagrams of the atoms in Figure 16.19.

(a) | 2 | He | 4
(b) | 4 | Be | 9
(c) | 13 | Al | 27
(d) | 20 | Ca | 40

▲ Figure 16.19

16.11 Divide into groups. Each group is to design and construct a model of an atom (element of your choice) showing the exact number of protons, neutrons and electrons.

16.12 Scientists discovered in about 1939 that a powerful explosion might be possible by splitting an atom.

Albert Einstein had many theories that helped scientists in developing the atomic bomb. He was so frightened about what might happen if Hitler and the Germans made the bomb first that he wrote to US President Franklin Roosevelt telling him about the bomb. This led to the Manhattan Project being set up, which involved over 200 scientists researching and developing the bomb. The first atomic bomb exploded in 1945 in the New Mexico desert. The temperature at the centre of the explosion was three times hotter than at the centre of the Sun. On 6 August 1945 an atomic bomb named 'Little Boy' was dropped on Hiroshima, Japan.

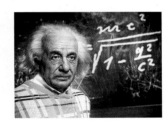
▲ Figure 16.20 *Albert Einstein*

Research the history of the first atomic bomb and answer the following questions:

(a) Who was the US president who made the decision to use the atomic bomb against Japan?

(b) On 9 August 1945 a second bomb was dropped on Japan.

   (i) Where was it dropped?

   (ii) What was its nickname?

(c) Which elements were used to make the two atomic bombs?

(d) What were the devastating effects of the atomic bombs?

▲ Figure 16.21 *'Little Boy',
the bomb dropped on
Hiroshima*

(e) Did the atomic bombs have any long-lasting effects on our society?

(f) Do you think scientists regret creating such a bomb?

Animated Scientist Biography

Watch an *Exploring Science* animation to find out more about Einstein and his discoveries.

CHEMICAL WORLD

Summary questions

16.13 Describe an atom.

16.14 Write and complete the following:

An element is a substance made up of only one type of _____. Elements cannot be _____ into simpler substances. Compounds are made up of two or more _____ which are chemically _____.

16.15 An atom is made up of three types of particle. Name them.

16.16 What is the atomic number of an atom?

16.17 What is the mass number of an atom?

16.18 Complete this sentence:

Protons and neutrons are found in the _____ and the _____ spin around in orbits, or _____.

16.19 Name the atom that has three electrons and four neutrons.

16.20 Distinguish between elements, compounds and molecules.

16.21 Copy and complete the table below identifying each of the substances listed as an element or a compound by placing a ✓ in the correct box.

Substance	Element	Compound
Carbon dioxide		
Carbon		
Hydrochloric acid		

16.22 An atom of phosphorus has the symbol $^{15}_{31}P$.

State the number of protons, neutrons and electrons in this atom.

Assessment questions

16.23 (a) The atom is made up of smaller particles called sub-atomic particles. These are protons, neutrons and electrons.

(15 marks)

Answer each of questions (i), (ii) and (iii) with one of the following words: protons, neutrons, electrons.

  (i) Sub-atomic particles with a negative charge and located in shells are called ...

 (ii) Sub-atomic particles with a positive charge and located in the nucleus are called ...

(iii) Sub-atomic particles with no charge and located in the nucleus are called ...

(b) An atom with 56 protons and 81 neutrons has an atomic number of _____ and a mass number of ___.

16.24 Use this table to help you answer the questions about the elements below.   **(15 marks)**

Element	Atomic number	Mass number
Oxygen	8	16
Chlorine	17	35
Gallium	31	70
Zinc	30	68
Tungsten	74	184

(a) State the number of protons in chlorine.

(b) Where in the atom are the protons found?

(c) How many neutrons are found in the zinc atom?

(d) Where are the electrons located in each atom?

(e) State the element in the table above that has the same number of protons and neutrons.

16.25 Copy and complete the table below for the substances shown in Figure 16.22.   **(15 marks)**

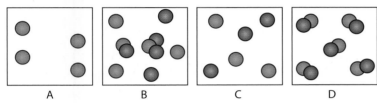

A   B   C   D

▲ **Figure 16.22**

Substance	Letter
A pure compound	
Only one element	
A mixture of elements and a compound	
A mixture of elements	

CHAPTER 17

THE CHEMIST'S COMPASS – THE PERIODIC TABLE

LO: CW5

What is the periodic table?

The periodic table is considered to be one of the most important tools of the chemist. **It shows a list of all the elements.** In the 1880s, scientists discovered a number of elements. They realised that some of these elements behaved in similar ways to others. A Russian chemist called Dmitri Mendeleev arranged them in order of the mass of the atoms of each element. He also lined up elements that behaved similarly. Only about half of the elements had been discovered by this time. Mendeleev left gaps in his table for elements that had yet to be discovered.

> **? Question**
>
> **17.1** Dmitri Mendeleev was passionate about chemistry. Research him and make notes on:
>
> **(a)** His life
>
> **(b)** His periodic table
>
> **(c)** His other achievements.

The modern periodic table

The modern periodic table has no gaps in it. The elements are not arranged according to atomic mass but by atomic number (for more on this see page 188). The table is arranged into:

- **Vertical columns, called groups, in which the elements with similar physical and chemical properties (behaviours) are grouped together**

- **Horizontal rows, called periods, which are in order of increasing proton number.**

Figure 17.1 — Periodic table (see page 184 for a larger version)

Period	1	2	3	4	5	6	7	8	9	10	11	12	13	14	15	16	17	18
1	1 H 1.00794																	2 He 4.0026
2	3 Li 6.941	4 Be 9.01218											5 B 10.811	6 C 12.0107	7 N 14.0067	8 O 15.9994	9 F 18.9984	10 Ne 20.1797
3	11 Na 22.9893	12 Mg 24.305											13 Al 26.9815	14 Si 28.085	15 P 30.9738	16 S 32.065	17 Cl 35.453	18 Ar 39.948
4	19 K 39.0983	20 Ca 40.078	21 Sc 44.9559	22 Ti 47.867	23 V 50.9415	24 Cr 51.9961	25 Mn 54.938	26 Fe 55.845	27 Co 58.9332	28 Ni 58.6934	29 Cu 63.546	30 Zn 65.38	31 Ga 69.723	32 Ge 72.63	33 As 74.9216	34 Se 78.96	35 Br 79.904	36 Kr 83.798
5	37 Rb 85.4678	38 Sr 87.62	39 Y 88.9059	40 Zr 91.224	41 Nb 92.9064	42 Mo 95.96	43 Tc [98]	44 Ru 101.07	45 Rh 102.906	46 Pd 106.42	47 Ag 107.868	48 Cd 112.411	49 In 114.818	50 Sn 118.71	51 Sb 121.76	52 Te 127.6	53 I 126.904	54 Xe 131.293
6	55 Cs 132.905	56 Ba 137.327	57–71	72 Hf 178.49	73 Ta 180.948	74 W 183.84	75 Re 186.207	76 Os 190.23	77 Ir 192.217	78 Pt 195.084	79 Au 196.967	80 Hg 200.59	81 Tl 204.383	82 Pb 207.2	83 Bi 208.98	84 Po [210]	85 At [210]	86 Rn [222]
7	87 Fr [223]	88 Ra [226]	89–103	104 Rf [267]	105 Db [268]	106 Sg [269]	107 Bh [270]	108 Hs [269]	109 Mt [278]	110 Ds [281]	111 Rg [281]	112 Cn [285]	113 Uut [286]	114 Fl [289]	115 Uup [290]	116 Lv [293]	117 Uus [294]	118 Uuo [294]

57 La 138.905	58 Ce 140.116	59 Pr 140.908	60 Nd 144.242	61 Pm [145]	62 Sm 150.36	63 Eu 151.964	64 Gd 157.25	65 Tb 158.925	66 Dy 162.5	67 Ho 164.93	68 Er 167.259	69 Tm 168.934	70 Yb 173.054	71 Lu 174.967
89 Ac [227]	90 Th 232.038	91 Pa 231.036	92 U 238.029	93 Np [237]	94 Pu [244]	95 Am [243]	96 Cm [247]	97 Bk [247]	98 Cf [251]	99 Es [252]	100 Fm [257]	101 Md [258]	102 No [259]	103 Lr [262]

▲ **Figure 17.1** *Periodic table (see page 184 for a larger version)*

? Questions

17.2 Complete the following sentence: Vertical columns of elements are called _____ and horizontal rows of elements are known as _____.

17.3 From the periodic table, identify:
(a) Three elements from group 2
(b) Three elements from period 2
(c) The element in group 1 period 3.

? Question

17.4 Refer to Figures 17.1 and 17.2. Complete this table to show that you understand how the periodic table is arranged.

Element	Symbol	Period	Group	Metal	Non-metal
Carbon					
	H				
		2	3		
Barium					
Chlorine					
	He				

Animated Scientist Biography

Marie Curie was a scientist who discovered two new elements: radium and polonium. Watch an *Exploring Science* animation to find out more about Marie Curie and her investigations.

◀ **Figure 17.2**
Marie Curie

Group names

The periodic table has four named groups. They are:

- Group 1 – the **alkali** metals
- Group 2 – the alkaline earth metals
- Group 7 – the **halogens**
- Group 8 – the **noble gases**.

We will look at each group in the rest of this chapter.

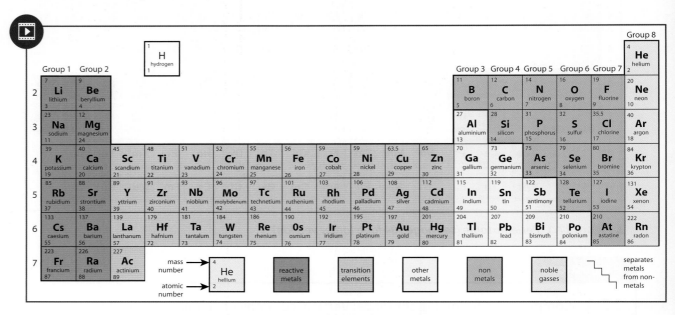

▲ **Figure 17.3** *Periodic table – each colour shows elements with similar properties*

Group 1 – the alkali metals

All the alkali metals have one electron in their outer shell. The atoms 'want' to get rid of this loose electron. As a result, the alkali metals are very reactive and behave similarly. Elements in this group include:

- Lithium (Li)
- Sodium (Na)
- Potassium (K).

Reactions of alkali metals with water

When an alkali metal such as lithium is added to water it floats on the surface of the water and forms a ball shape. Hydrogen gas is released and lithium hydroxide is formed, which dissolves in the water.

> lithium + water → lithium hydroxide + hydrogen

Sodium is more reactive than lithium. It may even catch fire (orange flame) as it fizzes about on the surface.

> sodium + water → sodium hydroxide + hydrogen

Potassium is even more reactive than sodium. Can you predict the products of the reaction between potassium and water?

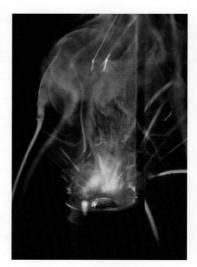

▲ **Figure 17.4** *Potassium reacting with water*

Reactions of alkali metals with air

All metals are shiny. Alkali metals look dull, but when they are cut a shiny surface is revealed. This shiny surface quickly goes dull again as the metal reacts with oxygen in the air, forming the metal oxide.

For lithium the reaction with oxygen is:

> lithium + oxygen → lithium oxide

For sodium the reaction with oxygen is:

> sodium + oxygen → sodium oxide

Group 2 – the alkaline earth metals

Elements in this group include:

- Beryllium (Be)
- Magnesium (Mg)
- Calcium (Ca).

All elements in this group have two electrons in their outer shell.
Group 2 elements are not as reactive as group 1 elements.

▲ Figure 17.5 *Alkaline earth metals – beryllium, magnesium, calcium, strontium and barium*

Group 7 – the halogens

The elements in group 7 have seven electrons in their atom's outer shell. (The word 'halogen' also contains seven letters!) Elements in this group include:

- Fluorine (F), in the form of compounds such as sodium fluoride, which is sometimes added to water to strengthen enamel in our teeth.
- Chlorine (Cl), which is sometimes added to water to kill bacteria.

Elements in this group are 'trying' to gain an electron because they want a full outer shell.

▲ Figure 17.6 *The halogens (chlorine, bromine and iodine)*

Group 8 (group 0) – the noble gases

The elements in group 8 are all gases and have full outer shells of electrons in their atoms. As a result, the noble gases are unreactive and thus very stable. Members of the noble gases include:

- Helium (He)
- Neon (Ne)
- Argon (Ar), which is used in filament lamps (light bulbs).

▲ Figure 17.7 *Helium, one of the noble gases, is sometimes used in balloons*

? **Questions**

17.5 Find out how these names were assigned to each of these groups:

(a) The alkali metals

(b) The alkaline earth metals

(c) The halogens

(d) The noble gases.

17.6 Select one element from each group and find out where it may be used.

17.7 How many naturally occurring elements are there?

Electron shell rules

- Electrons are found in shells, or orbits.

- The shells nearest the nucleus are filled first.

- The first shell can hold up to two electrons.

- The second and third shells can hold up to eight electrons each.

- Atoms that have a full outer shell of electrons are stable and do not react.

- In most atoms the outer shell is not full, and this makes them more likely to react.

What are ions?

All atoms would 'like' full outer shells and will either lose or gain electrons in order to achieve this. **When atoms lose or gain electrons they become charged particles and are called ions.** The elements that readily form ions make up groups 1, 2, 6 and 7.

- Group 1 – alkali metals. These have only one electron in the outer shell, which they lose to form a positive ion (+1), e.g. Na^{+1}.

- Group 2 – alkaline earth metals. These have two electrons in their outer shell so will lose two electrons to form a positive ion (+2), e.g. Mg^{+2}.

- Group 6 – non-metals. These have six electrons in their outer shell and so will gain two electrons for a full outer shell to form a negative ion (−2), e.g. O^{-2}.

- Group 7 – halogens. These have seven electrons in their outer shell and so will gain one electron to form a negative ion (−1), e.g. Cl^{-1}.

How are chemical bonds formed?

A compound forms when two different elements chemically combine. The question is why these elements react and combine with each other. They react to have a full outer shell of electrons. In a compound the atoms are joined by chemical bonds.

Making bonds involves atoms giving away, taking or sharing electrons. There are two ways for atoms to achieve this: ionic bonding and covalent bonding.

Ionic bonding

Ionic bonding produces a compound that is formed from a metal and a non-metal and is made up of ions. This occurs when one atom loses electrons and another atom gains electrons.

The metal atom will lose electrons to form a positive ion and the non-metal atom will gain electrons to form a negative ion. These positive and negative ions are strongly attracted to each other.

For example, sodium chloride (NaCl) is a compound formed from a metal (sodium) and a non-metal (chlorine). The sodium atom loses an electron and the chlorine atom gains an electron (Figure 17.8).

▲ **Figure 17.8** *A sodium atom gives an electron to a chlorine atom*

Covalent bonding

Covalent bonding produces a compound formed from non-metals in which each atom shares electrons with another atom. Neither atom wants to donate electrons as they both need electrons to achieve a full outer shell. The solution is that they share electrons.

For example, hydrochloric acid (HCl) is a compound formed from two non-metals (hydrogen and chlorine). A hydrogen atom bonds with a chlorine atom by sharing an electron with it. The outer shells of the two atoms overlap and they share one electron.

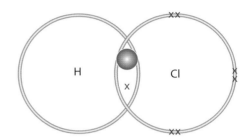

▲ **Figure 17.9** *A hydrogen atom and a chlorine atom share one electron*

Chemical formulas

Every compound has a formula – it tells you the type and number of atoms present in a compound. The **chemical formula** is made up of letters and numbers, e.g. CH_4, H_2O.

● The letters in the formula tell you the type of atoms it is made of.

● The numbers tell you how many of that atom there are.

The chemical formula for carbon dioxide is CO_2 as it contains 1 carbon atom and 2 oxygen atoms.

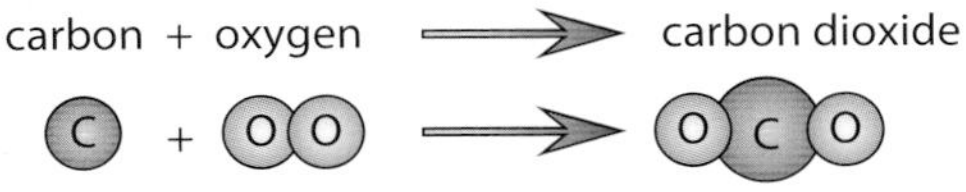

carbon + oxygen ⟶ carbon dioxide

Ⓒ + Ⓞ Ⓞ ⟶ Ⓞ Ⓒ Ⓞ

▲ **Figure 17.10** *Carbon dioxide is formed from a chemical reaction between carbon and oxygen*

You can use the periodic table to predict the ratio of atoms in compounds.

? Question

17.8 Copy and complete the following table.

Compound	Chemical formula	Atoms present
Methane	CH_4	1 C, 4 H
Water	H_2O	
Sulfuric acid	H_2SO_4	
Sodium hydroxide	NaOH	
Sodium chloride	NaCl	

THE CHEMIST'S COMPASS – THE PERIODIC TABLE

Combining metals and non-metals

When a metal and a non-metal are combined, the resultant compound is called after the name of the metal followed by the name of the non-metal, with its ending changed to '-ide'.
For example:

> sodium + chlorine → sodium chloride
> *Metal   Non-metal   Compound*

Sodium is in group 1 of the periodic table so it needs to lose one electron. Chlorine is in group 7 of the periodic table so it needs to gain one electron. So the ratio of atoms in the compound sodium chloride is 1:1: one sodium atom bonds with one chlorine atom.

 $Na + Cl \rightarrow Na^{+1} Cl^{-1}$

> **? Question**
>
> **17.9** What are the names of the compounds formed between:
>
> **(a)** Calcium and chlorine?
>
> **(b)** Lithium and bromine?
>
> **(c)** Magnesium and oxygen?

Combining non-metals and non-metals

Use the periodic table to predict the ratio of atoms in compounds. You need to work out the combining power of each atom. This is the number of bonds each atom can form. For example:

● Hydrogen is in group 1 of the periodic table, which shows it has only one electron and needs one more electron in order to be stable so that it can form one bond; so its combining power = 1.

● Carbon is found in group 4 of the periodic table, which shows it has four electrons in its outer shell and it requires four more electrons in order to be stable so it can form four bonds; so its combining power = 4.

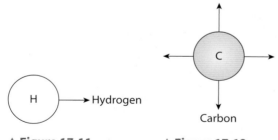

▲ **Figure 17.11**   ▲ **Figure 17.12**

For carbon and hydrogen to bond and stabilise, one carbon atom (combining power = 4) requires 4 hydrogen atoms (combining power = 1) to bond with it. This combination makes the carbon atom stable because of the four hydrogen electrons, and each of the four hydrogen atoms stable because of one carbon electron. The combination is shown in Figure 17.13. The resultant chemical formula is CH_4, which is methane (the main constituent of natural gas).

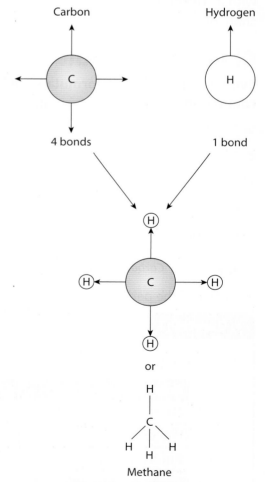

▲ **Figure 17.13** *Chemical formula for a compound containing carbon and hydrogen*

Note: Atoms do not always obey the octet rule (eight electrons in the outer shell). For example, hydrogen, beryllium and boron have too few electrons in the outer shell to form an octet.

? Question

17.10 In your group, copy and complete the following table using the periodic table.

Element	Symbol	Group number	Electrons needed	Combining power	Show bonds
Hydrogen	H	1	1	1	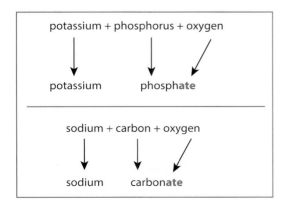
Carbon	C	4	4	4	
Nitrogen					
Oxygen					
Sulfur					
Chlorine					

? Questions

17.11 Using the periodic table work out the formula and the name of the compound formed between:

(a) Hydrogen and chlorine

(b) Nitrogen and hydrogen

(c) Carbon and oxygen.

17.12 Draw diagrams and show the bonding in a water molecule.

Combining metal atoms, non-metal atoms and oxygen

When naming compounds formed by combining a metal atom, a non-metal atom and oxygen, the name of the metal comes first, the name of the non-metal comes next and the ending is '-ate'. This occurs only when an oxygen atom is present. For example:

potassium + phosphorus + oxygen

↓   ↓   ↙

potassium   phosphate

_____

sodium + carbon + oxygen

↓   ↓   ↙

sodium   carbonate

Did you know?

Carbon is a very interesting element. It can form about 10 million compounds with almost all other elements in the periodic table. The human body's mass is 18.5% carbon.

? Question

17.13 Write the name of the compounds formed between the following:

(a) Potassium + nitrogen + oxygen

(b) Magnesium + carbon + oxygen

(c) Calcium + sulfur + oxygen

(d) Lithium + phosphorous + oxygen.

Hydrogen molecule (H_2)

Each hydrogen atom has one electron in its shell and so has a combining power of 1. This means that two hydrogen atoms will overlap their shells and bond, forming a hydrogen molecule (H_2).

▲ **Figure 17.14** *A hydrogen molecule*

Hydrogen
H_2

Oxygen molecule (O_2)

Each oxygen atom has six electrons in the outer shell and needs to gain two electrons to fill it and so has a combining power of 2. In an oxygen molecule, two oxygen atoms are bonded together and there is a double bond.

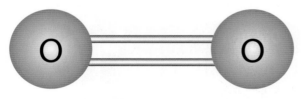

▲ **Figure 17.15** *An oxygen molecule*

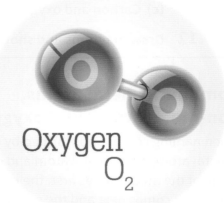

Oxygen
O_2

? Question

17.14 Refer to the periodic table to work out what a nitrogen molecule looks like.

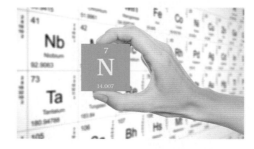

◄ **Figure 17.16**

Summary questions

17.15 How many naturally occurring elements are there?

17.16 Copy and complete the following table.

Element	Symbol
Helium	
Silicon	
Fluorine	
Chlorine	
Sodium	
Neon	
Argon	

17.17 Complete the following sentences: The elements in group _____ are called the alkali metals. Because they react vigorously with water they are stored under _____. Lithium, _____ and _____ are examples of alkali metals.

17.18 Look at Figure 17.17 and answer these questions using the letters A–E and the elements' names.

(a) Which two elements are in the same group?

(b) Which two elements are in the same period?

(c) Name the group to which elements A and B belong.

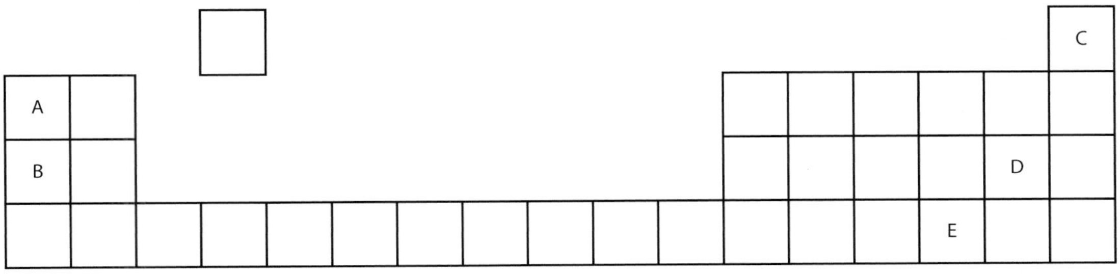

▲ **Figure 17.17**

17.19 From the periodic table, name:

(a) Three elements from group 3

(b) Three elements from period 3

(c) The element in group 1, period 4.

17.20 What are the names of the different types of atoms in the following compounds:

(a) Calcium nitrate?

(b) Potassium carbonate?

(c) Sodium bromide?

(d) Sodium carbonate?

Log on to **www.edcolearning.ie** for Additional Summary Questions

Assessment questions

17.21 Write down the atomic number and mass number of the element sodium.

17.22 An atom with 56 protons and 81 neutrons has an atomic number of _____ and a mass number of _____. Use the periodic table to help you answer questions about the elements listed in the table below. Write the answers in your copy book. **(30 marks)**

Element	Element	Compound name	Formula
Hydrogen (H)	Oxygen (O)	Water	H_2O
Nitrogen (N)	Hydrogen (H)	Ammonia	
Carbon (C)	Oxygen (O)		CO_2
Sodium (Na)	Chlorine (Cl)	Sodium chloride	
Magnesium (Mg)	Oxygen (O)		

(a) State the number of protons in chlorine. _____

(b) Where in the atom are the protons found? _____

(c) How many neutrons are found in a zinc atom? _____

(d) Where are the electrons located in each atom? _____

(e) State the element in the table above which has the same number of protons and neutrons. _____

17.23 Copy and complete the table below, using the periodic table of elements to predict the elements in the compounds. **(30 marks)**

Compound	Elements present
Sodium bromide	
Potassium carbonate	
Sodium carbonate	
Calcium nitrate	
Potassium oxide	

17.24 Question from Junior Cycle Science exam paper **(45 marks)**

Write your answers in your science copy book.

The Periodic Table was developed by Dmitri Mendeleev. It was published 150 years ago in 1869. To celebrate the International Year of the Periodic Table, The European Chemical Society has designed a new kind of Periodic Table called the '90 Elements that make up everything'.

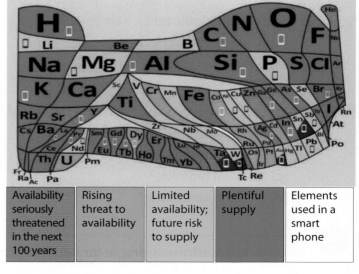

▲ **Figure 17.18**

The table has been drawn so that the area occupied by each element indicates how much of that element is in the Earth's crust and atmosphere.

(a) From the table, identify a gas which is a component of the Earth's atmosphere and which is in plentiful supply.

(b) Why should the use of the gas helium (He) in birthday balloons be avoided?

(c) The element indium (In) is used in smart phones. At current usage rates, indium will be used up in 50 years. Suggest one way humans could contribute to sustaining levels of this element for future generations.

The diagrams on the right show the arrangement of particles in the elements aluminium and chlorine at room temperature.

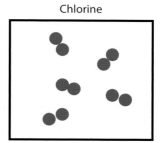
Aluminium   Chlorine

▲ **Figure 17.19**

(d) What evidence is there in the diagrams to support the classification of these substances as elements?

(e) Which of these elements is a solid at room temperature? Justify your answer.

(f) Aluminium reacts with chlorine to form the compound aluminium chloride. Use the Periodic Table on page 79 of the *Formulae and Tables* booklet to predict the ratio of aluminium to chlorine in this compound. Hence write the chemical formula for aluminium chloride.

(g) Elements can be classified as metals or non-metals.

The table shows some of the properties of three elements from the Periodic Table.

	Melting point (°C)	Boiling point (°C)	Conductor of electricity
Element 1	1538	2862	Yes
Element 2	−7	59	No
Element 3	−101	−34	No

Which element (**1**, **2**, or **3**) is most likely to be a metal? Justify your answer.

Which element (**1**, **2**, or **3**) is a liquid at room temperature (20°C)? Justify your answer.

 Log on to **www.edcolearning.ie** for Additional Assessment Questions

METALS AND NON-METALS – PROPERTIES AND USES

LO: CW4, CW6

Learning intentions

At the end of this chapter you will be able to:

✓ Classify substances as metals or non-metals

✓ Investigate properties of metals

✓ Apply the uses of metals and non-metals based on their properties.

Keywords

⊷ physical properties
⊷ melting point
⊷ conductivity
⊷ density
⊷ alloy
⊷ boiling point

What are physical properties of materials?

Physical properties are the characteristics and features that define any material. Every material has a different set of properties that makes it perfect for some jobs and useless for other jobs. For example, the plastic used in the handle of a brush is hard, strong and stiff, whereas the plastic used in the bristles is soft and flexible.

Ninety-two elements are found naturally on Earth. These can be classified as:

● Metals

● Non-metals

● Semi-metals or metalloids (e.g. silicon).

There are just a few semi-metals, and in this chapter we will be looking at metals and non-metals.

Metals

Most of Earth's naturally occurring elements are metals. Their different properties make individual elements ideal for a large variety of uses in everyday life. Look back to the periodic table on page 194.

▲ **Figure 18.1** *The handles of the brush and pan are made of hard plastic and the bristles of the brush are made of soft plastic*

Elements

Metals   Non-metals

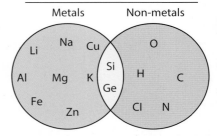

▲ **Figure 18.2** *Metals, semi-metals and non-metals*

The properties of metals

Metals have a number of physical properties in common, but each metal is also slightly different.

Melting point

The melting point is the temperature at which a solid material turns to a liquid. For example, the melting point of ice is 0°C. Most materials that are pure chemicals have a unique melting point.

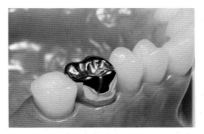
▲ **Figure 18.3** *A gold tooth – just one of the many uses of metal*

✒ Activity 18.1 Do metals have high or low melting points?

🧪 **Equipment needed**

Bunsen burner	Copper rod	Aluminium rod
Iron nail	Zinc rod	Tongs

Piece of metal e.g. a nail

Tongs

⚠ **Safety**
- Make sure to use tongs for holding the metal items in the flame.

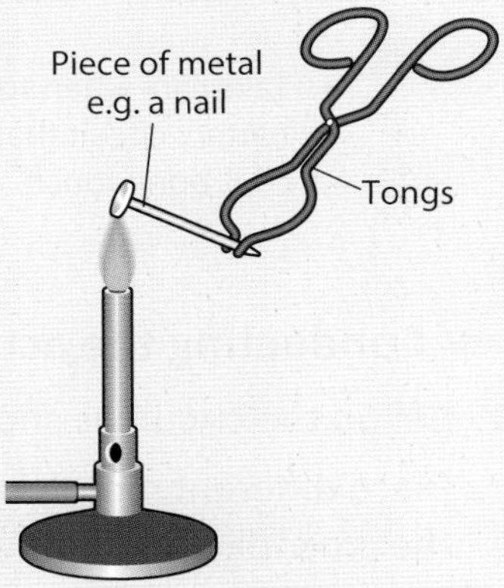

➡ **Conducting the activity**

1. Heat each metal, e.g. iron nail, in a strong Bunsen burner flame, using the tongs.

▲ **Figure 18.4** *Investigating the melting points of metals*

2. Make a note of what happens to each metal in your Student Activity Book and answer the questions that follow.

   (a) Do any of the metals melt?

   (b) What can you say about the melting points of these metals?

Conductivity of heat

✒ Activity 18.2 Are metals good conductors (or carriers) of heat?

🧪 **Equipment needed**

4 metal rods (different metals)

Bunsen burner	Tripod
Grease/wax	Pins

⚠ **Safety**
- Make sure the metal rods are stable on the tripod.

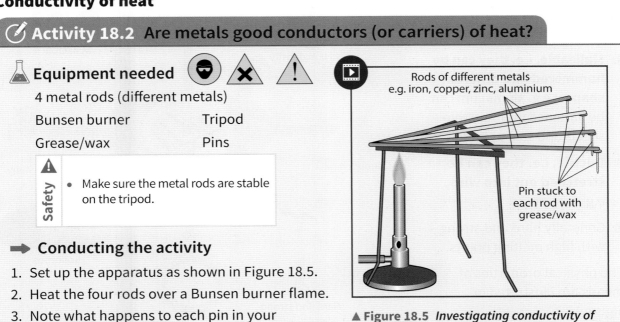

Rods of different metals e.g. iron, copper, zinc, aluminium

Pin stuck to each rod with grease/wax

➡ **Conducting the activity**

1. Set up the apparatus as shown in Figure 18.5.
2. Heat the four rods over a Bunsen burner flame.
3. Note what happens to each pin in your Student Activity Book.

▲ **Figure 18.5** *Investigating conductivity of heat for metals*

4. When writing up your results, place the metals in decreasing order of **conductivity** of heat.

Conductivity of electricity

✐ Activity 18.3   Are metals good conductors of electricity?

🧪 Equipment needed

Bulb

Crocodile clips

6-V battery or powerpack

Four different metals, e.g. iron, copper, zinc, aluminium

| ⚠ Safety | • | Take care when setting up the battery circuit that the crocodile clips don't touch. |

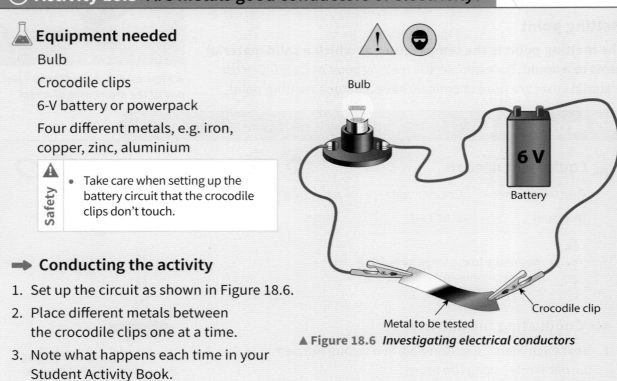

▲ **Figure 18.6** *Investigating electrical conductors*

➡ Conducting the activity

1. Set up the circuit as shown in Figure 18.6.
2. Place different metals between the crocodile clips one at a time.
3. Note what happens each time in your Student Activity Book.
4. When you write up your results, note whether metals are good conductors of electricity.

Other properties of metals

The short investigations in the previous activities show some of the physical properties of metals. Metals are also:

● **Malleable, i.e. they can be hammered into different shapes;** e.g. aluminium can be flattened into very thin sheets and sold as 'tinfoil'

● **Ductile, i.e. they can be stretched out into wire,** e.g. copper

● Generally hard and strong with high melting points.

The physical properties of metals are illustrated in Figure 18.7.

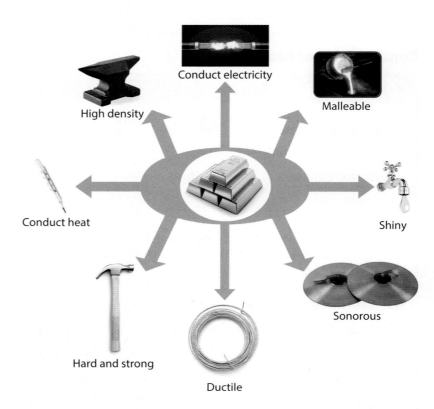

▲ **Figure 18.7** *The physical properties of metals*

Not all metals have all these properties. For example:

● The alkali metals are soft with low density, e.g. sodium and potassium
● Mercury is a liquid at room temperature.

Metals have high density

Many metals have a high **density**. This means they feel very heavy for their size. The reason for this is that there are a lot of atoms packed into a small volume.

Metallic bonding

Metal atoms are held tightly together by electrons. These electrons come from the outer shells of the atoms and hold the atoms together.

The metals are hard, strong and can conduct heat because of the atoms held tightly together. Metals can conduct electricity because the electrons are free to move between the atoms.

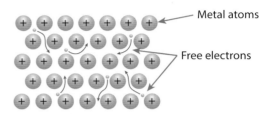

▲ Figure 18.8 *Metallic bonding*

⑦ Questions

18.1 Divide the class into groups. Each group is to choose and look at one metal. Within your group, discuss your chosen metal's properties and decide how it is best used.

An example is: Aluminium is strong and can be bent into shape but it is also light, so it is used to make aeroplanes.

18.2 Titanium is a transition metal that is used in hip replacements. Research the properties of titanium and list three properties that make it suitable for this use.

18.3 Research the properties of the metals listed below, and explain why each has been chosen for its use:

(a) Using copper to make wires

(b) Using iron to make bridges

(c) Using gold and silver to make jewellery.

18.4 Give two reasons why metal, rather than plastic, is a good choice for a saucepan.

Alloys

Sometimes metals are more useful when they are pure, e.g. pure copper is much better at conducting electricity than when it is mixed with other metals. However, **many metals are better and more useful for certain jobs when they are combined with other metals or a non-metal (such as carbon). These are known as alloys**. Some common alloys are listed in Table 18.1.

Table 18.1 Alloys, their composition and uses

Alloy	Composition	Use
Brass	Copper and zinc	Musical instruments, ornaments
Bronze	Copper and tin	Statues
Solder	Lead and tin	Soldering
Mild steel	Iron and carbon	Building reinforcement
Stainless steel	Iron, chromium and nickel	Knives, sinks
Alnico	Aluminium, nickel and cobalt	Powerful magnets

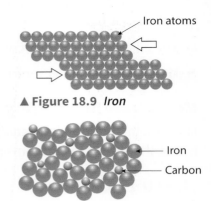

Figure 18.9 *Iron*

Steel

Pure iron has a regular arrangement of identical atoms (see Figure 18.9). The layers of atoms can slide over each other. This makes the iron soft, which allows it to change shape easily and makes it unsuitable for most uses.

Most pure iron is changed into alloys of steel, where small amounts of carbon and sometimes other metals are added to the iron. The carbon atoms disrupt the regularity of the iron atoms, making it more difficult for them to slide over each other (see Figure 18.10). This makes the alloy harder.

▲ Figure 18.10 *Steel*

? Question

18.5 There are three different types of steel, as shown in the table below:

Type of steel	Properties
Low carbon steel	Easily shaped
High carbon steel	Very hard, inflexible
Stainless steel	Corrosion-resistant

(a) Which of these alloys are suitable for car bodies? Give your reasons.

(b) Stainless steel is corrosion-resistant. What does this mean?

(c) Give some everyday uses of stainless steel.

(d) High carbon steel is used for blades for cutting tools and for building bridges. Why is this?

▲ Figure 18.11 *The Eiffel Tower is made of iron and needs repainting every 7 years*

Did you know?

The Eiffel Tower is made of iron. Iron goes rusty if air and water get on it. So the Eiffel Tower has to be painted every 7 years, and it takes an entire year of 25 painters working on it. That wouldn't happen with stainless steel!

? Question

18.6 Some alloys are called smart alloys. One smart alloy is nitinol. Research this alloy, looking particularly at the following questions.

(a) What metals are mixed together to form nitinol?

(b) Why is it called a smart alloy?

(c) Where is it used?

Non-metals

There are 22 non-metal elements. Many non-metals are liquids or gases. Examples are:

- Carbon
- Oxygen
- Sulfur
- Nitrogen.

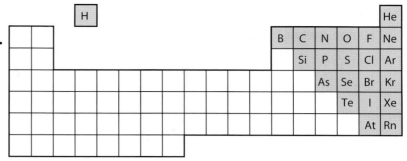

▲ Figure 18.12 *Periodic table for the non-metals*

Properties of non-metals

Non-metals have properties that are generally opposite to those of metals.

Melting point and boiling point

The forces that hold the atoms together in non-metals are weak and this means they melt and boil easily. The melting point and **boiling point** of some non-metals are given in Table 18.2.

Table 18.2

Non-metal	Melting point °C	Boiling point °C
Sulfur	113	445
Oxygen	−218	−183
Chlorine	−101	−35
Helium	−272	−269
Neon	−249	−248

Conductors of electricity

Non-metals are electrical insulators, which means electrical current cannot flow through them.

> ? **Questions**
>
> **18.7** Non-metals combine to make materials that are good insulators. Name one of these materials and state where it may be used and why.
>
> **18.8** Where might non-metals be used in everyday objects? Give five examples.

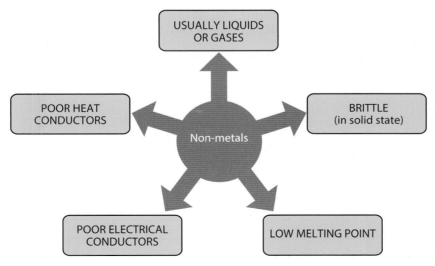

▲ Figure 18.13 *Non-metals*

Some exceptions

Not all non-metals have the above properties.

For example:

- Carbon in the form of graphite is a good conductor of electricity
- Carbon in the form of diamond is extremely hard with a high melting point.

▲ Figure 18.14 *Diamond*

✏ Activity 18.4 Which materials are good conductors or insulators of electricity?

🧪 **Equipment needed**

Bulb
Crocodile clips
Leads
Lead plate
Graphite
Euro coin
6V battery
Copper plate
Wood
Paper
Aluminium plate
Tinfoil
Piece of coal
Piece of plastic

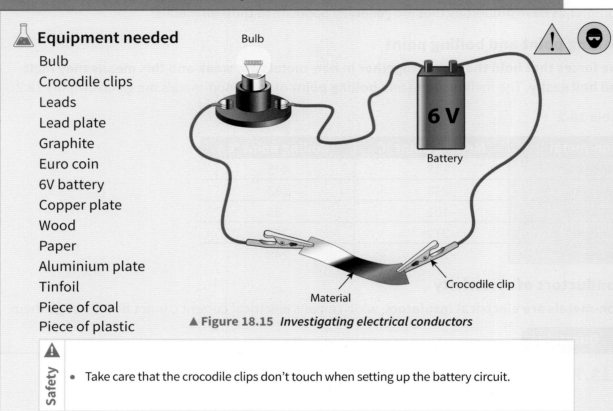

▲ Figure 18.15 *Investigating electrical conductors*

Safety
- Take care that the crocodile clips don't touch when setting up the battery circuit.

➡ Conducting the activity

1. Set up the circuit as shown in Figure 18.15.
2. Place different materials between the crocodile clips one at a time.
3. Note if the bulb lights and record the results in a table like the one below, showing whether the material is a conductor or an insulator of electricity (one has been done for you).

Results

Record your results in the copy of the following table in your Student Activity Book.

Material	Bulb lights	Insulator	Conductor
Wood	No	✓	
Copper			
Lead			
Coal			
Plastic			
Paper			

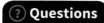

Questions

18.9 Coal and graphite are forms of carbon and are non-metals. Coal does not conduct electricity (it is an insulator), but graphite is a good conductor of electricity. Research these non-metals, looking at:

(a) The arrangement of carbon atoms in coal and graphite

(b) Why electrical current will flow through graphite but not coal.

18.10 The table shows the percentage of different metals in the €1 coin:

Coin	Colour	% Copper	% Zinc	Nickel
€1	Outer ring gold	75	20	5
€1	Centre silver	75	0	25

▲ Figure 18.16 *Euro coins*

(a) Why are alloys, rather than pure metals, used to make coins?

(b) What are the similarities and differences between the different alloys used for €1 coins?

(c) Which metal gives a gold colour to the coins? Explain how you can tell.

(d) Copper has an antibacterial effect. Explain why this is useful for coins.

Summary questions

18.11 Complete this sentence:

Metals are good conductors of _____ and _____.

18.12 Complete this sentence:

Copper can be drawn out into thin wire. This means it is a _____ metal.

18.13 Gold is a malleable metal. What does this mean?

18.14 What is unusual about the metal mercury?

18.15 Describe an alloy.

18.16 Give two examples of alloys.

18.17 Give the name for a metal which:

(a) Is used in hot-water pipes

(b) Is a liquid at room temperature

(c) Is the main element in steel

(d) Is used in expensive jewellery

(e) Is used to galvanise iron.

18.18 Suggest a reason for the following.

(a) Aeroplanes are made of aluminium, not steel.

(b) Tinfoil is made of aluminium, not steel.

(c) Gold rings are not pure gold.

(d) Copper is used in electrical wires.

18.19 Separate the following table of elements into metals and nonmetals. Write the answers in your copy book.

Elements
Iron
Carbon
Zinc
Chlorine
Hydrogen
Sodium
Gold

18.20 Use this list of elements to answer the following questions.

| iron | carbon | copper | zinc | mercury | sodium | chlorine | helium |

(a) Which metal and non-metal form steel?

(b) Which non-metal is used in swimming pools?

(c) Which two metals form the alloy brass?

(d) Which metal element is a liquid at room temperature?

(e) Which non-metal is used in a pencil?

(f) What is an alloy?

(g) Give two examples of alloys.

Assessment questions

18.21 The different properties make individual metals ideal for a large variety of uses in everyday life. Write out the metals from the list with the correct description: **(15 marks)**

Magnesium	Mercury	Copper
Lead	Aluminium	Silver
Potassium		

(a) The metal is used in thermometers.

(b) Coke cans are often made of this metal.

(c) This metal is a very good conductor of electricity.

(d) This metal is used in fireworks.

(e) Jewellery is often made of this metal.

18.22 Which two of the following are alloys. **(15 marks)**

Aluminium, brass, diamond, iron, bronze

18.23 Pure iron can be changed into an alloy called steel. **(30 marks)**

Type of steel	Properties
Low carbon steel	Corrosion-resistant
High carbon steel	Easily shaped
Stainless steel	Very hard, inflexible

(a) Match each type of steel to its property in a table in your copy book.

(b) State one use for each type of steel.

(c) Explain how the addition of carbon to pure iron can make the alloy harder.

PowerPoint summary   Weblinks

MATERIALS SCIENCE – FIT FOR PURPOSE

CHAPTER 19

LO: CW4, CW6

Learning intentions

At the end of this chapter you will be able to:

✓ Classify materials into different groups

✓ Investigate the properties of different materials

✓ Identify the choice of a material for a particular purpose and assess its fitness for purpose.

Keywords

- classify
- natural
- synthetic
- tensile strength
- compressive strength
- elasticity
- composites
- ceramics
- nanotechnology

What is a material?

A material is a substance that things are made from. Materials have different properties, and these are very important when choosing which material to use in a particular product.

How do we classify materials?

We can sort and **classify** materials into different groups by looking at their properties. For example:

- Solids, liquids and gases
- Elements, compounds and mixtures
- Metals and non-metals
- **Natural** and **synthetic** (manufactured).

▲ Figure 19.1 *The material for this mobile phone would have been chosen very carefully for its particular properties*

? Questions

19.1 Copy the following table and complete it using your knowledge of everyday materials and chemistry.

Material	State of matter	Element compound or mixture	Metal or non-metal	Natural or synthetic
Plastic				
Wood				
Butane				
Coal				
Glass				
Helium				
China				
Iron				
Quartz				

What are the properties of materials?

Every material has a different set of properties, which can make it perfect for some jobs and totally useless for others.

The properties can be categorised as:

- Strength
- Hardness
- Stiffness
- Elasticity
- Density
- Melting point
- Ability to conduct heat and electricity.

We look at each of these properties below.

Strength

Strength is how good a material is at resisting force. You can find out how strong a material is by how much force is needed to either break it or permanently change its shape. There are two different types of strength:

- Tensile strength
- Compressive strength.

▲ Figure 19.2

Tensile strength

Tensile strength is how much a material can resist a pulling force. For example, ropes and cables need a high tensile strength or they could snap.

The tensile strength of a material can be measured as the force it can withstand before it breaks. Look at Table 19.1 below. It shows the tensile strength of some metals.

▲ Figure 19.3 *A man using a rope on a field study in Patagonia*

Table 19.1 Tensile strength of some metals

Metal	Tensile strength force (MPa)
Aluminium	45
Copper	220
Cast iron	200
Steel	400
Brass	550
Tungsten	1510

? Question

19.2 Why, do you think, steel and not brass is used to make cables in the construction of bridges?

Compressive strength

Compressive strength is how well a material can resist a pushing force. For example, bricks need good compressive strength or they could be squashed by the weight of the bricks above them.

▲ Figure 19.4 *The bricks in this wall need good compressive strength*

Activity 19.1 Which paper has the greatest tearing strength?

We will be hanging a container on different kinds of paper (kitchen paper, napkin, tissue, newspaper, photocopying paper) and putting weights (marbles) into it to see how much weight the paper can take before it tears.

🧪 Equipment needed

Paper clip

String

Empty yoghurt carton

Marbles

Electronic balance

Different types of paper: kitchen paper, napkin, tissue, newspaper, photocopying paper

> ⚠ **Safety**
> • Take care that when the paper tears the marbles do not fall out of the container and on to the floor, where people could slip on them.

➡ Conducting the activity

1. Cut out the different types of paper to equal sizes (20 × 20 cm).

2. Make two holes opposite each other near the rim of an empty yoghurt carton.

3. Make a hole at the end of each piece of paper with a hole punch.

4. Using a paper clip and string, hang the carton from the first type of paper, as shown in Figure 19.5.

5. Gradually add marbles gently to the carton until the paper tears. Place the marbles gently in the yoghurt pot, as force will cause the paper to tear too soon.

6. Record the number of marbles and find the mass of marbles on an electronic balance.

7. Repeat steps 4 to 6 for the remaining squares of paper.

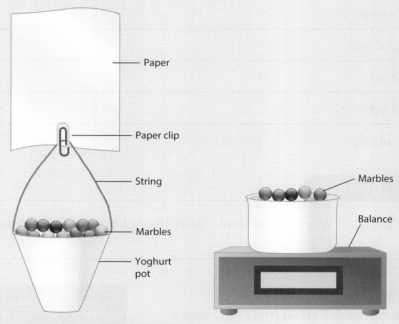

▲ Figure 19.5 *To find the tearing strength of paper*

8. Record all your results in the copy of the following table in your Student Activity Book and compare your results with those of the rest of the class.

Type of paper	Number of marbles	Mass of marbles (g)
Kitchen paper		
Napkin		
Tissue		
Newspaper		
Photocopying paper		

⑦ Questions

19.3 List all the different types of paper you can think of. Try to put them in order of how strong you think they are.

19.4 Why would you not make a shopping bag out of tissue paper?

19.5 What happens when paper gets wet?

Did you *know?*

Spider silk, which spiders use to make their webs, is very strong yet very light. It could have the potential to be made into bulletproof clothing. However, collecting it is difficult as it involves forcing the silk from the spiders.

Hardness

The hardness of a material is how difficult it is to cut into. Solids can be hard because their particles are held together by very strong bonds. The hardest material found in nature is diamond. Diamond can cut most materials, and this explains why many industrial drills have diamond tips.

▲ **Figure 19.6** *This dental drill has a diamond drilling point*

⑦ Questions

19.6 What would happen, do you think, if you rubbed a metal pen tip against the surface of a piece of wood? Make a prediction in terms of the hardness of the metal and the wood that you are comparing and then test it. Discuss what you observed.

19.7 Diamond is one of the hardest materials, so how could you cut a diamond?

▲ **Figure 19.7** *The centenary diamond – diamond is one of the hardest materials*

Stiffness

A stiff material does not bend or change shape when a force is applied. This is not the same as strength, because some materials, such as rubber, can be very strong but can bend and stretch very easily.

Materials such as steel are very difficult to bend, so they are very stiff. This explains why steel bars are inserted in concrete pillars during construction of large structures.

▲ **Figure 19.8** *Steel bars are used in construction because they are very stiff*

Elasticity

Elasticity is how much a solid can be stretched and return to its original shape and size.
For example, a rubber band is an elastic material. Solids are elastic because their particles are held together with stretchy bonds, so when you pull the material the bonds stretch but can then spring the particles back to their original position.

▲ Figure 19.9 *Elastic or resistance bands can be stretched and then they return to their original size*

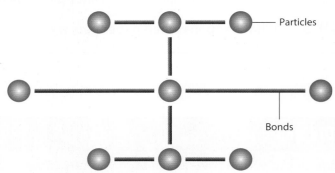

▲ Figure 19.10 *Particles in rubber being stretched*

? Question

19.8 For this question, each group of students must have a rubber band. Do the following tasks in your groups.

(a) Make a sketch of how the particles are arranged in the unstretched rubber band.

(b) Predict what will happen to the thickness of the rubber band as it is stretched.

(c) Sketch a particle diagram of the stretched rubber band.

(d) What do you think will happen to the stretchy bonds between the particles if the rubber band is stretched too far?

Density

Density is how much matter (mass) there is in a certain volume. Solids can be dense because their particles are packed closely together, so there is a large mass in a small volume of material.

? Question

19.9 Some solids have a low density; for example, aluminium, which is used to make aircraft. Research the main properties of aluminium and why it is suitable for making aircraft.

Melting point

As we saw in chapter 18, melting point is the temperature at which solid material turns to a liquid. Most materials that are pure chemicals have a unique melting point. Metals tend to have very high melting points, whereas plastics fall into two categories:

▲ Figure 19.11 *This aircraft is made from aluminium because of its low density*

● Plastics that melt when heated and therefore can be formed into different shapes

● Plastics that do not melt or soften when heated.

Ability to conduct heat and electricity

Metals are very good conductors of heat and electricity (see chapter 18). They are made up of atoms whose electrons can move easily, so heat and electricity can flow through. Non-metals such as plastic are not good conductors as their atoms are not easily freed, preventing the flow of electrons, so heat and electricity cannot flow through easily. These are good insulators and are therefore used as covering on electrical wires.

 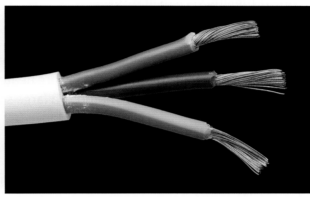

▲ Figure 19.12 *The saucepan is made of metal because it is a very good heat conductor; plastic is not a good electrical conductor and so it is very good as an insulator for electric cables*

How do we choose which material to use?

The possible use for a material depends on its properties. There are some key questions to answer when deciding which material would be the most suitable for a particular use:

- Will the material last?
- Will the material look good?
- Will the material be easy to process and use?
- What are the costs?
- What effect will this material have on the environment?

Developing new materials

Polymer scientists and chemical engineers develop new materials. These scientists study polymers and use their knowledge to develop new plastic and rubber products. They are made by:

- Chemical reactions (plastics, nylon and Lycra are made by chemical reactions)
- Mixing two or more materials – the result is known as a composite.

Materials are produced with specific properties suitable for a specific job.

? **Question**

19.10 Scientists have developed many new materials and one of these is Teflon, which is now used as a non-stick coating on cookware. Find out:

(a) What Teflon is made from

(b) The properties that make it suitable for its use.

▲ Figure 19.13 *This frying pan has a Teflon coating*

Metals

Metals have some basic properties in common (see chapter 18). Their strength makes them good for making things like bridges and car bodies, and because they are good conductors of heat they are ideal for cookware. Their conductivity of electrical charge makes them great for making electrical wires.

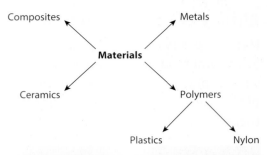

▲ Figure 19.14 *Classification of materials*

Plastics

Plastics are synthetic materials. Most plastics are made from crude oil. The term 'plastic' is used to describe substances that soften when they are heated. Plastics have many uses. It is hard to believe that plastics have only been made on a large scale since the 1930s.

Properties of plastics

- Plastics can be hard, strong and stiff.
- Some plastics have a low density so are good for lightweight goods.
- Some plastics are mouldable so can be easily made into different shapes.

These properties explain why plastics are suitable for TV and computer cases.

▲ Figure 19.15 *Plastics are suitable for TVs.*

The origins of plastics

Crude oil is a thick, black, foul-smelling liquid. Oil in this form is not of much use. The oil is a mixture of hydrocarbons (molecules made of hydrogen and carbon), which are separated in an oil refinery by fractional distillation. This is a process in which crude oil is heated until it boils and the hydrocarbon gases are passed into the bottom of a fractionating column. The hydrocarbon gases condense back into liquids and these are removed from the sides of the column. About 4% of all oil extracted is used to make plastics.

▲ Figure 19.16 *Hydrocarbons are separated in a fractionating column at an oil refinery*

Making plastics

The manufacture of plastics from crude oil involves two stages:

1. Simple hydrocarbons are separated from crude oil. They are known as monomers ('mono' means one, so monomers consist of only one molecule).

2. The monomers react together and form long chains called polymers ('poly' means many). All plastics are made up of repeating units (monomers) linked together to form polymers. This process is called polymerisation.

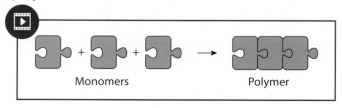

Monomers → Polymer

▲ Figure 19.17 *A model of polymerisation*

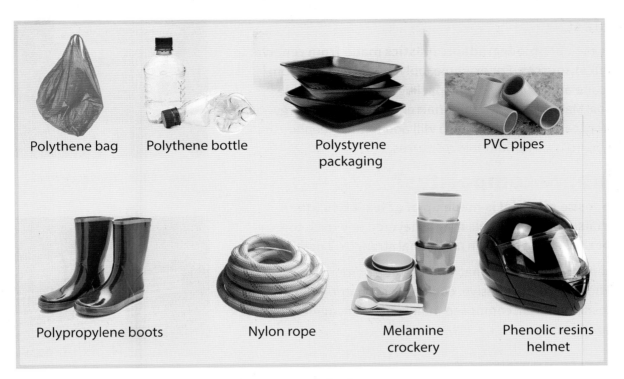

▲ Figure 19.18 *Products made from different types of plastic*

What is the environmental impact of plastics?

Plastic does not break down easily. It is not affected by air and water, and it is not biodegradable – bacteria and fungi cannot break it down. The first ever plastic bag will still be in existence, unless it was burned, which releases poisonous fumes. This is a major disadvantage of plastics (see chapter 23).

Landfill sites are full of plastic that will not break down, and plastic pollution affects every waterway, sea and ocean in the world. Around 80% of marine litter originates from land, and most of that is plastic. This has a severe impact on our environment.

Seabirds, turtles, whales and other sea life are eating the plastic and are dying from choking and starvation. Also, toxic chemicals are released into the water; fish easily become contaminated and get ill. This has a knock-on effect further up the food chain, right up to humans, who may ingest the contaminated fish.

Some plastics now contain an additive that promotes the breakdown of the plastic to water and carbon dioxide, but this can also affect our environment because carbon dioxide is one of the greenhouse gases that cause global warming. Despite the use of this additive in some plastic products, massive pollution still results from the use of plastics and waste from plastic products.

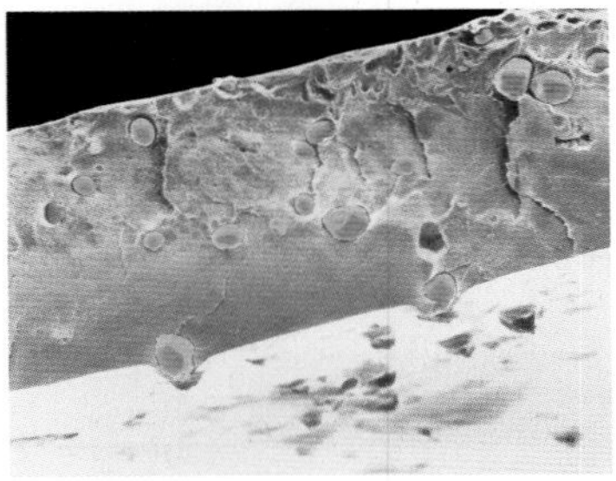

Many plastics are a fire risk. When they burn, poisonous fumes are created. Polyvinylchloride (PVC), which is found in guttering pipes and raincoats, for example, releases poisonous hydrogen chloride gas as it burns. In house fires, many deaths are caused by poisonous fumes and smoke produced as plastics burn.

> **? Question**
>
> **19.11**   How can we prevent plastic pollution in our waterways?

▲ Figure 19.19 *Biodegradable plastic bag*

> **? Question**
>
> **19.12**   Plastic pollution involves the accumulation of plastic products in the environment. Find out what effect plastic pollution has on our lands, ocean, animals and humans.

Bioplastics

Bioplastics are biodegradable plastics made from renewable biological sources. For example, polylactide is made from sugarcane and is used in some packaging and disposable nappies. Making this new material requires a lot of energy – which produces carbon dioxide, which will add to the greenhouse effect – and uses up valuable resources.

▲ Figure 19.20 *Cup made from bioplastic*

What are composites?

A composite material is made up of at least two other materials. These materials may be layered or woven together. **Composites** are used when additional strength is needed.

For example, plywood is made up of three or more thin layers of wood bonded with adhesive, concrete or cement – which is also a composite material, composed mainly of water, aggregates (rock, sand and gravel).

▲ Figure 19.21 *Pressed wood is a composite*

What is ceramic?

Ceramic is a non-metallic synthetic mixture. Ceramics are:

- Cheap
- Hard
- Resistant to high temperatures
- Long-lasting
- Low density compared to metals
- Poor conductors of electricity.

Traditional ceramics include bricks and tiles, but new ceramics are used for space shuttle tiles and joint replacements.

▲ Figure 19.22 *A traditional use for ceramics is in the making of roof tiles*

▲ Figure 19.23 *Spacecraft have ceramic tiles on their exterior*

▲ Figure 19.24 *Some joint replacements, like this shoulder replacement, are made from ceramic*

? Question

19.13 Rubber is a strong but soft and flexible material. It is used to make car tyres. Research rubber to answer the following questions.

(a) Is rubber a natural or a synthetic material?

(b) Where does rubber come from?

(c) What are the properties of rubber?

▲ Figure 19.25 *Rubber is used to make tyres*

What is nanotechnology?

Nanotechnology is the use of nanoparticles, which are tiny particles (atoms, molecules, ions) that are measured in nanometres (nm). There are one million nanometres in a millimetre.

Nanoparticles have a variety of uses.

- Nanoparticles are used to create water-repellent clothing because they can repel water and dirt.

- Nanoparticles are used in some medicines for cancer treatments because they are so small they are absorbed very quickly into cancer cells.

- Nano-sized silver particles have an antibacterial agent and are added to food packaging so food will keep fresher for longer.

- Nanoparticles are used in sunblocks to protect the skin against ultraviolet (UV) radiation from the Sun.

▲ Figure 19.26 *Nanoparticles are used in the manufacture of waterproof clothing*

CHEMICAL WORLD

? Question

19.14 Explain how nanoparticles in sunblocks and medicine for cancer treatment could improve people's lives.

Environmental impact of nanotechnology

Nano-sized silver particles have the ability to kill harmful bacteria, and several products containing these silver nanoparticles are already on the market, including:

- Socks, which contain silver nanoparticles to inhibit odour-causing bacteria

- Energy-efficient washing machines that disinfect clothes by generating silver nanoparticles.

Can these nanoparticles have a negative effect on our environment? There is an increased use of silver nanoparticles in consumer products and this material is being released into our sewerage systems, wastewater treatment systems and eventually our rivers, lakes and oceans. Scientists have discovered that these nanoparticles are extremely toxic and are destroying the good bacteria that are needed for wastewater treatment.

? Question

19.15 Find out what other negative impacts the overuse of nanoparticles has on our environment.

Summary questions

19.16 What is meant by the 'melting point' of a material?

19.17 List three advantages of manufacturing items from plastic instead of traditional materials.

19.18 Briefly outline two environmental disadvantages of plastics.

19.19 Some plastics are non-biodegradable. What does this mean?

19.20 Tony has a lump of black solid. It is light, breaks easily and does not conduct electricity. Is this a metal or non-metal?

19.21 Name eight different properties of materials.

19.22 There are many different types of plastic products, as shown in Figure 19.27. Each group should choose one product shown in the figure. List the properties of the plastic that the product is made from, and explain why this material is best suited to this product.

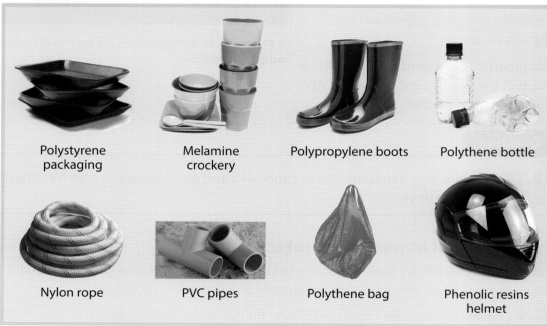

Polystyrene packaging   Melamine crockery   Polypropylene boots   Polythene bottle

Nylon rope   PVC pipes   Polythene bag   Phenolic resins helmet

▲ **Figure 19.27**

19.23 Some objects can be made of metal or plastic. Write down the advantages and disadvantages of metal or plastic for each of the following:

(a) Ruler

(b) Window frame

(c) Spoon

(d) Bucket.

19.24 In your copy, copy and complete the table below from your knowledge of materials.

Material	Properties	Uses
Metals		
Polymers		
Ceramics		
Composites		

Assessment questions

19.25 Materials can be sorted into different groups. Copy the following table and classify the materials as either natural or synthetic (manufactured) by placing a tick (✓) in the correct box. **(15 marks)**

Material	Natural	Synthetic
Sand		
Leather		
Nylon		
Cotton		
Polyester		

19.26 Copy and complete the sentence below to explain why plastic is a suitable material for making the case for a radio. **(15 marks)**

Plastics can be _____ so the case would protect the radio. Plastics can be low _____ so the radio would not be too heavy. Plastics can be _____ so it would be easy to make the case into the right shape for the radio.

19.27 Seamus investigated the tensile strength of four different types of plastic fishing wire. He suspended each fishing wire from a clamp and added weights to the end of the wire until it snapped. He repeated this experiment three times. His results are shown below.

Fishing wire	Mass (kg) that broke the wire
A	3.5
B	12.5
C	6.5
D	16

(a) Why did Seamus repeat the experiment three times?

(b) Seamus cut each fishing wire to exactly the same length. Explain why he did this.

(c) Suggest which wire Seamus should use to go fishing for a very large fish and explain why.

19.28 Copy and complete the following table using your knowledge of everyday materials and chemistry. Tick the relevant column in each case **(15 marks)**

Material	Composite	Ductile	Ceramic	Low melting point
Copper				
Roof tiles				
Plywood				
PVC				

PowerPoint summary   Weblinks

CHEMICAL WORLD

CHAPTER 20

RATES OF REACTIONS

LO: CW7

What is the 'rate of reaction'?

The rate of a chemical reaction tells us how quickly a chemical reaction happens. One of the slowest rates of reaction is the rusting of iron. A really fast reaction is an explosion, which is all over in a fraction of a second.

▲ Figure 20.1 *A nail rusting has a slow rate of reaction*

▲ Figure 20.2 *An explosion has a very fast rate of reaction*

In industry it is very important to know how long it will take for a reaction to occur. Reactions can take varying amounts of time from start to finish, so chemists measure how many reactants are used up and how much product is formed in a certain time.

▶ Figure 20.3 *Rate at which the reactants are used up or the product is formed*

What is particle theory?

During a chemical reaction the particles in the reactants are moving all the time. **The rate of a reaction simply depends on how often and how hard the reacting particles collide with each other.**

For the particles to react they must collide with enough energy to break the bonds in the molecules. Once the bonds are broken the atoms can rearrange to make the products.

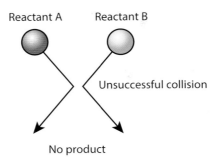

Reactant A   Reactant B

Unsuccessful collision

No product

▲ **Figure 20.4** *Particle theory – an unsuccessful collision*

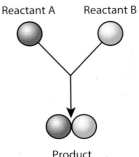

Reactant A   Reactant B

Product

▲ **Figure 20.5** *Particle theory – a successful collision*

Increasing the rate of a reaction involves increasing the number of successful collisions between the reacting particles. There are a number of factors that affect the behaviour of particles and have an overall effect.

 Activity 20.1   **What factors increase the rate at which a dissolvable tablet dissolves in water?**

 Equipment needed

5 conical flasks	Stopwatch	Graduated cylinder
Glass rod	Marker	5 dissolvable tablets
Thermometer	Wire gauze	Metal tongs
Tripod	Bunsen burner	Mortar and pestle

Conducting the activity

1. Label 5 conical flasks A–E.
2. Measure 50 cm³ of water into each conical flask.
3. **Conical Flask A:** Add the tablet and start the timer. Record the time (in seconds) it takes for the tablet to completely dissolve.
4. **Conical Flask B:** Add the tablet and start the timer. Stir continuously with a glass rod until the tablet dissolves. Record the time.
5. **Conical Flask C:** Heat the water to 30°C over a Bunsen burner. Add the tablet and start the timer. Record the time it takes the tablet to completely dissolve.
6. **Conical Flask D:** Break the tablet into four pieces of equal size. Add the four pieces of tablet to the conical flask and start the timer. Record the time it takes for the pieces of tablet to completely dissolve.
7. **Conical Flask E:** Crush up the tablet using a mortar and pestle. Add the powered tablet to the conical flask and start the timer. Record the time it takes the powder to completely dissolve.
8. Record all your results in the table in your Student Activity Book and note any conclusions you make from the results.

▲ Figure 20.6

Safety
- Use metal tongs when removing the conical flask from the Bunsen burner.

What happens to the rate of the reaction when you stir the solution?

Stirring the solution keeps the reactant particles in motion, increasing the chances of collisions and increasing the rate of reaction.

What happens to the rate of reaction as you increase the temperature?

When you raise the temperature the particles have more energy so they move around more quickly. This results in more collisions in a certain time, and so reactions get faster as we raise the temperature.

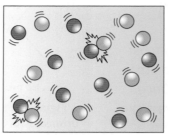 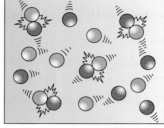

Reaction at 30°C   Reaction at 40°C

▲ **Figure 20.7** *As particles get more energy they move at a greater speed, and so there are more collisions and reactions get faster*

ⓘ Question

20.1 Plot the data in the table on a graph, with time on the *x*-axis and temperature on the *y*-axis. Describe what effect an increase in temperature has on the volume of carbon dioxide produced.

Volume of CO_2 produced		
Time (s)	20°C	30°C
0	0	0
20	7	9
40	14	16
60	18	19
80	21	24
100	25	25

What happens to the rate of reaction when you increase the surface area?

Surface area is the measure of how much surface (of the reactants) is exposed. When a large piece of solid material is cut into smaller pieces its surface area is increased. The smaller the particle size, the greater the surface area on which the reaction takes place, and so the faster the reaction.

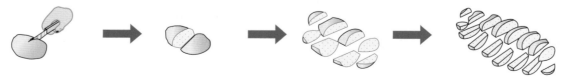

▲ **Figure 20.8** *You increase the surface area of the potato each time you cut it into smaller pieces*

✏ Activity 20.2 What is the effect of increasing surface area on the rate of production of carbon dioxide?

🧪 Equipment needed

😎 ⚠ ✖

Conical flask   Dilute hydrochloric acid   Marble chips (10 mm)

Electronic balance   Marble chips (5 mm)   Stopwatch or timer

Cotton wool

⚠ **Safety**
- Wear safety glasses.
- Handle acid with care.

> calcium carbonate + hydrochloric acid → calcium chloride + carbon dioxide + water

➡ Conducting the activity

1. Set up the apparatus as shown in Figure 20.10.
2. Place 5 g of marble chips (5 mm) into a conical flask. Add 50 cm³ of dilute hydrochloric acid.
3. Place cotton wool in the top of the flask.
4. Start the timer.
5. Record the loss in mass every 30 seconds in the table in your Student Activity Book.
6. Repeat steps 2 to 5 using the larger marble chips (10 mm). Record the results in the table in your Student Activity Book.

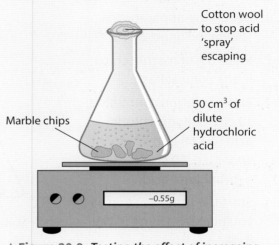

▲ **Figure 20.9** *Testing the effect of increasing the surface area on the rate of a reaction*

❓ Questions

Write the answers to these questions in your Student Activity Book.

20.2 Which marble chips have the larger surface area?

20.3 Why is it important to keep all other factors in the activity the same?

20.4 Plot both sets of results on graph paper in your Student Activity Book. Put Loss in mass (mass of gas given off) on the *y*-axis and Time on the *x*-axis.

20.5 Which size of marble chips reacts faster?

▶ **Figure 20.10** *The effect of increasing surface area on the rate of reaction: the steepest part of the curve is at the start, hence the fastest part of the reaction, but the curve becomes less steep as the reaction slows down and eventually becomes flat, indicating the end of the reaction*

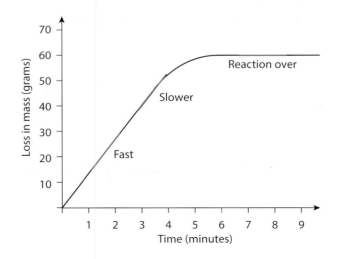

CHEMICAL WORLD

 Activity 20.3 What is the effect of concentration on rate of reaction?

Equipment needed

Conical flask	Hydrochloric acid (0.1 M)	
Bung	Water	
Glass tubing	Marble chips	
Basin	Stopwatch or timer	
Graduated cylinder		

Safety
- Always wear safety glasses.
- Handle the acid with care.

➡ Conducting the activity

1. Set up the apparatus as shown in Figure 20.13.

2. Place 5 g of marble chips in the conical flask.

3. Add a solution containing 10 cm³ of hydrochloric acid (0.1 M) and 40 cm³ of water (i.e. 50 cm³ of dilute hydrochloric acid).

4. Start the timer as soon as you place the bung in the flask.

5. Time how long it takes to collect 20 cm³ of gas.

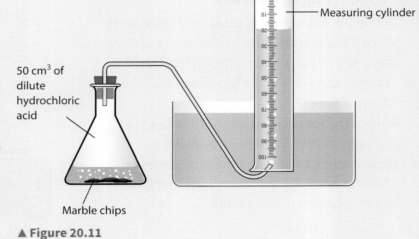

Measuring cylinder

50 cm³ of dilute hydrochloric acid

Marble chips

▲ Figure 20.11

6. Repeat steps 2 to 5 using different concentrations of acid as shown in the table.

7. Record your results in the table in your Student Activity Book.

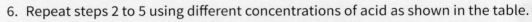

⑦ Questions

20.6 As you increase the concentration of acid there are more acid particles in the same volume. Use the particle theory and diagrams to explain why you think this may cause an overall increase in the rate of a reaction.

20.7 Have you ever tasted sour milk? Some foods react when exposed to air or bacteria, and turn into acids. Why do we store milk in a fridge, and why does refrigeration make it stay fresh for longer?

20.8 You are asked to make jelly for a party starting in 3 hours. What will you do to dissolve the jelly cubes in water as quickly as possible?

What happens to the rate of reaction as you increase the concentration of the acid?

When you increase the concentration, you increase the number of particles, which results in more collisions in a certain time and so you get an increase in rate of reaction (that is, the reaction gets faster).

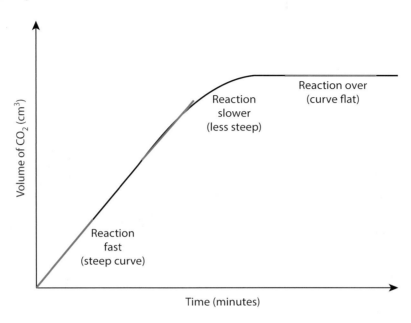

▲ Figure 20.12 *The effect of increasing concentration on the rate of reaction: the reaction is fastest at the start (steep curve), gradually becoming slower as the reaction proceeds. The curve on the graph goes flat when the reaction is complete*

▲ Figure 20.13 *A chemical reaction makes these light sticks glow*

Did you know?

Light sticks produce light because of a chemical reaction. Dropping a light stick into hot water makes it glow more intensely, demonstrating that the reaction occurs faster at higher temperatures.

What is the effect of using a catalyst?

Transition metals lie between group 2 and group 3 in the periodic table. Some well-known transition metals are iron, copper, chromium, nickel and gold. Transition metals and their compounds are important **catalysts. (A catalyst is a substance which alters the rate of a reaction without getting used up.)** How will a catalyst affect the rate of reaction?

Activation energy is the minimum amount of energy that reactant particles must have in order for them to react.

When you add a catalyst it lowers the activation energy; this makes it easier for the particles to react, so there is an increase in the rate of reaction.

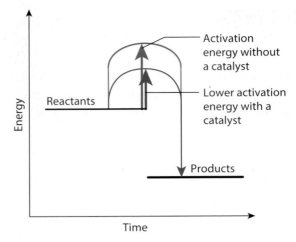

▲ Figure 20.14 *How a catalyst works*

Enzymes are natural catalysts in the human body. Without the enzyme amylase in our saliva it would take starch several weeks to break down.

Activity 20.4 What is the effect of a catalyst on the rate of a chemical reaction?

 Equipment needed

2 test tubes Spatula
Hydrogen peroxide (6%) Wooden splints
Manganese dioxide (catalyst)

Safety
- Wear safety goggles and gloves at all times when using the hydrogen peroxide.

➡ **Conducting the activity**

1. Place 5 cm³ of hydrogen peroxide into each of test tubes A and B.
2. Add a little manganese dioxide to test tube B.
3. Test each test tube with a glowing splint (oxygen will relight a glowing splint).
4. Record your results and answer the following questions in your Student Activity Book.

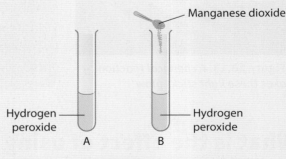

▲ Figure 20.15 *Investigating the effect of a catalyst*

(a) Did bubbles form in test tube A?
(b) What happened as soon as you added the catalyst manganese dioxide?
(c) Did the glowing splint relight in each test tube?
(d) Which test tube showed the greater rate of reaction?
(e) How did you judge the rate of reaction?

> ⓘ **Questions**
>
> **20.9** The catalyst manganese dioxide speeds up the reaction in Activity 20.4 without getting used up. How can you return the manganese dioxide to its original state? (Hint: it is insoluble in water.)

Biochemical reactions

There are several factors that can affect the rate of biochemical reactions, such as, respiration and photosynthesis (see chapter 10). The main factors that affect the rate of photosynthesis are light intensity, carbon dioxide and temperature.

✐ Activity 20.5   What is the effect of light intensity on photosynthesis?

🧪 Equipment needed

Beaker	Pondweed
Funnel	Water
Test tube	Lamp
Metre stick	

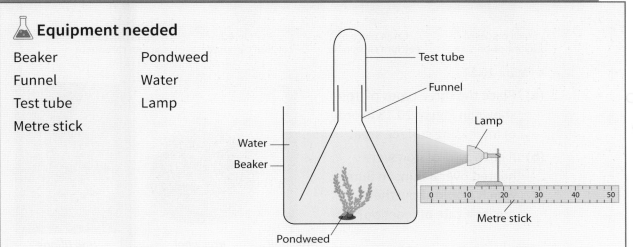

▲ **Figure 20.16** *Investigating the effect of light intensity on photosynthesis*

➡ Conducting the activity

1. Set up the apparatus as shown in Figure 20.16.
2. Place the light at the 10 cm mark on the metre stick and leave for 5 minutes.
3. Count the number of bubbles of oxygen produced in 1 minute.
4. Move the light to the 20 cm mark on the metre stick, leave for 5 minutes and count the number of bubbles of oxygen produced in 1 minute.
5. Repeat at the 30 cm, 40 cm and 50 cm mark.
6. Note your results in the table in your Student Activity Book and answer the following questions in the spaces provided.

   (a) How was the number of bubbles of oxygen affected by moving the light away from the plant?

   (b) What would happen to the bubbles if the apparatus were covered with a black sack?

   (c) Outline a test for the oxygen gas produced.

Summary questions

● 20.10 What are catalysts?

🔬 20.11 Explain how catalysts increase the rate of a chemical reaction.

🔬 20.12 Place the reactions in Figure 20.17 in order of increasing rate of reaction.

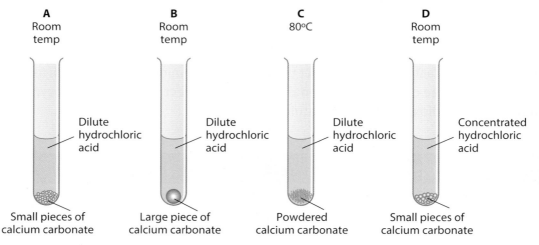

A Room temp	B Room temp	C 80°C	D Room temp
Dilute hydrochloric acid	Dilute hydrochloric acid	Dilute hydrochloric acid	Concentrated hydrochloric acid
Small pieces of calcium carbonate	Large piece of calcium carbonate	Powdered calcium carbonate	Small pieces of calcium carbonate

▲ Figure 20.17

🔬 20.13 (a) Place the three types of iron shown in Figure 20.18 in order of increasing surface area.

     (b) If each type of iron were heated over a Bunsen burner, which would show the greatest rate of reaction?

Iron nail   *Iron wool*   *Iron filings*

▲ Figure 20.18

Assessment questions

20.14 There are a number of factors that affect the behaviour of particles in chemical reactions. One of those factors is particle size. **(30 marks)**

Students reacted three different sized marble chips (calcium carbonate) with hydrochloric acid. They measured the loss in mass caused by carbon dioxide production during the reaction.

Marble chip A	4–6 mm diameter
Marble chip B	6–8 mm diameter
Marble chip C	9–11 mm diameter

(a) Which marble chip has the greatest surface area? Explain your answer.

(b) Draw a fully labelled diagram showing how this investigation was carried out.

(c) How did the students ensure this investigation was a fair test?

The students plotted a graph showing the loss of mass (g) against time (see Figure 20.19).

(d) Looking at the graph, which marble chip showed the greatest rate of reaction? Explain your answer.

(e) The students then repeated this investigation, adding powdered calcium carbonate to hydrochloric acid. Where on the graph, in relation to curves A, B and C, would you expect to draw the curve from this reaction? Explain why.

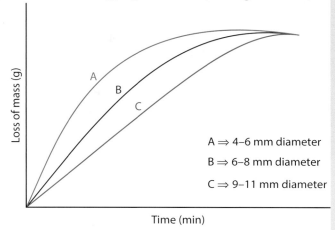

A ⇒ 4–6 mm diameter

B ⇒ 6–8 mm diameter

C ⇒ 9–11 mm diameter

▲ **Figure 20.19**

20.15 Different chemical reactions occur at different rates. There are a number of factors that can affect the rate of a reaction. Students carried out an experiment to investigate whether the concentration of hydrochloric acid had any effect on the time taken for magnesium metal to completely react (see Figure 20.20). The students recorded the following results.

(45 marks)

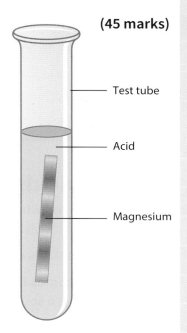

Test tube

Acid

Magnesium

Concentration of acid (mol/l)	Time taken for magnesium to react (s)
2.0	10
1.5	20
1.2	30
0.8	70
0.6	140
0.5	250

▲ **Figure 20.20**

(a) Draw a graph of the results.

(b) State a conclusion that students could have drawn from the shape of the graph about how changing the concentration of one of the reactants can affect the overall rate of the reaction.

(c) Use the graph to find the time taken for the magnesium to react if the concentration of acid used was 1 mol/l.

(d) State two other factors that could change the rate of a chemical reaction.

(e) Name the gas that is produced during this investigation and how you would test this gas to confirm its identity.

 Log on to **www.edcolearning.ie** for Additional Assessment Questions

PowerPoint summary   **Weblinks**

CHEMICAL WORLD

CHAPTER 21

ACIDS AND BASES

LO: CW8

What are acids?

What springs to mind when you hear the word **acid**? Most people think of acids as dangerous, corrosive liquids. Not all acids are like this, however. For example:

- Lemon juice contains an acid called citric acid
- Vinegar is a dilute solution of ethanoic acid.

The word 'acid' comes from a Latin word meaning 'sour'. The acids in food such as those listed above tend to have a sour, sharp taste. The acids you use in the laboratory are strong acids that are corrosive. So, be careful when using them! A substance that is an acid is said to be acidic. Table 21.1 shows some everyday acids and some laboratory acids.

Table 21.1 Some everyday acids and some laboratory acids

Everyday acids	Laboratory acids
Lemon juice (citric acid)	Hydrochloric acid (HCl)
Rain water (carbonic acid)	Sulfuric acid (H_2SO_4)
Vinegar	

Lemon

Rain water

Vinegar

Battery acid

▲ Figure 21.1 *Examples of acids*

What are bases?

There is another group of chemicals known as bases. They are the opposite of acids. Many bases are used by us every day. For example, bleach, washing soda, oven cleaner and toothpaste are all bases. A substance that is a base is said to be basic. Table 21.2 shows some everyday bases and some laboratory bases.

Many bases are as corrosive and as dangerous as acids. For example, caustic soda, which is used to clear drains, is a corrosive base and must be handled with care (and gloves!).

Table 21.2 **Some everyday bases and some laboratory bases**

Everyday bases	Laboratory bases
Toothpaste	Sodium hydroxide (NaOH)
Bleach	Calcium carbonate ($CaCO_3$)
Indigestion tablets	Limewater $Ca(OH)_2$

Toothpaste

Bleach

Indigestion tablets

▲ **Figure 21.2** *A selection of household bases*

Some bases will dissolve in water. They are known as alkalis. Drain cleaner (sodium hydroxide) is an example of an alkali. A substance that is an alkali is said to be alkaline. There is another group of substances that are neither acid nor base, including water and salt solution. They are said to be **neutral**.

? Question

21.1 We come across acids and bases every day but may not realise it. The food industry uses acids in many products, such as fizzy drinks, and bases are used in many cleaning products. Examine the labels on different food and cleaning products and see if you can identify any acids or bases.

How can you tell an acid from a base?

You cannot tell by looking at a substance whether it is an acid or a base or a neutral substance. You have to test it with an indicator.

What are indicators?

An indicator is a chemical that shows, by means of a colour change, whether a substance is an acid or a base. In the laboratory we use two types of indicator:

- Litmus paper
- Universal indicator.

What is litmus indicator?

Litmus paper is paper that has been treated with a water-soluble mixture of different dyes from lichens, which grow on the bark of trees or on rocks. There is blue litmus paper and red litmus paper.

Litmus paper will change colour from blue to red in acids and from red to blue in bases (or alkalis).

Remember: *b for base, b for blue litmus.*

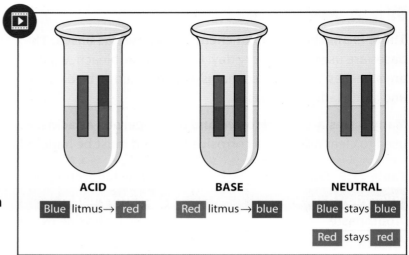

ACID	**BASE**	**NEUTRAL**
Blue litmus → red	Red litmus → blue	Blue stays blue
		Red stays red

▲ Figure 21.3 *Colour changes of litmus paper*

Activity 21.1 What household substances are acids, bases or neutral?

🧪 Equipment needed

Test tube rack   Test tubes

Litmus paper   Variety of household substances, laboratory chemicals and water

➡ Conducting the activity

1. Place a selection of household and laboratory chemicals in different test tubes. If the substance is a solid, try dissolving a spatula full of it in a small volume of water first.

2. Dip pieces of blue and red litmus paper into the liquid of each test tube.

3. Examine the papers and observe any colour changes.

4. Enter your results into the table in your Student Activity Book in the following way:

Safety
- Always wear safety glasses.
- Handle acids with care.

Substances being tested	Acidic	Basic	Neutral
Vinegar	✓		
Water			✓

? Question

21.2 **What effect do acids have on:**

   (a) Blue litmus paper?   **(b) Red litmus paper?**

What is universal indicator?

Universal indicator is a mixture of dyes that change to different colours according to how strong the acid or base is. Universal indicator gives a range of colours, as shown in Figure 21.4, which can be used to give a value on the **pH scale**.

What is the pH scale?

Some acids are safe to handle and even eat, whereas others such as car battery acid are very dangerous and corrosive. In order to compare the strengths of acids and bases, chemists devised a scale called the **pH scale**. **The scale is from 0 to 14**:

- 0–7 is an acid (the lower the number, the more acidic it is)
- 7 is neutral (pure water has a pH of almost 7)
- 7–14 is an alkali (the higher the number, the greater the alkalinity).

The pH can be measured using a pH meter or universal indicator.

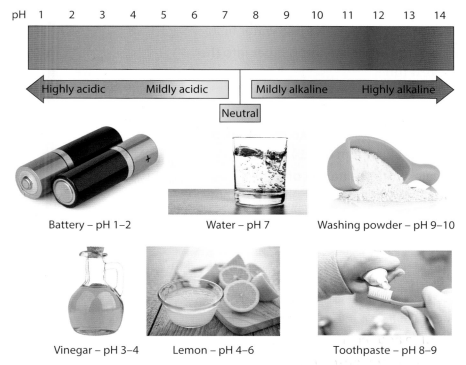

▲ Figure 21.4 *A variety of household substances and their position on the pH scale*

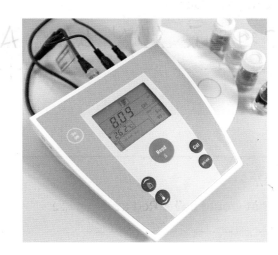

▲ Figure 21.5 *A pH meter*

? Question

21.3 What advantage does universal indicator have over litmus paper?

CHEMICAL WORLD

Activity 21.2 What is the pH of a variety of household substances?

 Activity video

Equipment needed

Test tube rack	Universal indicator or pH meter
Test tubes	Variety of household substances

➡ Conducting the activity

1. Place the substance being tested into a test tube. If the substance is solid, dissolve it in water first.
2. Place a piece of universal indicator paper into the liquid in the test tube.
3. Note the colour of the indicator and, using a colour chart, find its pH.
4. Draw a pH scale in your Student Activity Book by drawing a number line from 0 to 14.
5. On the pH scale, write the names of the substances tested and indicate their pH, as shown in Figure 21.7.

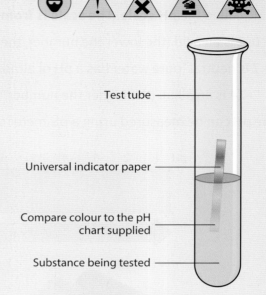

Test tube

Universal indicator paper

Compare colour to the pH chart supplied

Substance being tested

▲ Figure 21.6 *Investigating the pH of a substance*

```
0   1   2   3   4   5   6   7   8   9   10  11  12  13  14
                    |           |
              Orange juice    Water
```

▲ Figure 21.7 *A pH number line*

Did you know?

When you are stung by a nettle, hairs on the nettle leaf inject methanoic acid into your skin. A dock leaf contains chemicals that when rubbed over the sting neutralise this acid and cool down the skin.

⍰ Questions

21.4 What is the pH scale?

21.5 Name a substance that would have:

   (a) A pH below 7

   (b) A pH of 7

   (c) A pH above 7.

   Say which is acidic, basic or neutral.

21.6 Some people add lemon to tea instead of milk. When the lemon is added, the tea changes colour slightly. Why does this happen?

Making indicators

Activity 21.3 How do you make your own indicator using red cabbage?

Equipment needed

Bunsen burner	Red cabbage
Test tube rack	Beaker
Tripod	Water
Test tubes	Glass rod
Dropper	A range of acid, base and neutral substances
Wire gauze	

Safety
- Always wear safety glasses.
- Allow glassware to cool down before you move it.

Conducting the activity

1. Tear up some red cabbage leaves and add them to a beaker containing approximately 100 cm³ of water.

2. Heat the water to boiling and stir the leaves using a glass rod. The water turns purple as the indicator is extracted from the leaves.

3. Allow the solution to cool.

4. Add acidic, neutral and alkaline solutions to different test tubes.

5. Using a dropper add 5–6 drops of the red cabbage indicator to each test tube. Stopper the tubes and shake.

6. Note the colour in each test tube and summarise your results in the table in your Student Activity Book.

Note: If you store the red cabbage indicator in the fridge it will last longer.

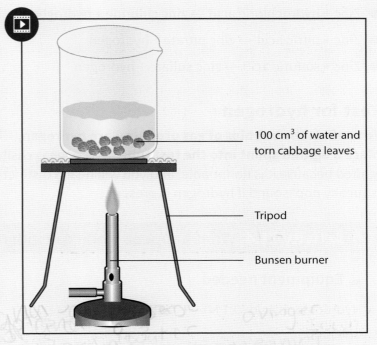

100 cm³ of water and torn cabbage leaves

Tripod

Bunsen burner

▲ Figure 21.8 *Extracting the indicator from red cabbage*

Question

21.7 State the colours of the red cabbage indicator in acid, base and neutral solutions.

Reactions of acids

Acids are part of our everyday life and we must understand their key reactions. **Acids react with many substances. A salt is always produced.**

Acid and metal

An acid always reacts with a metal to produce a salt and hydrogen gas.
For example, the reaction between zinc and hydrochloric acid produces a salt called zinc chloride and hydrogen gas.

The word equation for this reaction is:

| metal + acid → salt + hydrogen |

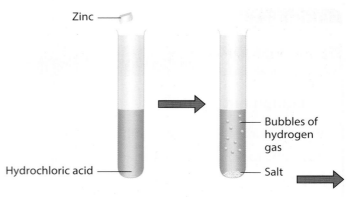

▲ **Figure 21.9** *Acid and metal*

Note: When naming the salt the first part is the name of the metal (e.g. zinc) and the second is based on the acid used (e.g. hydrochloric acid). So:

● Zinc + hydrochloric acid → zinc chloride + hydrogen

● Zinc + nitric acid → zinc nitrate + hydrogen

● Zinc + sulfuric acid → zinc sulfate + hydrogen.

Test for hydrogen

To confirm the bubbles of gas produced are hydrogen, place a lighted splint into the test tube. Hydrogen is easily ignited because it is flammable, and you will hear a distinctive 'squeaky pop' sound if hydrogen is present.

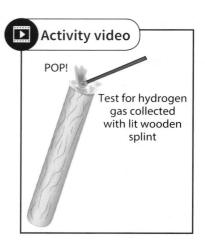

▲ **Figure 21.10** *Testing for hydrogen*

✎ Activity 21.4   What happens when calcium reacts with hydrochloric acid?

🧪 Equipment needed

Hydrochloric acid (0.1 M)   Test tube
Calcium   Test tube rack
Cotton wool   Wooden splint

Safety
⚠ • Keep the test tube in the test tube rack at all times because it can become very hot.

➡ Conducting the activity

1. Place 10 cm³ of hydrochloric acid in the test tube.

2. Add a few granules of calcium.

3. Stopper the test tube with some cotton wool and allow gas to collect inside it for about 30 seconds.

4. Remove the stopper and place a lighted splint into the test tube. Record what happens in the space provided in your Student Activity Book.

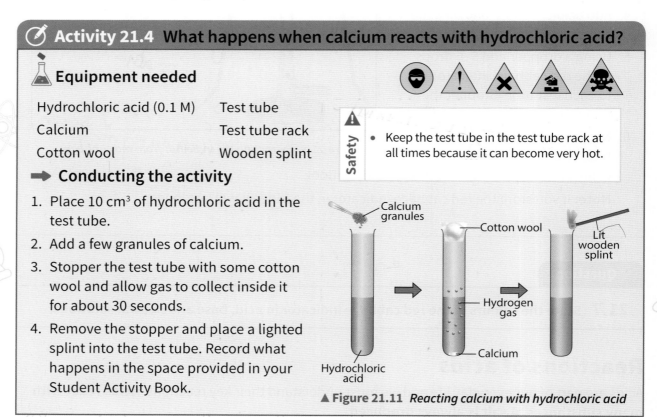

▲ **Figure 21.11** *Reacting calcium with hydrochloric acid*

Answer the following based on Activity 21.4.

21.8   What is the name of the salt formed?

21.9   Name the gas produced.

21.10   Outline what happened when you tested the gas with a lighted splint.

What is neutralisation?

We have already mentioned that an acid is the chemical opposite of a base. So, what would happen if an acid and a base were mixed together?

The answer is they react together and neutralise, or cancel, each other. **They react to produce a salt and water.** Both salt and water are neutral. These reactions are known as **neutralisation** reactions.

an acid + a base $\rightarrow$ a salt + water

$HCL + NaOH \rightarrow NaCl + H_2O$

Neutralisation can be done in a very accurate way by acid–base titration. The acid is placed in a burette and the base and indictor are placed in a conical flask. The conical flask is placed under the burette and the acid is added slowly to the base until the indicator changes colour when the salt and water are formed (neutralisation).

Titrations allow you to find out exactly how much acid is needed to neutralise a base.

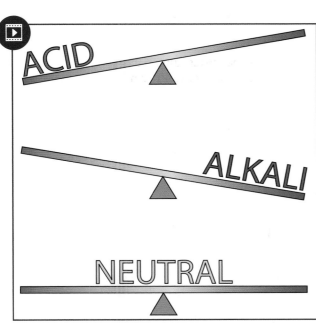

▲ **Figure 21.12** *Colour changes at different pHs*

▲ **Figure 21.13** *A student reading a burette*

 **Activity 21.5** How do you titrate hydrochloric acid (HCl) against sodium hydroxide (NaOH) and prepare a sample of sodium chloride (NaCl)?

 Activity video

Safety
- Always wear safety glasses.
- Handle acid and base with care.

Equipment needed

Burette	Evaporating dish	Dilute hydrochloric acid (0.1 M)
Pipette	Bunsen burner	Dilute sodium hydroxide (0.1 M)
Pipette filter	Tripod	An indicator
Conical flask	Wire gauze	Electronic balance
White tile	Beakers	
Retort stand	Funnel	

➡ **Conducting the activity**

1. Using a pipette filter, measure 25 cm³ of dilute sodium hydroxide into a conical flask.
2. Add 3–4 drops of indicator, e.g. litmus, and place the flask on a white tile so that you can see any change of colour more easily.
3. Using a funnel, fill the burette to the 0 cm³ mark with the dilute hydrochloric acid.
4. Slowly and with continuous swirling of the conical flask, add the acid from the burette until the indicator just changes colour. In the table provided in your Student Activity Book, note the volume of acid added.
5. Repeat the titration, taking care to add the acid drop by drop near the end point.
6. Calculate the average volume of acid from these two titrations.
7. Repeat the experiment without using any indicator and add the volume of acid calculated in step 6.
8. The conical flask contains a solution of sodium chloride in water.
9. Place a sample of the sodium chloride solution into an evaporating dish and rest the dish on the wire gauze over a tripod. Light a Bunsen burner under the tripod and evaporate off the water to leave the sodium chloride behind.
10. Use an electronic balance and find the mass of sodium chloride salt produced.

Remember: *A*cid is *a*bove in a burette. *B*ase is *b*elow in a flask.

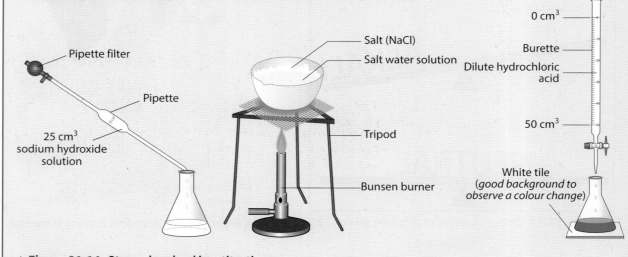

▲ **Figure 21.14** *Stages involved in a titration*

⑦ Questions

From the results of the titration, answer the following:

21.11 What was the colour of the indicator when you added it to sodium hydroxide in the conical flask?

21.12 What was the colour of the universal indicator at the end point?

21.13 What was the average volume of acid needed to neutralise the base?

21.14 What is the mass of the sodium chloride salt produced?

21.15 What is neutralisation?

21.16 Explain acid-base titration.

What is particle theory?

What happens during a neutralisation reaction is explained by **particle theory** (see chapter 13). The common laboratory acids all have one atom in common: the hydrogen atom.

- Hydrochloric acid (HCl)
- Nitric acid (HNO_3)
- Sulfuric acid (H_2SO_4)

What happens to acids in water?

When laboratory acids are dissolved in water, the hydrogen atoms separate from the other atoms; it is these free hydrogen particles (ions) that make a solution acidic. The more hydrogen ions (H^+) there are, the lower the pH will be.

Acids are compounds that **dissociate** (break) into their ions when placed in water. The strong acid hydrogen chloride is one example – it breaks up into H^+ ions and Cl^- ions when placed in water:

$$HCl \rightarrow H^{+1} + Cl^{-1}$$

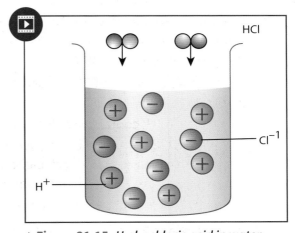

▲ Figure 21.15 *Hydrochloric acid in water*

What happens to bases in water?

The common laboratory base sodium hydroxide (NaOH) will also dissociate when added to water.

$$NaOH \rightarrow Na^{+1} + OH^{-1}$$

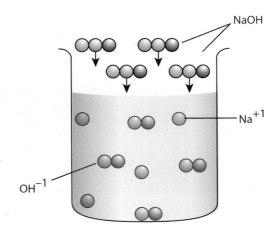

▲ Figure 21.16 *Sodium hydroxide in water*

Neutralisation

When you add an acid to a base they neutralise – all the ions are rearranged and the products salt and water are formed.

$$H^+ + OH^{-1} \rightarrow H_2O$$

$$Na^{+1} + Cl^{-1} \rightarrow NaCl$$

Did you know?

If soil is too acidic, most crops will not grow well. Farmers can spread powdered limestone or lime on the soil to neutralise it.

? Question

21.17 A bee sting is acidic and a wasp sting is alkaline. The bee sting can be neutralised by rubbing a mild base such as baking soda or toothpaste on it. How would you treat a wasp sting?

Acid and carbonate

Acids can also be neutralised by reacting them with carbonates (which are also bases). In this type of neutralisation, carbon dioxide gas is also produced.

an acid + a carbonate $\rightarrow$ salt + water + carbon dioxide

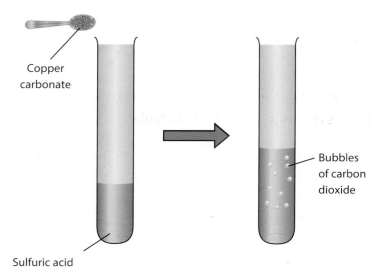

Copper carbonate

Bubbles of carbon dioxide

Sulfuric acid

▲ **Figure 21.17** *The reaction of an acid and a carbonate*

Did you know?

Have you ever had indigestion? It is caused by the hydrochloric acid in your stomach. The pain can be relieved by taking an antacid (anti-acid) chemical, which is a base.

Activity 21.6 Which brand of indigestion tablet is the most effective at neutralising an acid?

Equipment needed

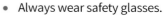

Conical flask	Mortar and pestle
Burette	De-ionised water (purified water with no dissolved salt ions)
White tile	Universal indicator
Retort stand	Two brands of indigestion tablet
Pipette	Hydrochloric acid (0.1 M)
2 beakers	

Safety
- Always wear safety glasses.
- Handle acid with care.

➡ Conducting the activity

1. Grind to powder one tablet from the first brand using a mortar and pestle.
2. Place the powder into the conical flask. Wash out the mortar with de-ionised water and transfer the washings to the conical flask.
3. Add 25 cm³ of de-ionised water to the conical flask and swirl to mix after adding a few drops of universal indicator with a pipette.
4. Fill a burette with dilute hydrochloric acid (0.1 M).
5. Place the conical flask on the white tile under the burette (the white tile makes it easier to see any colour changes). Add the hydrochloric acid from the burette into the conical flask slowly, until the indicator changes colour (end point).
6. Record the total volume of acid added in the table in your Student Activity Book.
7. Repeat steps 1 to 6 with a second tablet from the first brand.
8. Repeat steps 1 to 6 twice with the second brand of indigestion tablet.
9. Calculate the average volume of Cl neutralised by each tablet over the two titrations.
10. Draw a bar chart or line graph showing the results for each brand of tablet using the graph paper in your Student Activity Book.

⑦ Questions

Answer the following based on Activity 21.6.

21.18 Why do you think it is important to repeat each experiment twice for each brand of tablet?

21.19 Why did you place the conical flask on a white tile while carrying out titration?

21.20 From your observations during the activity:

(a) What colour was the universal indicator when added to the indigestion tablet solution?

(b) What was the colour change at the end point?

(c) Which brand of indigestion tablet was the most effective at neutralising the acid?

CHEMICAL WORLD

Summary questions

- **21.21** Complete the following:

  Acidic solutions turn blue litmus _____ and their pH is always _____ than 7 and they have a sour taste.

- **21.22** Name and give the formulas of two acids and two bases used in the lab.

- **21.23** What are alkalis?

- **21.24** What effect do acids have on:

  (a) Blue litmus paper?

  (b) Red litmus paper?

- **21.25** What is neutralisation?

- **21.26** Explain acid–base titration.

- **21.27** **(a)** Name an Indicator.

  (b) What colour will this indicator be in sulfuric acid?

- **21.28** Describe how to investigate the pH of everyday substances, e.g. lemon juice, oven cleaner, vinegar.

- **21.29** Petra has a solution that she thinks might be acidic. Describe three tests she could do to check whether or not it is acidic.

- **21.30** Thomas tested some solutions with universal indicator. He wrote down their pHs: 1, 5, 7 and 14. But he forgot to write down the names of the solutions. Can you help him by matching the pHs to the correct solutions? Copy and complete the table below.

Solutions tested	pH (1, 5, 7, 14)
Distilled water	
Sulfuric acid	
Sodium hydroxide	
Vinegar	

Assessment questions

21.31 The table below shows the preferred soil pH for some plants.   **(30 marks)**

Plant	Preferred pH
Apple	5–6.5
Potato	4–6.5
Blackcurrant	6–8
Mint	7–8
Onion	6–7
Strawberry	5–7
Lettuce	6–7

(a) Describe how to test a sample of soil to find its pH. As part of your description, name each piece of equipment you would use. (A labelled diagram may help your answer.)

(b) List the plants that grow well in acidic soil.

(c) Name the plant that grows well over the largest range of pH values.

(d) If you tested the soil and it was too acidic, explain how you could increase its pH.

21.32 A group of students made some indicator solutions from three **(30 marks)** different coloured flower petals. The first step involved crushing and grinding the petals to release their colour into water.

(a) Name and draw a diagram of the apparatus used to grind up the petals with water.

(b) They added their indicators to an acidic solution and an alkaline solution and here are their results.

Colour of indicator in water pH = 7	Colour of indicator in acidic solution pH = 1	Colour of indicator in alkaline solution pH = 12
Yellow	Yellow	Yellow
Red	Red	Green
Purple	Pink	Blue

State the colour of the red petal indicator in nitric acid. Explain your answer.

(c) If the purple petal indicator were placed in a solution of salt and water, would you expect a colour change? Explain your answer.

(d) In your opinion, which flower petal makes the best indicator? Explain why.

21.33 **Question from Junior Cycle Science exam paper** **(15 marks)**

A student carried out an experiment to investigate the reaction between an acid and a base. A pH indicator and a thermometer were used to monitor changes in pH and temperature during the reaction.

(a) Name a pH indicator the student could have used during this investigation.

(b) What colour is this indicator when placed in acid?

(c) When an acid and a base react, they neutralise each other to produce a neutral solution. On the pH scale, what number represents a neutral solution?

(d) The student noted a rise in temperature as the acid-base reaction took place. Is this an example of an endothermic or an exothermic reaction?

(e) The diagram shows an energy profile diagram for the reaction between an acid and a base.

On a copy of the diagram, show the activation energy for this reaction.

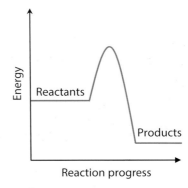
▲ **Figure 21.18**

Questions (d) and (e) relate to material covered in chapter 22.

 Log on to **www.edcolearning.ie** for Additional Assessment Questions

PowerPoint summary   Weblinks

CHAPTER 22

ENERGY TRANSFER IN CHEMICAL REACTIONS

LO: CW9

Learning intentions

At the end of this chapter you will be able to:

✓ Describe exothermic and endothermic reactions

✓ Explain activation energy

✓ Produce simple energy profile diagrams to illustrate energy changes.

Keywords

○— exothermic
○— endothermic
○— bond energy
○— energy profile diagrams
○— activation energy

What energy changes occur during a chemical reaction?

One piece of evidence to show that a chemical change or reaction has taken place is to identify a change in temperature. In a chemical reaction, heat energy is usually released or taken from its surroundings.

What is an exothermic reaction?

An exothermic reaction is a reaction in which energy is transferred from the chemicals to the surroundings. This is where the temperature of the reaction mixture usually rises. For example, combustion, such as in the burning of fuels or fireworks, is an exothermic reaction.

▲ **Figure 22.1** *An exothermic reaction is taking place on this barbeque*

▲ **Figure 22.2** *An exothermic reaction takes place when fireworks burn*

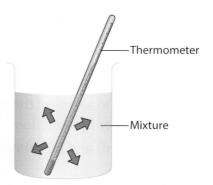

Thermometer

Mixture

▲ **Figure 22.3** *Heat is transferred from the chemicals to the surroundings in an exothermic reaction*

What is an endothermic reaction?

An endothermic reaction is where energy is absorbed by the chemicals from the surroundings in order for the reaction to take place. The reaction mixture usually shows a fall in temperature.

For example, ammonium chloride dissolving in water is an endothermic reaction.

◀ **Figure 22.4** *Solid barium hydroxide and solid ammonium chloride in a flask on a damp piece of wood. As the two chemicals mix, an endothermic reaction occurs, causing a drop in temperature that freezes the water between the conical flask and the block of wood*

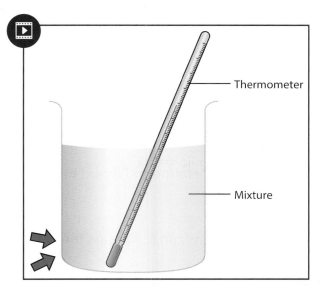

Thermometer

Mixture

▲ **Figure 22.5** *Heat is absorbed by the chemicals from the surroundings in an endothermic reaction*

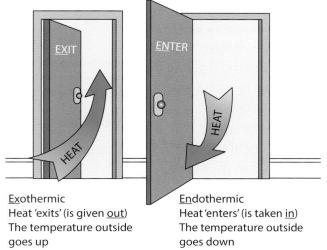

EXIT

ENTER

HEAT

HEAT

Exothermic
Heat 'exits' (is given <u>out</u>)
The temperature outside goes up

Endothermic
Heat 'enters' (is taken <u>in</u>)
The temperature outside goes down

▲ **Figure 22.6** *Heat can be lost or gained during a reaction*

✏ Activity 22.1 What energy changes occur in chemical reactions?

🗻 Equipment needed

4 polystyrene cups (labelled A–D)

Graduated cylinder

Thermometer

Sodium hydroxide (0.1 M)

Hydrochloric acid (0.1 M)

Sodium hydrogen carbonate solution

Citric acid

Ammonium nitrate

Water

Dilute sulfuric acid (0.1 M)

Magnesium ribbon

| Safety | • Always wear safety glasses. • Handle acid and base with care. |

➡ Conducting the activity

Reaction A

1. Measure 10 cm³ of sodium hydroxide solution using a graduated cylinder and place it in polystyrene cup A.

2. Measure the temperature with the thermometer and record the result in the table in your Student Activity Book.

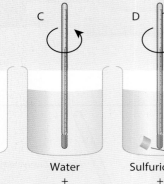

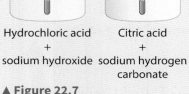

Hydrochloric acid + sodium hydroxide   Citric acid + sodium hydrogen carbonate   Water + ammonium nitrate   Sulfuric acid + magnesium ribbon

▲ Figure 22.7

3. Add 10 cm³ of hydrochloric acid. Stir with the thermometer; measure the temperature and record the result in your table.

Reaction B

4. Add 10 cm³ of sodium hydrogen carbonate solution to polystyrene cup B. Measure the temperature and record the results in your table.

5. Add 10 cm³ of citric acid. Stir with the thermometer; measure the temperature and record the result in your table.

Reaction C

6. Place 10 cm³ of water in polystyrene cup C. Measure the temperature and record the result in your table.

7. Add 1 g of ammonium nitrate. Stir with the thermometer; measure the temperature and record the result in your table.

Reaction D

8. Add 10 cm^3 of dilute sulfuric acid to polystyrene cup D. Measure the temperature and record the result in your table.

9. Add 1 g of magnesium ribbon. Stir with the thermometer; measure the temperature and record the result in your table.

---

⑦ Questions

Answer these questions based on Activity 22.1.

22.1 Did you find more exothermic or endothermic reactions?

22.2 The first reaction is between an acid and a base. What do you call this type of reaction?

22.3 What gas is produced in reaction B?

22.4 What gas is produced in reaction D?

22.5 Why did you use polystyrene cups and not glass beakers?

22.6 What is the clue in the terms 'exothermic' and 'endothermic' that indicates that they are linked to heat energy?

How are bonds made and broken?

During a chemical reaction, old bonds are broken (reactants) and new bonds are formed (products). Breaking bonds requires energy, so it is an endothermic process; but energy is released when new bonds are formed, so bond formation is an exothermic process.

Bond breaking – endothermic

Figures 22.8, 22.9 and 22.10 illustrate endothermic reactions.

Bond formation – exothermic

Figure 22.11 and Figure 22.12 illustrate exothermic reactions.

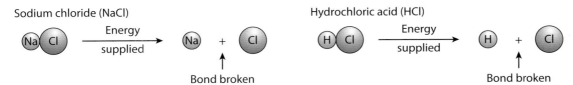

▲ **Figure 22.8** *The bonds in sodium chloride are broken*

▲ **Figure 22.9** *The bonds in hydrochloric acid are broken*

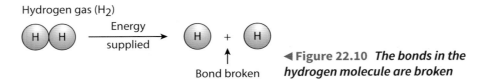

◀ **Figure 22.10** *The bonds in the hydrogen molecule are broken*

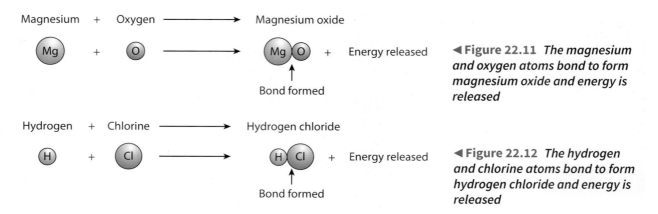

Magnesium + Oxygen ⟶ Magnesium oxide

Mg + O ⟶ Mg O + Energy released

Bond formed

◀ **Figure 22.11** *The magnesium and oxygen atoms bond to form magnesium oxide and energy is released*

Hydrogen + Chlorine ⟶ Hydrogen chloride

H + Cl ⟶ H Cl + Energy released

Bond formed

◀ **Figure 22.12** *The hydrogen and chlorine atoms bond to form hydrogen chloride and energy is released*

What is bond energy?

Bond energy is the energy required to break different bonds. The units are kilojoules per mol (kJ/mol). A mole (symbol 'mol') is the unit used to measure the amount of a substance. Table 22.1 shows the amount of energy required to break different bonds.

Table 22.1 The amount of energy required to break different bonds

Bond	Bond energy (kJ/mol)
H—H	436
Cl—Cl	242
H—Cl	431
C—H	413
C—C	347
C—O	335

What are energy profile diagrams?

We can show the energy transfer in reactions on energy profile diagrams. The diagrams show us the energy stored in the reactants compared to the energy stored in the products, so they tell us whether a reaction is exothermic or endothermic.

Activation energy, shown in energy profile diagrams, is the minimum energy that colliding particles must have for a reaction to occur.

Energy profile diagram for an exothermic reaction

Figure 22.13 shows an exothermic reaction because the products are at a lower energy than the reactants, so energy has been given out. The difference in height (ΔH) is the symbol for the 'change in energy' in a reaction.

ΔH is negative for an exothermic reaction. The difference in energy is given out as heat, so the temperature of the surroundings rises.

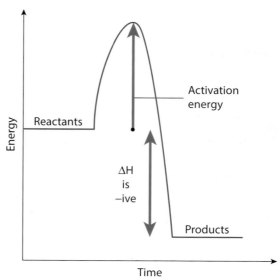

▲ **Figure 22.13** *An exothermic reaction energy profile diagram*

Energy profile diagram for an endothermic reaction

In Figure 22.14 the products are at a higher energy than the reactants so this shows an endothermic reaction. Extra energy was required to form the products, which was taken in from the surroundings; therefore, the temperature of the surroundings falls. ΔH (change in energy) is positive for endothermic reactions.

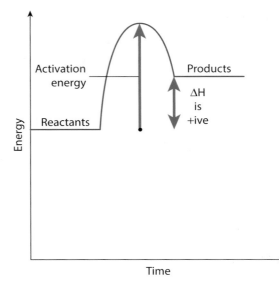

▶ **Figure 22.14** *An endothermic reaction energy profile diagram*

ⓘ Question

22.7 In your group, decide whether each of the following reactions are endothermic or exothermic and give reasons for your decision.

Reaction A: Two chemicals are mixed together in a fume cupboard at room temperature. The reaction starts to fizz and a gas is produced, and the mixture soon catches fire with a purple flame.

Reaction B: When two chemicals are combined in a beaker the outside of the beaker frosts up and it gets stuck to the desk due to the formation of ice.

Reaction C: When a piece of sodium is added to chlorine gas in a flask a bright light is seen and a drop of water on the flask soon vaporises.

Reaction D: Butane from the Bunsen burner is ignited to heat some water.

Is energy transfer always heat?

Energy transfer is not always heat.

Photosynthesis, which is a reaction that takes place in plants, requires light energy (not heat energy). Photosynthesis is a process in which light energy from the Sun is converted to chemical energy (see chapter 10). The chemical energy is stored in the form of glucose (sugar).

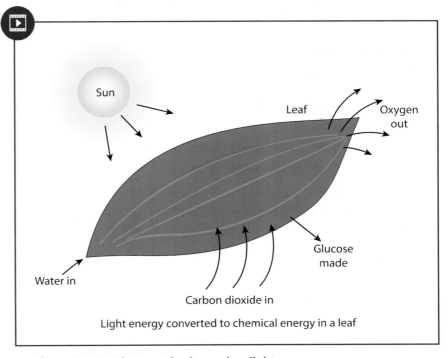

▲ **Figure 22.15** *Photosynthesis requires light energy*

22.8 **What is a glow stick and how does it work?**

Light sticks or glow sticks are used by campers, divers and trick-or-treaters. They are plastic tubes containing different chemicals. When a chemical reaction takes place it releases energy in the form of light – this is called chemiluminescence.

Research the names of the three chemicals found in glow sticks.

▲ **Figure 22.16** *Glow sticks*

Summary questions

22.9 Sodium reacts with water in an exothermic reaction. What does this suggest about the energy needed to break the bonds compared with the energy released when they are made?

22.10 Distinguish between an exothermic reaction and an endothermic reaction.

22.11 Look at this table and answer the questions below.

Reaction	Starting temperature (°C)	Final temperature (°C)
A + B	19	27
C + D	20	25
E + F	19	17

(a) For each reaction say whether it is exothermic or endothermic. How can you tell?

(b) The volume of solution was the same in each reaction. Which had the largest energy change?

22.12 Draw energy profile diagrams for exothermic and endothermic reactions.

22.13 When hydrochloric acid and sodium hydroxide react in a beaker, the temperature rises:

$$HCl + NaOH \rightarrow NaCl + H_2O \qquad \Delta H = -58 \text{ KJ/mol}$$

(a) Is this reaction exothermic or endothermic?

(b) Draw an energy profile diagram to show this change.

Assessment questions

22.14 The graph in Figure 22.17 shows an energy profile diagram for an exothermic reaction.

(15 marks)

Match A, B, C and D with the relevant words:

Products,

Activation energy,

Reactants,

Heat change.

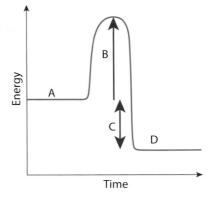

▲ **Figure 22.17**

22.15 Enzymes are biological catalysts that help reactions to take place at quite low temperatures. This explains why they are used in biological washing powders.

(30 marks)

Hydrogen peroxide is a poison that can build up inside living things. An enzyme in the liver can break down this toxin very quickly.

| enzyme |
| hydrogen peroxide → water + oxygen |

(a) Describe how this could be demonstrated in the laboratory. As part of your description, draw a labelled diagram and name each piece of equipment used.

(b) The gas produced during this reaction is oxygen. Describe a test for this gas.

(c) This reaction will show an increase in temperature. Is this reaction an endothermic or an exothermic reaction? Explain your answer.

(d) Draw an energy profile diagram and explain how a catalyst can increase the rate of a chemical reaction.

22.16 Cold packs are applied externally to swollen or injured body parts to relieve pain and swelling. They contain ammonium nitrate and water; when you squeeze the bag the ammonium nitrate comes in contact with the water and a chemical reaction occurs.

(30 marks)

(a) Is this reaction an example of an endothermic or an exothermic reaction? Explain your answer.

(b) A student was asked to investigate the energy changes that take place in a chemical reaction between a piece of magnesium and hydrochloric acid. Describe how this should be carried out. As part of your description, name each piece of equipment and draw a labelled diagram.

(c) The student recorded a rise in temperature. Explain what this indicates about this chemical reaction.

(d) Draw an energy profile diagram for this type of reaction.

22.17 **Question from Junior Cycle Science exam paper questions (d) and (e) on page 249 are relevant for this chapter.**

 Log on to **www.edcolearning.ie** for Additional Assessment Questions

ENVIRONMENTAL IMPACT OF MATERIALS

LO: CW10

Learning intentions

At the end of this chapter you will be able to:

✓ Explain the complete life cycle of a material

✓ Describe sustainable development

✓ Research and present information on new materials and sources of energy.

Keywords

- environment
- life cycle
- extraction
- transportation
- manufacturing
- raw materials
- sustainable development
- carbon footprint
- electrolysis
- molten
- distribution
- recycling
- composting

What impact do materials have on the environment?

Materials can have an impact on the **environment** in a range of different ways and at different times during their **life cycle**. For example, **extraction**, **transportation**, **manufacturing** and uses of **raw materials** consume energy and produce carbon dioxide (which contributes to global warming). However, when a material is recycled or re-used the wider impact on the environment is much reduced.

What is sustainable development?

Sustainable development is where demands on the environment by people can be met without harming the environment for future generations. The rules are simple:

- Leave the world better than you found it

- Take no more than you need

- Try not to harm the environment and make amends if you do.

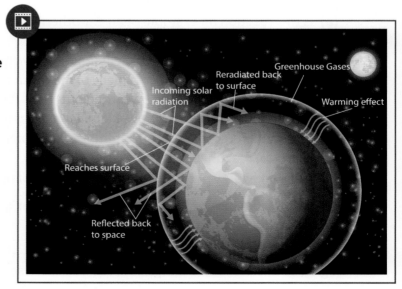

▲ Figure 23.1 *The greenhouse effect*

What is the life cycle of a material?

Have you ever considered where the goods we use come from or where they go when you finish with them? **Every product we use goes through a life cycle, and each stage of the life cycle has environmental impacts.**

One impact is carbon dioxide. Any stage in a product's life that releases carbon dioxide into the atmosphere affects the environment, and the total effect is calculated as the **carbon footprint** of the product.

The carbon footprint is a measure of the amount of carbon that is produced from activities that we carry out (see chapter 41). However, if we reduce the use of materials at each stage then this will lessen the impact on the environment.

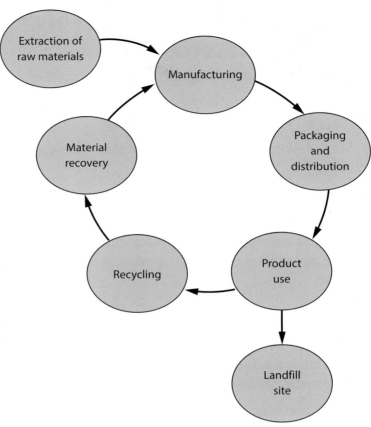

▲ Figure 23.2 *The life cycle of a product*

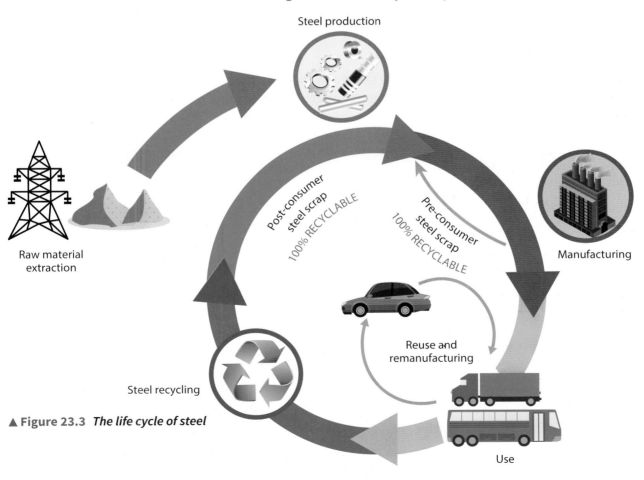

▲ Figure 23.3 *The life cycle of steel*

What are the stages in the life cycle of a material?

We will look at the individual stages in the life cycle of a material. They are:

- Stage 1 – extraction of the raw material
- Stage 2 – manufacturing
- Stage 3 – distribution
- Stage 4 – usage
- Stage 5 – disposal.

? Question

23.1 Draw a diagram showing the stages in the life cycle of an aluminium (fizzy drink) can.

Stage 1 – extraction of the raw material

All products are made from materials found in or on Earth. Large machinery is used to dig rock out of large areas called quarries. The extraction of a raw material is the start of a product's carbon footprint.

A few unreactive metals, such as gold, are found as the metal itself rather than as a compound, but most metals are extracted from rocks (ores) using a chemical reaction. A metal ore is a naturally occurring solid material from which a metal can be extracted.

There are two ways of extracting metal from its ores:

- Chemical reduction using carbon
- Electrolysis.

We will look at both of these here. The position of the metal in the reactivity series determines which method

▲ **Figure 23.4** *Gold*

is used. The reactivity series is shown in Table 23.1. It allows us to see how metals react. The most reactive metal is placed at the top of the table and the least reactive metal is placed at the bottom. The most reactive metals have a greater tendency to lose electrons and form ions.

Table 23.1 The reactivity series

Extraction	Element	Reactivity
Extraction using electrolysis	Potassium Sodium Calcium Magnesium Aluminium Carbon	Most
Extraction by reduction with carbon	Zinc Iron Tin Copper	
Do not need extraction	Silver Gold	Least Found as an element

Reduction with carbon

A more reactive metal can displace a less reactive metal from its compound. This is what happens when carbon is reacted with the compounds formed by the metals below it in the reactivity series.

For example:

$$\text{copper oxide + carbon} \xrightarrow{\text{heat}} \text{carbon dioxide + copper}$$

The copper oxide loses oxygen – it is reduced.
The carbon gains oxygen – it is oxidised.

On an industrial scale this would happen in a blast furnace (at +500°C). Coke, a pure sample of carbon, is used to extract copper or iron.

▲ Figure 23.5 *Extracting iron from ore*

✐ Activity 23.1 Can you extract copper metal from copper oxide using carbon?

🧪 Equipment needed

Tripod	Copper oxide
Bunsen burner	Crucible
spatula	Charcoal powder (carbon)
Metal tongs	Pipe clay triangle

Safety
- Make sure that the crucible has cooled down completely before you remove it from the tripod.

➡ Conducting the activity

1. Transfer one spatula of copper oxide into a crucible.

2. Carefully add one spatula of charcoal powder on top of the copper oxide, completely covering it and without mixing it.

3. Strongly heat the crucible for 5 minutes with a Bunsen burner.

4. Allow the crucible to cool and then look closely at where the powders meet in the crucible.

5. Note in the space provided in your Student Activity Book any reaction that occurs and the colour of any metal produced.

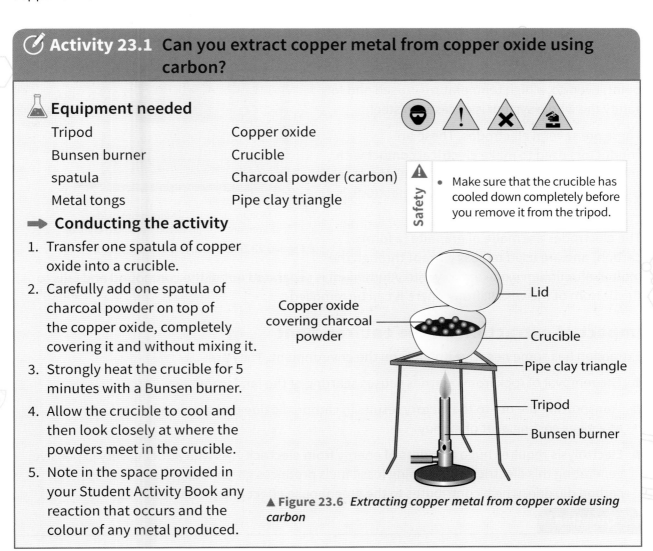

▲ Figure 23.6 *Extracting copper metal from copper oxide using carbon*

Electrolysis – extracting with electricity

Metals that are higher than carbon in the reactivity series have to be extracted using **electrolysis**. **When electric current is passed through a molten sample of a metal compound, the compound will split up and release the metal.**

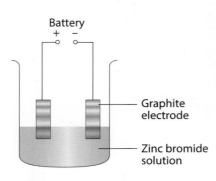

▲ **Figure 23.7** *Using electrolysis for extraction*

▲ **Figure 23.8** *The Statue of Liberty has a covering of copper*

Did you know?

The covering of the Statue of Liberty in the United States is made of copper – about 80 tonnes of it, in fact. Its surface reacts with gases in the air to form copper carbonate – which is why it is green.

Electrolysis of aluminium

Aluminium oxide has a high melting point, and to reduce costs it is dissolved in molten cryolite, an aluminium compound with a lower melting point. Even so, a high temperature is used and for safety the whole system is encased in steel.

There are several electrodes. These are conductors used to make electrical contact with some part of the circuit – the negative electrode is called a cathode, and the positive electrode is called the anode.

The electrodes are made of graphite (a form of carbon) and are used to pass current through the

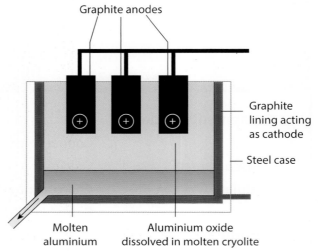

▲ **Figure 23.9** *Electrolysis of aluminium*

molten aluminium oxide and cryolite. Aluminium is separated out of the compound and falls to the bottom of the vessel, from where it can be removed.

Impact of extraction on the environment

Extraction has some negative impacts on the environment. They are:

- The removal of rock from quarries causes scarring of the landscape

- Transporting the ore to the factory results in carbon dioxide emissions from the fuel, as well as costing a lot of money

- Electrolysis requires huge amounts of energy from electricity. As well as being very expensive, generating this electricity by burning fossil fuels produces greenhouse gases such as carbon dioxide, which contributes to the greenhouse effect and global warming.

⑦ Question

23.2 **The supply of copper-rich ores is limited. Scientists have discovered two ways for extracting copper from low-grade ores. These are called bio-leaching and photomining.**

Research what these terms mean and how copper is extracted by the two methods.

Stage 2 – manufacturing

Most production requires a great deal of energy, which results in greenhouse gas emissions. When companies plan new products they must consider their impact on the environment.

When a product is made from recycled materials, less energy is needed to transport and process raw materials, which reduces manufacturing costs and makes it a more attractive option.

▲ Figure 23.10 *A paper mill*

Stage 3 – distribution

Each stage of the life cycle of a material requires some form of **distribution**. The finished product needs to be transported from factories to warehouses then to stores and eventually your home. This transportation requires the use of fossil fuels for energy, which can contribute to global warming and climate change.

Everyone can play their part to help: it is important to buy locally grown foods, as this reduces energy use compared to buying food shipped or flown into the country.

Planning ahead can reduce the number of times it is necessary to drive to the shops, or using public transport will reduce the use of fuel, which in turn will benefit the environment.

▲ Figure 23.11 *Road freight distribution*

Stage 4 – usage

Using a product may require energy, so we need to purchase items that are energy efficient. Some consumable products such as detergents work well at low temperatures; this saves energy as there is no need to heat the water.

▲ Figure 23.12 *Biological dishwasher detergents contain enzymes that help to break down particles of food on dishes in warm water instead of hot water, so the dishwasher is more energy efficient*

> **? Question**
>
> 23.3 Biological washing powders contain enzymes that help to remove stains from clothes. These work best at moderate temperatures (40°C) and not at high temperatures. Find out the names of the enzymes found in the biological washing powders and why they work best at lower temperatures.

Stage 5 – disposal

How we manage our goods at the end of their current life, when they are no longer used, can make a big difference to our environmental footprint.

Landfill

When organic materials go to landfill (often called dumps) they decompose and form methane gas. This is a greenhouse gas that contributes towards global warming.

Many landfill sites collect this gas and use it to generate electricity, or as a fuel for equipment such as a boiler.

▲ Figure 23.13 *A landfill waste disposal site*

Reduce, reuse, recycle – the three Rs

Most of our rubbish is sent to the dump or landfill sites. This is not good for our environment. We can all contribute to improving this by following the three Rs – reduce, reuse, recycle.

Reduce

We need to reduce the amount of waste going to our landfill sites and we can do this in a number of ways, such as:

- Buying products that do not have a lot of packaging, or look for products that are packed in materials that can be recycled
- Reducing paper waste by reading newspapers and magazines online instead of buying the paper version
- Organising a carpool with friends, or walking or cycling to school, as cars use a lot of energy and create a lot of pollution.

Reuse

This is where you do not throw things away but try and find ways to use them again. For example:

- Bring your own bags to the shop instead of buying new ones
- Bring your lunch to school in a lunch box or maybe a plastic ice-cream container
- Use shoe boxes, coffee jars and other types of containers for storing things
- Adapt clothes to make a different garment
- Purchase second-hand items, such as books, clothes and furniture, which not only is good for the environment, but saves money as well.

Recycle

If a product ends up in a landfill site its atoms are no longer useful, but if it is recycled the atoms can remain useful for longer. Recycled items are put through a process that makes it possible to create new products out of the materials from the old one.

It is very important to recycle for the following reasons.

- **Less extraction of resources: Recycling** reduces the need to extract raw materials. There is only a certain amount of materials – for example, metals and oil – in the earth, so recycling helps to conserve these resources.

- **Less energy:** Mining, extracting and manufacturing need lots of energy. For example, aluminium is extracted by electrolysis, which is very expensive as it requires a lot of energy. Recycling an aluminium can uses only 5% of the energy required to manufacture one from raw materials.

- **Less money:** Energy is not cheap, so recycling saves money too.

▲ **Figure 23.14** *Recycling saves resources and money*

- **Less rubbish:** Recycling results in less rubbish in landfill sites, which means less environmental damage and less methane gas.

Recycling is collected and delivered to a special processing plant

Using the latest technology all material streams are separated

Plastic elements are melted and treated to make new materials

Recycling Process

The recycled plastic is now used in the production of new products

The plastic is back on the shelf for you to buy in as little as six weeks

1 PET	2 HDPE
3 V	4 LDPE
5 PP	6 PS	7 OTHER

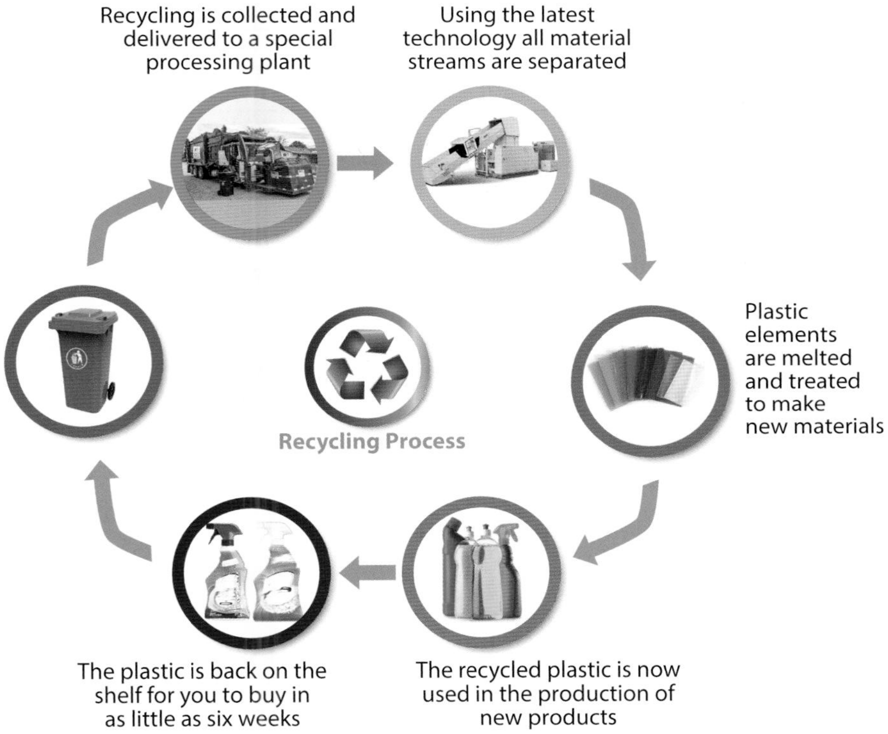

Plastic recycling (the numbers show the grade of plastic and are used for sorting when recycling)

▲ **Figure 23.15** *Recycling process for plastics*

Recycling glass

▲ **Figure 23.16** *Recycling saves resources and money*

Recycling symbol	What it means
	Glass recycling – the glass can be recycled through a bottle bank. Used glass is collected and melted and used in the manufacture of glass bottles and glassware. There is a 14% saving in energy compared to the production from raw materials
	Green dot – some of the purchase price goes towards recycling of the product's packaging. Note: it does not mean the packaging is recyclable
(alu)	Aluminium recycling
	Steel recycling
	Mobius loop – the packaging can be recycled
	Paper recycling – the product uses a percentage of recycled materials
FSC	Wood recycling – the product contains wood from sustainably managed forests
	Be tidy – 'Do not litter'

✐ Activity 23.2 How can we make old paper into new, reusable paper?

🧪 Equipment needed

Newspaper	Filter paper
2 beakers	Water
Glass rod	Cornflour
Bunsen burner	Decoration (e.g. dried flowers)
Tripod	Aluminium foil
Funnel	Rolling pin

⚠️ Safety
- The water will be boiling, so take care not to touch or tip the beaker.

➡ Conducting the activity

1. Set up the apparatus as shown in Figure 23.17.
2. Cut up four sheets of newspaper into small pieces and place them in a beaker.
3. Cover the paper with water and stir to a paste.
4. Place the beaker on the tripod and heat with a Bunsen burner until it starts to boil. Allow it to cool.
5. Add cornflour (5 g) and a little more water and stir the mixture (to form a pulp).
6. Heat the mixture again to boiling over the Bunsen burner.
7. Filter the pulp by filtration.
8. Spoon the pulp onto a sheet of aluminium foil and spread it out with a rolling pin. Add decorations if you wish.

CHEMICAL WORLD

9. Place a sheet of foil on top to cover and leave in a warm place to dry overnight. You now have recycled paper.

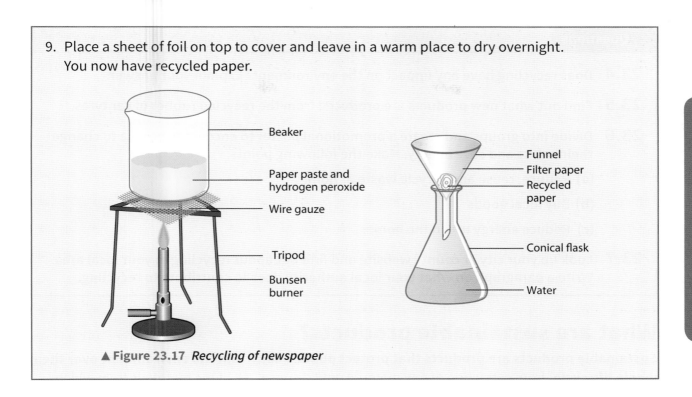

▲ Figure 23.17 *Recycling of newspaper*

What is composting?

Composting keeps organic waste such as food scraps from landfill sites. When organic materials decompose in landfill they produce methane gas, which is a greenhouse gas 20 times more potent than carbon dioxide. **But during composting the material decomposes in the presence of oxygen and so methane is not produced.**

You can have a compost bin in your own garden and use it to dispose of certain types of food and plant materials. Over time these materials will

▲ Figure 23.18 *A composting recycling centre*

break down through a natural process called decomposition (by micro-organisms) resulting in compost, which can be used to supply nutrients to the soil in your garden.

Energy recovery

Energy recovery is the conversion of non-recyclable waste material into heat, electricity or fuel through combustion or landfill gas recovery.

▲ Figure 23.19 *Generating electricity from a landfill site*

▲ Figure 23.20 *A gas recovery well on a landfill site*

▲ Figure 23.21 *A tyre recycling facility*

23.4 Does recycling have any impact on the environment? Explain your answer.

23.5 Find out what new products are produced from the recycled rubber of car tyres.

23.6 Divide into groups and create a promotional poster to encourage people to change their habits and save energy. Make the following points:

(a) Reduce, reuse and recycle waste at home

(b) Buy local goods

(c) Reduce energy use in the home.

23.7 Look up your city or county website and find out about recycling in your local area. Write a paragraph on what your local authority does to contribute to recycling.

What are sustainable products?

Sustainable products are products that protect public health and the environment over their whole life cycle, from extraction of raw material until disposal. All of the materials from which they are made can be returned to the earth after composting, or they can be repeatedly recycled as raw materials. For example, some clothing companies have collections of products that are either recyclable or biodegradable. This includes T-shirts and sneakers that are fully compostable.

Cradle-to-cradle design

Cradle-to-cradle design shows how to design products that will not damage the environment. These are non-toxic, non-harmful materials that have no negative effects on the environment. They can be used over and over again instead of becoming waste in a landfill site (cradle-to grave materials). In the cradle-to-cradle model all materials fall into one of two groups.

● **Technical materials:** These are synthetic materials that will cause no harm to the environment because they can be used over and over again. For example, the metals aluminium and steel can be recycled repeatedly; this explains why drink cans are a truly renewable material because they can be recycled and the can retains the same characteristics as the original material. Polystyrene (plastic) is another example of a completely recyclable material which after collection is sorted from other plastics for recycling. It can be used many times without loss of quality and stays in a continuous cycle.

▲ **Figure 23.22** *These plastic bottles will be recycled and used to make swimming pools*

▲ **Figure 23.23** *This house has been insulated with straw*

- **Biological materials:** This is organic material that once used can be disposed of in any natural environment. It provides food for bacteria and microbiological life and it decomposes into soil causing no harm to the environment. Examples of these materials include: cork, bamboo, hay and straw. Buildings and structures can be made from these materials.

▲ **Figure 23.24** *Organic cotton fabric is a cradle-to-cradle material because it can be disposed of in any natural environment and decomposes into soil*

Packaging

In our modern society we have become more dependent on packaging as households have become increasingly busy and convenience has become an important factor in purchases. While packaging does improve safety and convenience, it also has a number of disadvantages.

It can be expensive and can cause damage to our environment because most of the waste produced by packaging ends up in landfill. For example, some meat products are packed in polyethylene, which is a petroleum-based plastic and therefore cannot be recycled.

▲ **Figure 23.25**

Sustainable packaging is very important so that we can reduce the waste in our landfill sites.

- Many food processors have reduced their packaging by offering reusable and refillable containers: e.g. branded coffee where the refill packaging is manufactured from cardboard or paper which can be recycled and composted.

- Supermarkets are buying products from suppliers that use recyclable material in their packaging. Polyethylene terephthalate (PET) is 100% recyclable, making it ideal for packaging. It is light and easily crushed and so is easy to transport to the recycling plant.

- The biodegradable plastic polylactide (PLA) is processed from the starch of plants such as corn or sugarcane and is ideal for shopping bags because it is a compostable material.

The key factors when choosing a sustainable material are that it is made from easily grown materials, is recyclable and is locally available.

? Question

23.8 A company called Ecolean has developed ecologically sustainable food packaging that is not a fossil fuel-based material, but is made with the natural material chalk (limestone).

Research answers to the following questions:

(a) Where is limestone formed in nature?

(b) What is the name of this new packaging material?

(c) Explain why this new material has less impact on our environment than other packaging.

(d) What products is this new sustainable packaging material used for?

(e) How many countries does Ecolean sell its products in?

Summary questions

23.9 Name two ways that a metal can be extracted from its ores.

23.10 Human activities have damaged the environment, and this cannot easily be repaired. List five resources that you think will eventually run out.

23.11 What is electrolysis?

23.12 List the five stages in the life cycle of a material.

23.13 Explain the 3Rs.

23.14 Which greenhouse gases are often produced during human activities?

23.15 Why do processes using electricity add to a product's carbon footprint?

23.16 Think of ways in which you can apply the 3Rs. In other words, what would you reduce, reuse and recycle in your own home?

23.17 Explain how sustainable products are good for the environment.

23.18 What is meant by cradle-to-cradle design?

Assessment questions

23.19 This table shows the environmental impact of four different shopping bags **(30 marks)**

	Polyethylene (mass = 6 kg)	Paper (52 kg)	Reusable nonwoven polypropylene (42 kg)		Reusable polyethylene with 40% recycled content (44 kg)	
	1 use	1 use	1 use	8 uses	1 use	8 uses
Nonrenewable energy. GJ	763	2,620	3,736	467	2,945	368
Greenhouse gas emissions metric tons of CO_2 equivalent ● = 0.010	0.040	0.080	0.262	0.033	0.182	0.023
Freshwater consumption, gal ● = 10	58	1,000	426	85	250	40

▲ **Figure 23.26**

(a) In your opinion, which bag causes less damage to the environment? Explain why, using the data in the table.

(b) (i) Explain the term 'carbon footprint'.

(ii) Which bag shows the greatest carbon footprint? Explain why.

(c) The 3Rs play a large role in protecting our environment. Outline, using the data in the table, why you think this statement is true.

23.20 According to the United Nations, combating plastic pollution is one of **(15 marks)** the key environmental challenges of our generation. Copy and complete this table showing which items can and cannot be recycled.

Item	Can be recycled	Cannot be recycled
Clingfilm		
Milk carton		
Bubble wrap		
Yoghurt carton		
Crisp packet		

23.21 Figure 23.27 shows the stages in the recycling of a drinks can. **(30 marks)**

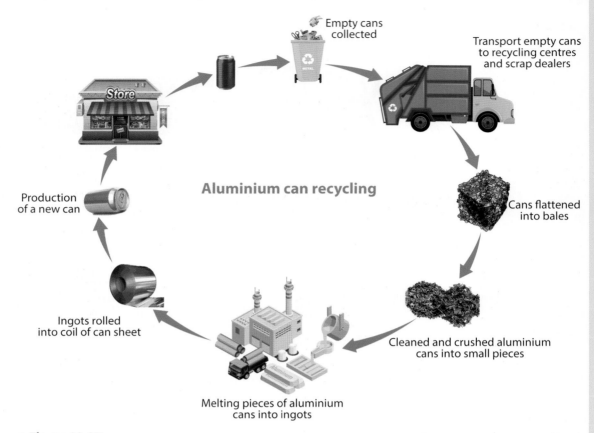

Aluminium can recycling

Empty cans collected

Transport empty cans to recycling centres and scrap dealers

Store

Production of a new can

Cans flattened into bales

Ingots rolled into coil of can sheet

Cleaned and crushed aluminium cans into small pieces

Melting pieces of aluminium cans into ingots

▲ Figure 23.27

(a) Which stages in the life cycle contribute to global warming? Explain.

(b) What greenhouse gas is released that increases the carbon footprint of the can?

(c) One advantage of recycling cans is that it can reduce the manufacturing costs. Outline two more advantages of recycling.

(d) The extraction of raw materials is the first stage in the life cycle of the can. State two negative impacts this may have on the environment.

PowerPoint summary   Weblinks

PHYSICAL WORLD

LEARNING OUTCOMES: LO

PW1. Students should be able to select and use appropriate measuring instruments

PW2. Students should be able to identify and measure/calculate length, mass, time, temperature, area, volume, density, speed, acceleration, force, potential difference, current, resistance, electrical power

PW3. Students should be able to investigate patterns and relationships between physical observables

PW4. Students should be able to research and discuss a technological application of physics in terms of scientific, societal and environmental impact

PW5. Students should be able to design and build simple electronic circuits

PW6. Students should be able to explain energy conservation and analyse processes in terms of energy changes and dissipation

PW7. Students should be able to design, build, and test a device that transforms energy from one form to another in order to perform a function; describe the energy changes and ways of improving efficiency

PW8. Students should be able to research and discuss the ethical and sustainability issues that arise from our generation and consumption of electricity

CHAPTER 24

MAKING ACCURATE MEASUREMENTS

LO: PW1, PW2

Learning intentions

At the end of this chapter you will be able to:

✓ Make measurements of length, mass, time, area and volume

✓ Work with units relevant to your measurements

✓ List examples of where measurements are made in everyday life.

Keywords

- ⚬— accurate
- ⚬— units
- ⚬— length
- ⚬— zero error
- ⚬— opisometer
- ⚬— volume
- ⚬— trundle wheel
- ⚬— vernier caliper
- ⚬— mass
- ⚬— balance
- ⚬— timer
- ⚬— graduated cylinder
- ⚬— meniscus

Measurements

There are certain skills you need in order to be good at physics. Measuring is most definitely one of these skills. Some of the quantities you will measure are:

- Length
- Time
- Volume.
- Mass
- Area

It is very important that your measurements are **accurate** and that they are given in **units** that can be understood internationally.

> **? Question**
>
> **24.1** Spend 5 minutes making a list of where measurements are used in everyday life. Then one member of your group will read out your list to the rest of the class.

Why is it important to be accurate?

Some measurements need to be more accurate than others.
Some measurements have to be perfectly accurate. For example, if you have to replace a broken window pane the new piece of glass has to be the right size. If it is too small it will fall out, and if it is too big it will not fit into the window. To get the right size you have to make accurate measurements.

All sorts of items have to be measured with accuracy. A DVD has to be the right size to fit into the drive. Pieces of Lego are manufactured to a high degree of accuracy so they fit together. Accuracy is extremely important with things such as medicines: for example, the amount of insulin taken by a person with diabetes must be just right to maintain a correct blood sugar level.

> **? Question**
>
> **24.2** List three everyday items that are manufactured using accurate measurements.

Why do we need units?

It would be unhelpful to be asked to fetch 'a long piece of wood'. Nor would it be helpful to be asked to fetch 'a piece of wood of length 3'. Three what? Centimetres? Metres? Can you guess how long 3 metres is?

We use a system of SI units. The name comes from the French Système Internationale d'Unités – the International System of Units. By using an international system of units, scientists, engineers, manufacturers, office workers and other people from various countries can understand each other.

ⓘ Question

24.3 **The problem:** You are shopping online and you see a shirt that you really like. The shirt is made in France, which uses a different measurement for clothes sizes.

The task: Go online to find a chart that will allow you to compare clothes sizes in Ireland and France. Print or copy this out. Now make a list of five items of your own clothes and give their Irish sizes and their French sizes.

Instruments for measurement

In this chapter we will look at different instruments that are used to make measurements.

ⓘ Question

24.4 We mentioned that we may need to measure quantities such as length, mass, time, area and volume. Research answers to the following questions for each quantity.

(a) What are the instruments that could be used for the measurements?

(b) Can some of the quantities be measured with different instruments?

(c) How old are these measuring instruments? Were they in use 100 years ago?

(d) Would these instruments be expensive to buy?

(e) How many of these instruments do you already have in your school laboratory? Present your findings in the form of a reference sheet.

As you read on further, compare your answers with the measuring instruments we suggest.

Measuring length

Length is measured in:

- Millimetres (mm)
- Centimetres (cm)
- Metres (m)
- Kilometres (km).

Remember:

10 mm	is the same as	1 cm
100 cm	is the same as	1 m
1000 m	is the same as	1 km

Measuring items

Case 1:

To measure the length of a copy book you would use a ruler or a metre stick. The most suitable units would be centimetres.

? Question

24.5 Why, do you think, would the metre or the millimetre not be suitable units for measuring your copy book?

Note: Be careful not to confuse the end of a ruler and the zero mark on the ruler. Sometimes the zero mark is exactly at the end of the ruler, but not always. Make sure the zero mark is at one edge of the copy book and then note the position on the ruler corresponding to the other end. This gives the length of the copy book.

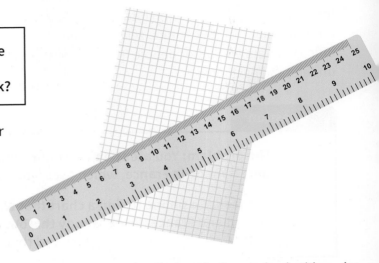

▲ Figure 24.1 *Measuring the length of a copy book with a ruler*

Case 2:

To measure the length of a curve you would use an opisometer. Start with the wheel of the opisometer at the left side. Move the wheel along the curve until you come to the end of the curve. Now place the wheel on the zero mark of a metre stick and roll the wheel along the metre stick until the wheel stops at the left side. The position on the metre stick where the wheel stops corresponds to the length of the curve.

Did you know?

If you make the mistake of including the space between the end of the ruler and the zero mark in your measurement, you will have made a **zero error**.

Case 3:

Large curved lengths are often measured with a trundle wheel.

Case 4:

To measure the diameter of a coin you would use a vernier caliper.

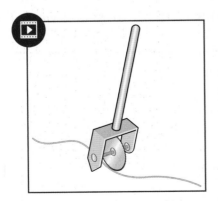

▲ Figure 24.2 *An opisometer*

▲ Figure 24.3 *A trundle wheel*

▲ Figure 24.4 *A vernier caliper*

PHYSICAL WORLD

Activity 24.1 How can we measure without measuring instruments?

 Equipment needed

String, about 2 metres long   Lunch box

Goal posts   Bicycle

 Safety • Take care not to get in the way of others as you move around the school.

Conducting the activity

The problem: In groups, you will need to measure some items around the school, but the measuring instruments must remain in the science room. You may use a piece of string about 2 metres long, which you can then take back to the science room.

The task:

Do the following and record your measurements in the grid in your Student Activity Book.

(a) Measure the perimeter of a lunch box.

(b) Measure the distance between the uprights of a goalpost.

(c) Measure the diameter of the handlebar of a bicycle.

(d) Compare your measurements with the other groups.

? Question

24.6 Why might the measurements of all the groups be slightly different?

Sample calculation 1

Convert 8.6 cm to millimetres.

Answer:

1 cm ⟶ 10 mm

8.6 cm ⟶ 10 × 8.6 = 86 mm

Sample calculation 2

Convert 67 mm to cm.

Answer:

10 mm ⟶ 1 cm

1 mm ⟶ $\frac{1}{10}$ cm

67 mm ⟶ $\frac{1}{10}$ × 67 = 6.7 cm

Sample calculation 3

Convert 7.2 km to metres.

Answer:

1 km ⟶ 1000 m

7.2 km ⟶ 1000 × 7.2
= 7200 m

Measuring mass

The mass of an object is the amount of matter in the object. Mass is measured in grams (g) or kilograms (kg). Smaller quantities, such as the mass of a chemical you would use in a classroom activity, would usually be measured in grams. The kilogram is more suitable for the mass of a person or the mass of a large bag of potatoes.

1 kilogram is the same as 1000 grams.

The instrument used to measure the mass of an object is called an electronic **balance**. Most food items that you buy in a supermarket come in packaging with the value of the mass written on it. For example, a box of breakfast cereal (not including the packaging) might have a mass of 500 g. This allows you to know exactly how much you are getting for your money.

▲ Figure 24.5 *An electronic balance*

Did you know?

In science the words 'mass' and 'weight' do not have the same meaning. Later in the book we will look at weight and learn its exact meaning. The problem for many people is that in everyday language we use weight and mass as if they were the same. But in science you have to be more precise with your choice of words.

Measuring time

Time can be measured in many units. Examples are: second, minute, hour, day, week. In science we use the second, and the symbol for the second is 's'. The instrument we would use is a stopwatch or an electronic **timer**. You could also use the timer on your mobile phone.

▶ Figure 24.6 *A stopwatch is used for measuring time*

Sample calculation 4

How many seconds are there in a week?

Answer:

There are 7 days in a week, therefore 1 week ⟶ 7 days

There are 24 hours in a day, therefore 1 week ⟶ 7 × 24 = 168 hours

There are 60 minutes in an hour, therefore 1 week ⟶ 168 × 60 = 10 080 minutes

There are 60 seconds in a minute, therefore 1 week ⟶ 10 080 × 60 = 604 800 seconds

That is a lot of seconds!

Measuring area

? Question

24.7 Measuring area is studied in maths classes and is something we do quite often in a science course. Working in small groups, discuss the following and then design a reference sheet to refer to in your work:

(a) What geometrical shapes do you meet most often in maths classes? (The *Formulae and Tables* booklet might help you here.)

(b) What formulae could you find to calculate the area of the various shapes from part (a)?

(c) Could you use any of these formulae to calculate the area of a leaf? Briefly explain your answer.

(d) What unit would you use for area?

(e) If you find more than one unit, give examples of where each unit would be used.

The price of a house or an apartment for sale depends on many factors. One of these is the total area of the floors. The scientific system for measuring floor space is the metre squared (m^2). Most countries around the world use this system.

Measuring volume

The volume of an object is the amount of space an object takes up. The unit for volume is the centimetre cubed (cm^3) or the metre cubed (m^3). In your maths class you will learn how to calculate the volume of regular shapes such as a rectangular box. In science we also have to be able to calculate the volume of irregular shapes such as a small stone you would find on a beach.

Measuring the volume of a regular shape

The volume of this box = 10 cm × 5 cm × 8 cm

= 400 cm^3

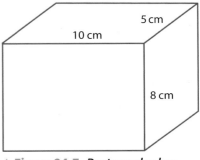

▲ Figure 24.7 *Rectangular box*

(?) Questions

24.8 What is the word formula for the calculation used for the volume of the box?

24.9 Could your formula work for calculating the volume of a small stone? Explain your answer.

Sample calculation 5

Calculate the volume of a rectangular box of length 1 m, width 70 cm and height 12 cm.

Answer:

The volume of the box = length × width × height

= 100 × 70 × 12

= 84 000 cm^3

Note: Be careful with the trick in this question. You must change the 1 m to cm. **Make sure that all the units are the same.**

Sample calculation 6

Calculate the volume of a cube with a side of length 15 cm.

Answer:

In a cube, length = width = height

Therefore volume = 15 × 15 × 15 = 3375 cm^3

Activity 24.2 **How can we measure the volume of an irregular shape?**

Equipment needed

Water   Overflow can

Graduated cylinder   A stone

 Safety • Be careful not to spill water on the floor to avoid the danger of somebody slipping.

➡ **Conducting the activity**

1. Pour water into the overflow can until some spills out into the **graduated cylinder**.

2. When the water stops spilling out you know that the level of the water is exactly at the level of the spout.

3. Carefully read the level of the water in the graduated cylinder and write down the value in the space provided in your Student Activity Book.

4. Place the stone into the overflow can and allow it to sink to the bottom. Take care not to splash water.

5. Carefully read the new level of the water in the graduated cylinder and write down the value your Student Activity Book.

6. Subtract the first value from the second to get the volume of the stone.

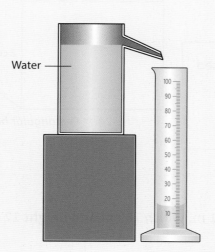

▲ **Figure 24.8** *Overflow can and graduated cylinder*

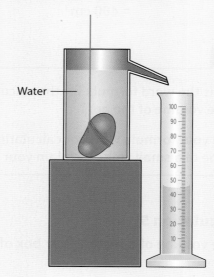

▲ **Figure 24.9** *Graduated cylinder showing meniscus*

Meniscus

The top surface of water in a graduated cylinder is curved a little, as you can see in Figure 24.9. This is called the **meniscus**.

When reading a graduated cylinder you must allow for the meniscus. Always **take a reading corresponding to the bottom of the meniscus** to get the correct water level.

? Question

24.10 Measuring the volume of a small object.

Look at Figure 24.10 and answer the questions below.

(a) What is the volume of liquid in the graduated cylinder on the left of the diagram?

(b) Take the reading of the level of the liquid in the graduated cylinder on the right of the diagram.

(c) Calculate the volume of the irregular object that was placed in the graduated cylinder.

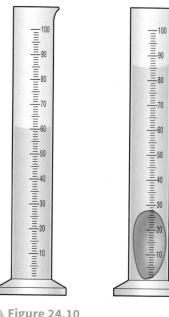

▲ Figure 24.10

Ethics in measurement

When you buy petrol or diesel for a car the amount you pay depends on the volume of fuel you put into the tank. If the pump is faulty the amount you pay for is not the amount you put into the car.

? Questions

24.11 Discuss the problems that arise when a customer is overcharged for the petrol or diesel that they bought.

24.12 Discuss the problems that arise when a customer is undercharged for the petrol or diesel that they bought.

24.13 List five other examples of where faulty measuring machines could lead to problems in shops.

24.14 Research the organisation in Ireland responsible for checking that petrol pumps and weighing scales in shops, etc. are working correctly. Make a note of how this organisation can be contacted if someone needed to make a complaint.

Summary questions

24.15 Name three different units that can be used to measure length.

24.16 A scientist is unlikely to measure a length in inches today. Why do you think this is so?

24.17 Name two instruments that could be used to measure a curved length.

24.18 What would be the difference in the use of the two instruments you named in the answer to question 24.17?

24.19 Name the instrument used to measure the diameter of a coin.

24.20 What is the meaning of the word 'mass'?

24.21 Name two units that could be used to measure mass.

24.22 What unit would be most suitable to measure the mass of the quantity of a chemical in a class experiment?

24.23 **(a)** Name six different units for measuring time that are used by people in their everyday lives.

(b) Name the unit for measuring time that is used in science.

24.24 What is the meaning of the word 'volume'?

24.25 Convert the following times to seconds:

(a) 6 minutes   **(b)** 12 hours   **(c)** 2 days   **(d)** 4 weeks

24.26 Convert:

(a) 1 week to minutes   **(c)** 1 week to seconds

(b) 1 week and 2 days to minutes   **(d)** 1 week and 2 days to seconds

24.27 What is your age at midday today in seconds?

(A little help: Assume that you were born at exactly midday on your birthday.)

24.28 Copy and complete the table below for the instruments listed.

In each case state the physical quantity the instrument measures.
Also state the unit used for that measurement.

Instrument	Quantity measured	Unit
Ruler		
Vernier caliper		
Opisometer		
Electronic balance		
Trundle wheel		
Stopwatch		

24.29 Convert:

(a) 320 km to m   **(d)** 3 km to cm   **(g)** 11.1 mm to cm

(b) 900 m to km   **(e)** 1.2 km to cm   **(h)** 1.2 m to mm

(c) 7.2 m to cm   **(f)** 6 cm to mm   **(i)** 1.4 km to mm

24.30 Convert:

(a) 3.4 kg to g   **(b)** 0.85 kg to g   **(c)** 1 250 g to kg   **(d)** 750 g to kg

24.31 Calculate the volume of a rectangular box of length 62 cm, width 40 cm and height 12 cm.

24.32 Calculate the volume of a rectangular box of length 2 m, width 60 cm and height 25.5 cm.

24.33 Calculate the volume of a cube with a side of length 25 cm.

Assessment questions

24.34 (a) Name a suitable instrument to measure the lengths of the sides of the block. **(15 marks)**

(b) Name something you might find in your home that could have a length, width and height similar to the measurements of the block.

(c) Calculate the volume of the block using the metre as your unit.

(d) Calculate the volume of the block using the centimetre as your unit.

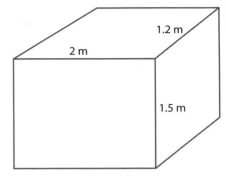

▲ **Figure 24.11**

24.35 The passage below is about measurements that are used in everyday life and science. **(15 marks)**

Copy the paragraph and fill in the spaces using the words given below.

kilometre   second   hours   metre   minutes

The time taken to prepare food depends very much on the meal you have in mind. To make a sandwich usually takes a few _____ while to prepare a dinner to celebrate a special occasion may take two or three _____. The distance from your home to your school may be measured in the _____ or the _____ depending on whether you live near or far from the school. If you live near your school the time to travel to school is usually measured in minutes but for measurements of time in science we use the _____ as our unit.

24.36 A group of people decide to open a takeaway pizza restaurant. They will make five different size pizzas with a variety of toppings. The price of the pizza will depend only on the size and not on the topping. The pizzas will be circular in shape and the size of the pizzas will be the diameter value. The following is their price structure. **(30 marks)**

Pizza size (cm)	Price (€)
10	3
15	6
20	9
25	12
30	15

(a) When rolling the dough what instrument will the chef use to measure the diameter of the pizza?

(b) Suggest a better way of knowing the diameter of the pizza without actually measuring it directly.

(c) Draw a graph of the data in the table above with pizza size on the *x*-axis and price on the *y*-axis.

(d) Is there any relationship between the size of a pizza and the price?

(e) Using the price structure above, what would be the price of a 5 cm pizza?

(f) 'The larger pizza is better value for money.' Give a mathematical reason why this statement is true.

24.37 A pendulum usually consists of a heavy weight, called a bob (often spherical in shape) attached to a string, as illustrated in Figure 24.12. It will swing from side to side when released. It can be used in science to calculate a value for the acceleration caused by the Earth's gravitational force. **(30 marks)**

(a) What instrument would you use to measure the time taken for the bob to swing over and back?

(b) A student measured the time for 40 full swings over and back as 63 s.

    (i) What would be the time for one full swing?

    (ii) What is the advantage of measuring the time for 40 full swings compared to measuring the time for just 1 full swing?

▲ Figure 24.12

(c) The length of a pendulum is measured from the point of suspension (where the string is tied to the support) to the centre of the bob. To do this accurately you may need to measure the diameter of the spherical bob.

    (i) Name an instrument that could be used to measure the diameter of the spherical bob.

    (ii) From Figure 24.12, what unit of measurement would be suitable for measuring the diameter of the bob?

    (iii) Suggest a reason in relation to accuracy why it would not be wise to use a string that is slightly elastic (can be stretched).

(d) The student shown in Figure 24.12 carried out the activity beside an open window through which a strong breeze was blowing. How might this affect the measurements of the time for a full swing?

PowerPoint summary   Weblinks

WHAT IS DENSITY AND WHY DO SOME THINGS FLOAT?

CHAPTER 25

LO: PW2, PW3

Learning intentions

At the end of this chapter you will be able to:

- ✓ Explain density
- ✓ Use the correct units when measuring density
- ✓ Calculate values of density using a mathematical formula
- ✓ Carry out activities to measure densities of solids
- ✓ Explain flotation
- ✓ Investigate patterns and relationships between physical observables.

Keywords

- ⚷ density
- ⚷ flotation
- ⚷ mass
- ⚷ volume
- ⚷ overflow can
- ⚷ g cm⁻³
- ⚷ kg m⁻³
- ⚷ graph

Density

When you go shopping for a new school bag you will often see several bags on display. To give the customer an idea of the size of the bag the shopkeeper might stuff the bag full of crumpled-up tissue paper. This helps you to visualise the size of the bag. The bag looks full but feels very light when stuffed with the tissue paper. But when this bag is full of books, it is much heavier.

▲ Figure 25.1 *A full school bag – if there is tissue paper in it, it will be light; if there are books in it, it will be heavy*

The paper used in books is more tightly packed than the paper in crumpled-up pieces of tissue paper. In a bag full of books there is more paper in the same size or volume of bag. The mass of the books is greater than the mass of the tissue paper, even though the volumes are the same. We would say that the **density** of the books is greater than the density of the tissue paper.

Density of a substance tells you how much mass is packed into a particular volume. Experience will tell you that a bag full of books will be heavier than a bag of crumpled tissue paper. A mathematical formula explains it, and can be used in other situations:

Low density

High density

▲ Figure 25.2

$$\text{density} = \frac{\text{mass}}{\text{volume}} \text{ (Density is the mass divided by the volume.)}$$

Activity 25.1 What is the relationship between mass and volume?

 Equipment needed

Set of brass weights   Overflow can

Water   Graduated cylinder

Safety
- Be careful not to spill water on the floor to avoid the danger of somebody slipping.

➡ **Conducting the activity**

1. Choose five different size brass weights: 25 g, 50 g, 100 g, 200 g and 500 g.

2. Using the method for measuring the volume of irregular objects in activity 24.2 on page 280, you should measure and record in the table in your Student Activity Book the volume of the five weights.

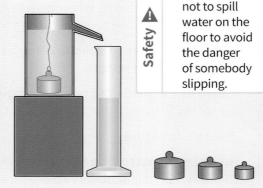

▲ Figure 25.3

⑦ Questions

25.1 Do you notice any pattern between the values of the mass and the values of the volumes?

25.2 Take each pair of values and see what happens when you: **(a)** add, **(b)** subtract, **(c)** multiply and **(d)** divide the values.

25.3 Draw a graph with the mass values on the *y*-axis and the volume values on the *x*-axis. Graph paper is provided for you in your Student Activity Book. What do you notice about your graph?

3. Repeat the activity, only this time use five small objects that are made of different materials – wood, metal, plastic, etc. Record your results in the table in your Student Activity Book.

⑦ Question

25.4 Do you notice any pattern between the mass values and the volume values of these new objects?

Units for density

There are two sets of units that can be used for density:

First,

$$\text{since density} = \frac{\text{mass}}{\text{volume}}, \text{ units of density} = \frac{\text{units of mass}}{\text{units of volume}}$$
$$= \frac{\text{gram}}{\text{cm}^3}$$

In science we write this as **gram cm^{-3}** or simply **g cm^{-3}**.

The minus sign in front of the number 3 is to remind you that the cm^3 are below the line in the formula.

Second,

$$\text{density} = \frac{\text{mass}}{\text{volume}}, \text{ units of density} = \frac{\text{units of mass}}{\text{units of volume}}$$
$$= \frac{\text{kilogram}}{\text{m}^3}$$

In science we write this as **kilogram m^{-3}** or simply **kg m^{-3}**.

Helpful hint: Look at the following triangle:

$$\frac{\text{mass}}{\text{density} \times \text{volume}} \qquad or \qquad \frac{M}{D \times V}$$

In a calculation you may be asked to find:

- The value of density
- The value of mass
- The value of volume.

Place your finger over the quantity you are measuring in the triangle above and the instruction for your calculation is right in front of you. This is what you get:

- To calculate the value of density: $\quad \text{density} = \dfrac{\text{mass}}{\text{volume}}$
- To calculate the value of mass: $\quad \text{mass} = \text{density} \times \text{volume}$
- To calculate the value of volume: $\quad \text{volume} = \dfrac{\text{mass}}{\text{density}}$

Sample calculation 1

Brian noted that 100 cm^3 of a liquid had a mass of 80 g. Calculate the density of this liquid.

Answer:

$$\text{density} = \frac{\text{mass}}{\text{volume}} = \frac{80}{100}$$
$$= 0.8 \text{ g cm}^{-3}$$

Sample calculation 2

The rectangular block in Figure 25.4 has a length of 5 m, a width of 3 m and a height of 2 m. The mass of the block is 21 000 kg. Calculate the density of the block.

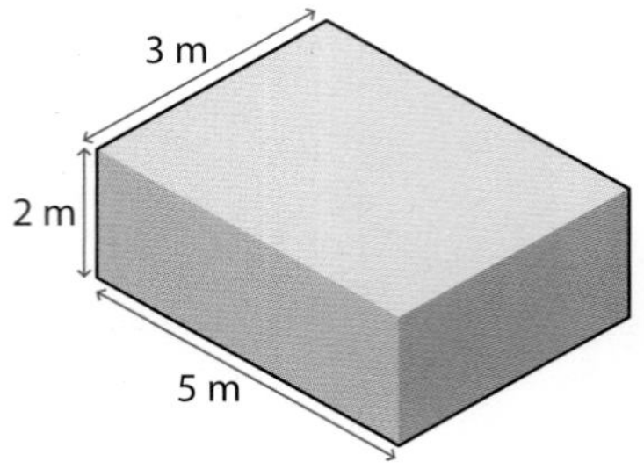

Answer:

First you have to calculate the volume of the block:

Volume = length × width × height

Volume = 5 × 3 × 2

Volume = 30 m³

Then use your answer in the formula:

$$\text{density} = \frac{\text{mass}}{\text{volume}} = \frac{21\,000}{30} = 700 \text{ kg m}^{-3}$$

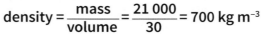

▲ **Figure 25.4** *Rectangular block*

Sample calculation 3

A substance has a density of 19 g cm⁻³. Calculate the mass of 8 cm³ of this substance.

Answer:

Mass = density × volume

Mass = 19 × 8

Mass = 152 g

Sample calculation 4

The density of a stone is 5 g cm⁻³. Calculate the volume of this stone if it has a mass of 17 g.

Answer:

$$\text{volume} = \frac{\text{mass}}{\text{density}} = \frac{17}{5} = 3.4 \text{ cm}^3$$

Sample calculation 5

A student measured the values of the volume for five different pieces of cork. Each piece of cork had its mass value written on it. She presented the data as shown in the table below.

Mass (g)	2	4	6	8	10
Volume (cm³)	10	20	30	40	50

Draw a graph with values of mass on the y-axis and values of volume on the x-axis.

(a) What do you notice about the shape of the graph?

(b) Divide any mass value by its corresponding volume value. Do you notice any pattern?

(c) What unit would you get when a mass value is divided by a volume value?

Answer:

See Figure 25.5 on page 289.

(a) The graph is a straight line passing through the origin.

(b) Every time you divide the mass value by the volume value you get the same answer of 0.2:

$$\frac{2}{10} = 0.2 \qquad \frac{4}{20} = 0.2 \qquad \frac{6}{30} = 0.2$$

(c) The unit would be $\quad \dfrac{\text{unit of mass}}{\text{unit of volume}} \quad = \quad \dfrac{\text{g}}{\text{cm}^3} \quad = \quad \text{g cm}^{-3}$

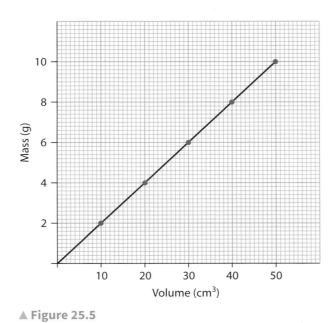

▲ **Figure 25.5**

By now you have noticed that there is a relationship between the mass and the volume of objects made of the same material: for example, the brass weights. This relationship leads to the idea of density. You have also seen some maths calculations based on the density formula.

> **② Question**
>
> **25.5** In your group discuss the practical difficulties of measuring the density of each of the following. Then each take one of the list to tell the rest of the class what the difficulties are.
>
> **(a)** A sponge   **(b)** An inflated balloon   **(c)** A sample of soil   **(d)** An ice cream.

Now that you have discussed the above, do you better understand the need for very clear instructions before undertaking an activity?

Values of density

Table 25.1 gives some values of density for a range of materials.

Table 25.1 Values of density

Material	Density (kg m⁻³)	Density (g cm⁻³)
Polystyrene	20	0.02
Cork	200	0.2
Paraffin oil	800	0.8
Ice	900	0.9
Water	1 000	1
Aluminium	2 700	2.7
Mercury	13 600	13.6
Gold	19 300	19.3
Osmium	22 600	22.6

PHYSICAL WORLD

Be careful with the units for density. Table 25.1 shows how the numerical value of density depends on the units you choose. For water, the density is 1 if you use g cm^{-3} and the density is 1000 if you use kg m^{-3}.

The density of water is exactly 1 g cm^{-3}. This is not a coincidence. This value was used many years ago when scientists were deciding on an exact meaning for the kilogram.

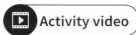 Activity video

Did you know?

Water is at its most dense at a temperature of 4° Celsius. If you heat water above this temperature it will become less dense. If you cool water below this temperature it will also become less dense.

Questions

25.6 What is the most dense material and what is the least dense material to be found on Earth?

25.7 Name a material in space that might be more dense than a material you will find on Earth.

Flotation

We observe many examples of **flotation** in our everyday lives. Boats float in the sea, twigs float in rivers, and we know that icebergs are huge floating blocks of ice. Why do some objects float and other objects sink? The answer to this question lies in knowing about the density of the objects.

▲ Figure 25.6 *Leaves on water – an example of flotation*

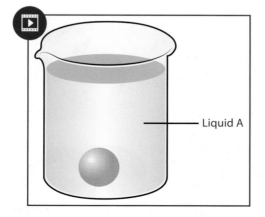

▲ Figure 25.7 *A solid sinks in liquid A*

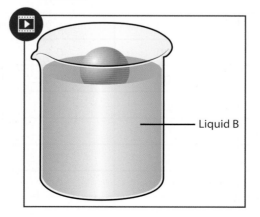

▲ Figure 25.8 *A solid floats in liquid B*

WHAT IS DENSITY AND WHY DO SOME THINGS FLOAT?

✂ Activity 25.2 Why do some objects float and other objects sink?

⚗ Equipment needed

Water	Paraffin oil	Ice cubes
Cork	Brass weight	3 plastic beakers

 Safety
- Be careful not to spill the water or the oil on the floor to avoid somebody slipping.

➡ Conducting the activity

1. Half fill one beaker with water and half fill the other with paraffin oil.
2. Place the cork, the ice cube and the brass weight on the surface of the water. Which objects remain floating? Record your observations in the table provided in your Student Activity Book.
3. Place the cork, the ice cube and the brass weight on the surface of the oil. Which objects remain floating? Record your observations in your table.
4. Pour some of the oil into a third beaker and then pour some water on top of the oil. Record your observations in the space provided in your Student Activity Book.

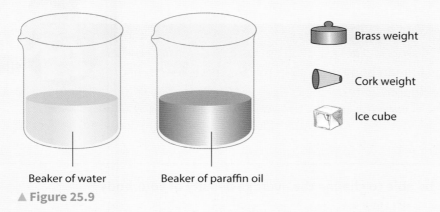

Brass weight

Cork weight

Ice cube

Beaker of water   Beaker of paraffin oil

▲ **Figure 25.9**

? Questions

25.8 Using the information in Table 25.1 on page 289 about ice, water, cork and paraffin oil, when will an object float and when will an object sink?

25.9 Brass is not included in Table 25.1. Based on your activity, what can you say about the density of brass?

25.10 How does the information in Table 25.1 about oil and water help to explain your observation in the last part of your activity?

Figure 25.10 shows three different liquids, each with different densities. The liquid on the top has the smallest value of density while the liquid on the bottom has the greatest value of density.

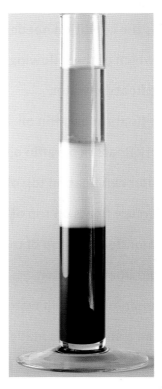

▲ **Figure 25.10** *Less dense liquids can float on top of more dense liquids*

How can seemingly heavy objects float?

Have you ever wondered why a ship that is made of a metal is able to float in water?

If the metal is more dense than the water you might expect the ship to sink. However, the ship is hollow and the inside of the ship is filled with air.

The average density of the ship and the air in it is less than the density of the water. The ship is therefore able to float.

▲ Figure 25.11 *A laden cargo ship can float in water*

Did you know?

The average density of the human body is 0.985 g cm^{-3}. As this is less dense than water, we are able to float in water.

⑦ Questions

25.11 How might you be able to change the average density of your body?

25.12 What is the condition needed for a solid to float in a liquid?

25.13 What is the condition needed for one liquid to float on top of another liquid?

25.14 State which of the following are true and which are false.

  (a) Ice floats in water.

  (b) Ice floats in paraffin oil.

  (c) Cork floats in paraffin oil.

  (d) Water can float on top of paraffin oil.

  (e) Mercury floats on top of water.

  (f) Water floats on top of mercury.

  (g) Gold floats in water.

  (h) Aluminium sinks in water.

25.15 How can a ship that is made of a metal float in water when the metal is more dense than water?

Summary questions

25.16 Why is a bag full of books heavier than a bag stuffed with tissue paper?

25.17 What is the mathematical way to explain the meaning of density?

25.18 Write down the values of the density of water, aluminium, gold, mercury and osmium in the two different units that we use for density.

25.19 What are the two sets of units that can be used to measure density?

25.20 An object has a mass of 48 g and a volume of 6 cm³. Calculate the density of this object.

25.21 If 250 cm³ of a liquid had a mass of 200 g, what would be the value of the density of the liquid?

25.22 A liquid has a density of 1.2 g cm⁻³ and the volume of this liquid is 20 cm³. Calculate the mass of this liquid.

25.23 Calculate the volume of an object if it has a mass of 96 g and a density of 12 g cm⁻³.

25.24 A rectangular block has a length of 8 cm, a width of 5 cm and a height of 3 cm.
It has a mass of 1440 g. Find:
  (a) The volume of the block
  (b) The density of the block.

25.25 To measure the density of a rectangular block:
  (a) What four measurements do you need to make?
  (b) How do you calculate the volume of the rectangular block using these measurements?
  (c) How do you calculate the density of the rectangular block using your measurements?

25.26 In an activity to measure the density of an irregular solid, Ciara noted the following measurements:
  ● The mass of a small stone was 27 g.
  ● The reading of the level of water in the graduated cylinder was 10 cm³ before the stone was placed into the overflow can.
  ● The reading of the level of water was 19 cm³ after the stone was placed into the overflow can.
  (a) Calculate the volume of the stone.
  (b) Calculate the density of the stone.

25.27 A rectangular block has a length of 1.5 m, a width of 50 cm and a height of 40 cm.
It has a mass of 810 kg.
  (a) Calculate the density of the block.
  (b) State the unit of density used here.
  Hint: Be careful with your units!

25.28 A rectangular block has a length of 30 cm, a width of 18 cm and a height of 10 cm.
It has a mass of 10.8 kg.
  (a) Calculate the density of the block.
  (b) State the unit of density used here.
  Hint: Be careful with your units!

 Log on to **www.edcolearning.ie** for Additional Summary Questions

Assessment questions

25.29 Question from Junior Cycle Science exam paper   (15 marks)

A student was asked to measure the density of a block.

The dimensions of the block are shown in the diagram (Figure 25.12).

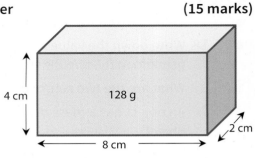

The mass of the block is 128 g.

(a) Calculate the volume of the block.

(b) Calculate the density of the block. Include the unit for your answer.

▲ Figure 25.12

25.30 A student measured the values of the volume for five different pieces of metal. Each piece of metal had its mass value written on it. She presented the data as shown in the table below.   (30 marks)

Mass (g)	20	40	60	80	100
Volume (cm³)	5	10	15	20	20

(a) Draw a graph with values of mass on the *y*-axis and values of volume on the *x*-axis.

(b) **(i)** What do you notice about the shape of the graph?

(ii) Can you explain why the shape of the graph is different to the shape of the graph in sample calculation 5 in this chapter?

(c) **(i)** Divide any mass value by its corresponding volume value. Do you notice any pattern?

(ii) Is there any break in the pattern?

(d) **(i)** What value of volume would be needed for the 100 g mass in order to obtain a straight-line graph with the above data?

(ii) The student measured the volume of a 400 g piece of metal and found it to be 50 cm³. Is this the same metal that was used in obtaining the data table above? Explain your answer.

Log on to **www.edcolearning.ie** for Additional Assessment Questions

PowerPoint summary   Weblinks

MEASURING SPEED AND ACCELERATION

CHAPTER 26

LO: PW1, PW2, PW3

Learning intentions

At the end of this chapter you will be able to:

- ✓ Measure and calculate values of speed
- ✓ Measure and calculate values of velocity
- ✓ Measure and calculate values of acceleration
- ✓ Investigate patterns and relationships.

Keywords

- 🔑 motion
- 🔑 speed
- 🔑 velocity
- 🔑 acceleration
- 🔑 ms^{-1}
- 🔑 $km\ h^{-1}$
- 🔑 distance–time graph
- 🔑 speed–time graph

Motion

Motion, or movement, is happening around us every day. You arrived in school today as a result of motion – by bus, by car, by bicycle or by walking. There are many different methods of transportation, some being faster than others. There are also many different types of motion. For example:

- A DVD spins in a circular manner quite fast
- A guitar string moves when you pluck it – we say that it vibrates
- A car or train moves in linear motion.

▲ Figure 26.1 *A DVD player*

▲ Figure 26.2 *A moving train*

Activity 26.1 What is the relationship between distance and time?

 Equipment needed

Trundle wheel

Chalk

Stopwatch or timer

Safety
- The exercise should be carried out in a safe environment where the person walking or running cannot trip or come to harm.
- The person running or walking should wear appropriate footwear and be in good general health.

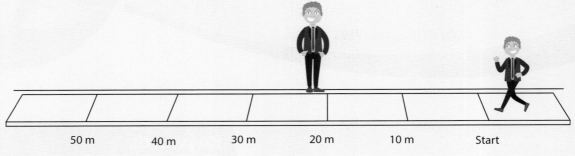

| 50 m | 40 m | 30 m | 20 m | 10 m | Start |

▲ **Figure 26.3**

➡ **Conducting the activity**

1. Outside if possible, mark a starting place with chalk.

2. Using the trundle wheel measure and mark distances of 10 m, 20 m, 30 m, 40 m and 50 m from the starting place.

3. As a student walks quickly from the starting place, measure and record the time on the stopwatch when they pass each of the five marks. Record the times in the table in your Student Activity Book.

4. Repeat the procedure for a student who sprints the same 50 m. Record the times in the table.

? Questions

26.1 Do you notice any pattern between the values of distance and the values of time for the student walking or for the student running?

26.2 Take each pair of values and: **(a)** add, **(b)** subtract, **(c)** multiply and **(d)** divide the values. Do this separately for the walker and the runner.

26.3 Draw two graphs, with distance values on the *y*-axis and time values on the *x*-axis for both the runner and the walker. Graph paper is provided in your Student Activity Book. What do you notice about the graph?

5. Repeat the procedure for a student who changes from walking to running and running to walking as they get to each mark.

? Question

26.4 Do you notice any pattern for this student?

Sample data for this activity

A student picks a starting point and marks six positions at certain distances from the starting point.

She records the time it takes a person walking to reach each of the six positions.

She records the time it takes a person jogging to reach each of the six positions.

The data recorded is given below.

Distance from starting point (m)	10	20	30	40	50	60
Time to reach distance for walker (s)	6	12	18	24	30	36
Time to reach distance for jogger (s)	3	6	9	12	15	18

Draw a graph with distance on the *y*-axis and time on the *x*-axis (a distance–time graph). Use the same set of axes for the walker and the jogger.

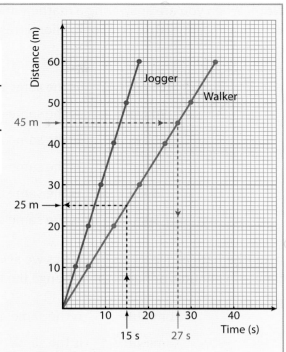

▲ **Figure 26.4**

Notice:

● That the jogger travelled the distance of 60 m in a shorter time

● That the jogger was moving faster than the walker

● That the graph for the jogger is steeper than the graph for the walker (we say that the graph for the jogger has a greater slope than the graph for the walker)

● After 15 s the walker had travelled a distance of 25 m from the starting point

● The walker had travelled a distance of 45 m from the starting point after a time of 27 s.

Objects moving in a straight line

While there are many types of **motion**, in this chapter we examine one type: objects moving in a straight line. We use certain words to describe motion, such as:

● **Speed**   ● **Velocity**   ● **Acceleration**.

We will look at what these mean in the following sections.

We have to be very careful with the units for motion because not everyone uses the SI units, although that is what we will use here.

Speed

In activity 26.1 you noticed a pattern between the distance travelled by a person and the time to travel this distance.

In the language of mathematics we say: $\text{speed} = \dfrac{\text{distance}}{\text{time}}$

Units for speed

Since $\text{speed} = \dfrac{\text{distance}}{\text{time}}$, units are $\dfrac{\text{unit of distance}}{\text{unit of time}} = \dfrac{\text{metre}}{\text{second}} = \dfrac{\text{m}}{\text{s}}$

Instead of writing $\dfrac{\text{m}}{\text{s}}$ we usually use m/s or ms^{-1}.

Note: When you are answering a mathematical question about speed you might be given the distance in centimetres (cm) or in kilometres (km). You must always change the distance value to metres.

Remember:

100 cm	is the same as	1 m
70 cm	is the same as	0.7 m
16 cm	is the same as	0.16 m
1 km	is the same as	1000 m
4 km	is the same as	4000 m
7.5 km	is the same as	7500 m

In mathematical questions in physics we always use seconds for values of time. If the value for time is in minutes or hours then change the time value to seconds.

Remember:

1 minute	is the same as	60 s
5 minutes	is the same as	$60 \times 5 = 300$ s
1 hour	is the same as	$60 \times 60 = 3600$ s

Did you know?

- In science we measure speed in metres per second (**ms⁻¹**).
- Most European countries measure the speed of cars in kilometres per hour (kph) or **km h⁻¹**.
- In the United Kingdom the speed of cars is measured in miles per hour (mph).
- Scientist Albert Einstein said that nothing can travel faster than the speed of light.

Calculating speed

Helpful hint: look at the triangle:

Where D = distance

S = speed

T = time

$$\frac{D}{S \times T}$$

Place your finger over the quantity you are measuring in the triangle above and the instruction for your calculation is right in front of you.

- **To calculate speed:** $\text{speed} = \dfrac{\text{distance}}{\text{time}}$
- **To calculate time:** $\text{time} = \dfrac{\text{distance}}{\text{speed}}$
- **To calculate distance:** $\text{distance} = \text{speed} \times \text{time}$

Sample calculation 1

Calculate the speed of a car that travels 400 m in a time of 10 s.

Answer:

$$\text{speed} = \frac{\text{distance}}{\text{time}} = \frac{400 \text{ m}}{10 \text{ s}} = 40 \text{ ms}^{-1}$$

Sample calculation 2

Calculate the speed of a train that travels a distance of 1.8 km in a time of 1 minute.

Answer:

$$\text{speed} = \frac{\text{distance}}{\text{time}} = \frac{1.8 \text{ km}}{1 \text{ min}} = \frac{1800 \text{ m}}{60 \text{ s}} = 30 \text{ ms}^{-1}$$

Sample calculation 3

How long does it take a car travelling at a speed of 40 ms^{-1} to travel a distance of 720 m?

Answer:

Be careful with a question that starts with the words 'how long' because the word 'long' can refer to both distance and time. In this question you are being asked about time.

$$\text{time} = \frac{\text{distance}}{\text{speed}} = \frac{720 \text{ m}}{40 \text{ ms}^{-1}} = 18 \text{ s}$$

Sample calculation 4

Calculate the distance travelled by a person running at a speed of 5 ms^{-1} for 2 hours.

Answer:

$$
\begin{aligned}
\text{distance} &= \text{speed} \times \text{time} \\
&= 5 \times 2 \times 60 \times 60 \\
&= 36\,000 \text{ m}
\end{aligned}
$$

Sample calculation 5

The graph in Figure 26.5 represents the distance a jogger is from a chosen starting point.

(a) Calculate the average speed of the jogger as he moved between points A and B.
(b) Calculate the average speed of the jogger as he moved between points C and D.
(c) Do you notice any connection between the speed values and the slope of the graph between points A and B and between points C and D?
(d) What is the jogger doing between points B and C?
(e) What is happening between points D and E?

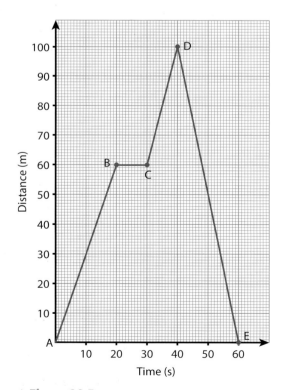

▲ Figure 26.5

Answer:

(a) Average speed = $\dfrac{\text{distance}}{\text{time}} = \dfrac{60\text{ m}}{20\text{ s}} = 3\text{ ms}^{-1}$

(b) Average speed = $\dfrac{\text{distance}}{\text{time}} = \dfrac{40\text{ m}}{10\text{ s}} = 4\text{ ms}^{-1}$

(c) Between A and B the graph rises by 60 m in 20 s, an average rise of 3 m in 1 s.

Between C and D the graph rises by 40 m in 10 s, an average rise of 4 m in 1 s.

It would appear that a steeper or **greater slope means a larger value of speed**.

(d) Between points B and C the jogger is not moving. For a time interval of 10 seconds he stays at a distance of 60 m from the chosen starting point.

(e) Between points D and E the distance from the chosen starting point is being reduced, i.e. the jogger is returning to the starting point.

Did you know?

Words don't always mean the same in science as they do in general conversation. When talking normally with friends we often use words that can have more than one meaning. For example, the word 'cool' does not always refer to the fact that something is cold. But in science we need to be very precise with the meaning of words.

Velocity

The words 'speed' and 'velocity' have similar meanings but there is a very important difference between them. **The velocity of an object tells you the speed at which it is travelling and the direction in which it is travelling.** The direction of a moving object is usually given using points of the compass, for example: north, south, east or west.

▲ Figure 26.6 *Skydivers – after falling for a short time, skydivers reach a 'terminal velocity'*

Unit for velocity

The unit we use for velocity is the same as the unit we use for **speed: m/s or ms⁻¹**.

Acceleration

In normal conversation many people would use the word 'acceleration' to refer to an object that is increasing its speed, i.e. going faster. In science this is not fully correct.

> **? Question**
>
> **26.5** Using the internet, research the term 'terminal velocity' as it applies to:
>
> **(a)** Rain drops   **(b)** Hailstones.
>
> **Present your findings to the class.**

Acceleration is about the rate of change in velocity. Remember that a change can be an increase or a decrease. Acceleration could refer to a car slowing down. In this case we would have a negative acceleration, or a deceleration.

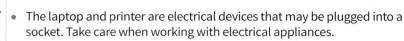

Activity 26.2 How can you identify acceleration?

Equipment needed

Laptop with data logging software installed

Printer

Speed sensor

Trolley

Motion track

Protractor

Set of books

> **Safety**
> • The laptop and printer are electrical devices that may be plugged into a socket. Take care when working with electrical appliances.
> • Take care not to drop heavy equipment such as the trolley and the track.

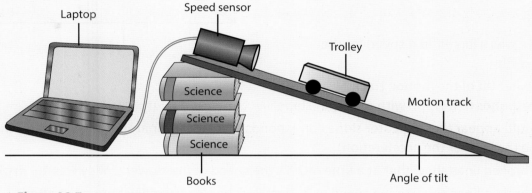

▲ Figure 26.7

Conducting the activity

1. Arrange the motion track so it is tilted at an angle of 20° above the horizontal. Books can be used to tilt the track.
2. Release the trolley from rest at the top of the track.
3. Using the speed sensor connected to the laptop, record the speed of the trolley as it rolls down the tilted track. The speed will increase as it rolls down the track.
4. On the laptop display a graph of speed on the *y*-axis and time on the *x*-axis.
5. Print a copy of this graph. Write on it the angle of tilt that was used.
6. Repeat the above steps for an angle of tilt of 30°.

? Questions

26.6 Compare the two graphs. Have they the same shape? How do they differ?

26.7 Which angle of tilt caused the greater acceleration?

Sample data for this activity

A student recorded values of speed and time for a trolley rolling down a motion track using data logging equipment. The motion track was tilted at two different angles, one tilt being larger than the other.

PHYSICAL WORLD

The following data was recorded.

Time (s)	1	2	3	4	5
Speed for smaller tilt (ms⁻¹)	0.6	1.2	1.8	2.4	3.0
Speed for larger tilt (ms⁻¹)	0.9	1.8	2.7	3.6	4.5

Draw a graph with speed values on the *y*-axis and time values on the *x*-axis (a speed–time graph). Draw both graphs on the same set of axes.

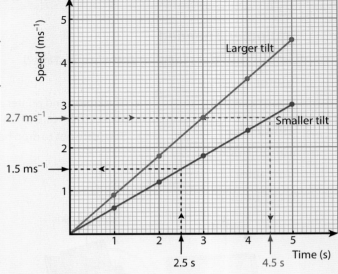

▲ Figure 26.8

Notice:

- There was a larger final speed for the larger tilt
- A greater tilt of the motion track corresponds to a graph with a steeper slope
- It would appear that a greater slope corresponds to a greater final speed (the greater the slope the greater the acceleration)
- The broken lines show that at a time of 2.5 s the speed of the slower trolley was 1.5 ms⁻¹
- The broken lines show that a speed of 2.7 ms⁻¹ for the slower trolley happened after 4.5 s.

You will need to know this formula for acceleration:

$$\text{acceleration} = \frac{\text{final speed} - \text{first speed}}{\text{time taken for the change in speed}}$$

Unit for acceleration

The unit we use for acceleration is ms⁻¹ divided by the second.

This can be written two ways: m/s² or ms⁻².

Sample calculation 6

A car is moving at a speed of 4 ms⁻¹. After 12 s it is moving at a speed of 28 ms⁻¹. Calculate the acceleration of the car.

Answer:

$$\text{acceleration} = \frac{\text{final speed} - \text{first speed}}{\text{time taken for the change in speed}}$$

$$= \frac{28 - 4}{12}$$

$$= \frac{24}{12}$$

$$= 2 \text{ ms}^{-2}$$

Sample calculation 7

A train starts from rest in a station and after 2 minutes it is moving at a speed of 90 ms⁻¹. Calculate the acceleration of this train.

Answer:

The words 'from rest' mean that the first speed of the train was zero. Remember to change the minutes to seconds.

$$\text{acceleration} = \frac{\text{final speed} - \text{first speed}}{\text{time taken for the change in speed}}$$

$$= \frac{90 - 0}{2 \times 60}$$

$$= \frac{90}{120} = 0.75 \text{ ms}^{-2}$$

Sample calculation 8

A car was travelling at a speed of 50 ms⁻¹. After a time of 14 seconds the speed of the car had changed to 8 ms⁻¹. Calculate the acceleration.

Answer:

$$\text{acceleration} = \frac{\text{final speed} - \text{first speed}}{\text{time taken for the change in speed}}$$

$$= \frac{8 - 50}{14}$$

$$= \frac{-42}{14}$$

$$= -3 \text{ ms}^{-2}$$

This could be considered as a deceleration.

Ethics

? Question

26.8 Split into small groups and discuss the following. When the discussion is finished, select one person from your group to present the ideas from the discussion to the whole class.

(a) Reducing the speed limits on roads is the most effective way of avoiding accidents.

(b) Reducing speed limits on motorways near large cities reduces carbon dioxide emissions from cars.

(c) In the last 30 years the demand for cheap air travel has been greater than the demand for faster air travel.

Summary questions

● **26.9** What is the meaning of speed?

● **26.10** What units are used for speed?

⚹ **26.11** Convert the following to metres:

(a) 17 cm

(b) 9 cm

(c) 4 km

(d) 7.2 km

⚹ **26.12** Convert the following to seconds:

(a) 6 minutes

(b) 4 hours

(c) 1 day

⚹ **26.13** Calculate the speed of a car that travels a distance of 450 m in a time of 90 s.

⚹ **26.14** Calculate the speed of a car that travels a distance of 2.4 km in 2 minutes.

⚹ **26.15** Calculate the time taken for a car to travel 50 m if the speed of the car is 20 ms⁻¹.

⚹ **26.16** Calculate the distance travelled by a train in 50 s if it has a speed of 70 ms⁻¹.

⚛ **26.17** When a car is first observed it has a speed of 20 ms⁻¹. After a time of 10 s it is observed that the speed is 50 ms⁻¹. Calculate the acceleration of this car.

⚛ **26.18** A car starts from rest and after a time of 20 s it has a speed of 40 ms⁻¹. Calculate the acceleration of this car.

⚛ **26.19** When a car is first observed it has a speed of 30 ms⁻¹. After a time of 6 s the speed has been reduced to 12 ms⁻¹. Calculate the value of the deceleration.

Assessment questions

26.20 Question from Junior Cycle Science exam paper (15 marks)

The graph below represents the journey of a cyclist.

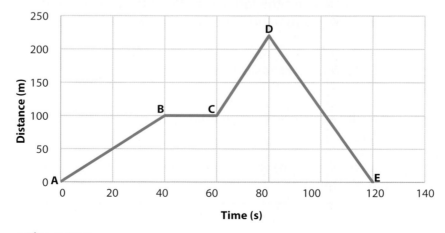

▲ Figure 26.9

Answer the questions on the following page.

(a) Name an instrument that could be used to measure the time taken for the journey.

(b) Calculate the average speed of the cyclist as he travelled from point **A** to point **B**.

(c) Describe the cyclist's motion between points **B** and **C** of his journey.

(d) The cyclist's speed as he travelled from point **A** to point **B** was less than his speed as he travelled from point **C** to point **D**. What evidence is there in the graph to support this?

(e) Describe what the cyclist did at point **D**.

26.21 The graph below represents the motion of a cyclist.   **(30 marks)**

Make sure to carefully notice the labels on the y-axis, i.e. speed

(a) Calculate the acceleration between points A and B.

(b) Calculate the acceleration between points C and D.

(c) Calculate the deceleration between points D and E.

(d) What is the value of the acceleration between points B and C?

What is implied by this value of the acceleration?

(e) Draw a graph to represent the following information:

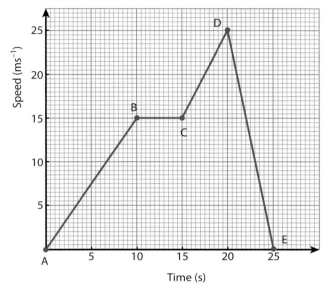

▲ **Figure 26.10**

'A cyclist starts from rest at a point A. She accelerates for 15 s until a speed of 20 ms⁻¹ is reached. She travels at this same speed for 10 more seconds. She applies the brakes and comes to a stop in the next 5 s.'

CHAPTER 27

FORCE, WORK, POWER AND PRESSURE

LO: PW2, PW3

Learning intentions

At the end of this chapter you will be able to:

✓ Explain force

✓ List some examples of forces

✓ Explain the relationship between the force you put on a spring and the extension of the spring caused by the force

✓ Explain a moment of a force

✓ Explain levers and what they are used for

✓ Explain the words 'work', 'power' and 'pressure'

✓ Carry out simple calculations for work, power and pressure.

Keywords

🔑 force
🔑 friction
🔑 weight
🔑 mass
🔑 extension
🔑 directly proportional
🔑 moment of a force
🔑 lever
🔑 pressure
🔑 work
🔑 joule
🔑 power
🔑 watt

? Question

27.1 What is the meaning of force? Split into groups and take 5 minutes to agree on the meaning of the word 'force'.

What is force?

Remember our need to be very precise with the meaning of words. A famous scientist, Isaac Newton (1643–1727), wrote a very exact meaning of **force**. If we take Newton's ideas and use simple and modern English we could say:

● **A force can cause a stationary object to move**

● **A force can cause a moving object to move more quickly, to move more slowly or to change the direction in which it is moving.**

▲ Figure 27.1 *Isaac Newton (1643–1727)*

Animated Scientist Biography

Watch an *Exploring Science* animation to find out more about Newton and his ideas.

Unit of force

The unit used to measure force is the newton and the symbol is N.

▲ Figure 27.2 *The magnetic force attracts the iron paper clips*

▲ Figure 27.3 *There is friction between a car's tyres and the road – this is what stops the car from skidding and helps it to stop when brakes are applied*

Different types of force and their effects

(?) Question

27.2 Use the internet to research different types of forces. Present your findings in the form of a poster.

In particular, pay attention to:

(a) The force of gravity: its value on different planets, its role in the formation of the early universe

(b) Magnetic force: its everyday uses and some possible uses in the area of medicine

(c) Electric force: clothes sticking together in a tumble dryer, and lightning

(d) Force of **friction**: the benefits of friction and friction as a nuisance

(e) Contact and non-contact forces.

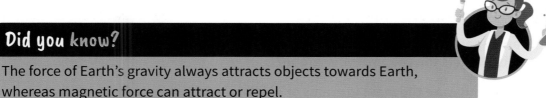

Did you know?

The force of Earth's gravity always attracts objects towards Earth, whereas magnetic force can attract or repel.

Weight and mass

In the physical world the words '**weight**' and '**mass**' have very different meanings. These are summarised in Table 27.1.

Table 27.1 The differences between weight and mass

Weight	Mass
…is the force pulling an object towards the centre of the Earth.	…is the amount of matter in an object.
…is measured in newtons.	…is measured in grams or kilograms.
…has a direction, i.e. is a force that acts towards Earth.	…does not have a direction.
…can change. Weight gets smaller as you rise upwards from ground level.	…does not change. The mass of an object remains constant.

Converting mass to weight

Activity 27.1 How can we see the relationship between weight and mass?

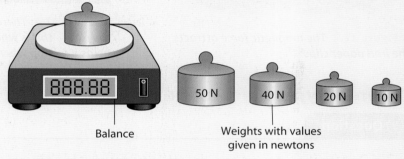

Equipment needed

Electronic balance to measure mass

Set of five different brass weights where the weights are given in newtons

Graph paper

888.88

Balance

50 N 40 N 20 N 10 N

Weights with values given in newtons

▲ Figure 27.4

⚠ Safety
* Take care not to drop the weights on the floor as they could cause injury or result in someone tripping.

➡ Conducting the activity

1. In the table provided in your Student Activity Book write down the weights given in newtons of the five different brass weights.

2. For each one find the mass and record the mass value beside the weight value.

⑦ Questions

27.3 What pattern do you notice between the two sets of values?

27.4 Draw a graph with the weight values on the *y*-axis and the mass values on the *x*-axis. What is the shape of your graph?

27.5 Did you measure the mass in grams or in kilograms? Did it make any difference to the relationship between weight and mass?

There is a very simple formula to convert mass to weight:

$$\text{weight (in newtons)} = \text{mass (in kilograms)} \times 10$$

Sample calculation 1

What is the weight of an object of mass 6.5 kg?

Answer:

weight = mass × 10

weight = 6.5 × 10

weight = 65 N

Sample calculation 2

Calculate the weight of an object of mass 200 g.

Answer:

Remember to change the unit of mass to the kilogram.

200 g = 0.2 kg

weight = mass × 10

weight = 0.2 × 10

weight = 2 N

The value of weight can change

Earth pulls objects towards it. **This pulling force is called weight.** The size of the pulling force depends on how near the object is to the surface of Earth at sea level.

- As objects rise above ground level the pulling force of Earth decreases. The weight of the object decreases. The weight of an object on the top of Mount Everest is smaller than the weight at sea level.

- The International Space Station is 400 km above the surface of Earth. Objects would have a smaller weight at this height.

- Since the Moon is smaller than Earth, the gravity force is smaller on the Moon. An object would have a weight six times smaller on the Moon compared to Earth.

Did you know?

In pictures of astronauts in the International Space Station you will see them floating around. You might think that they have no weight at all. However, there is a gravity force at 400 km above Earth.

The International Space Station moves in such a way that it creates a situation of zero gravity. Carry on to do Leaving Certificate physics and you will find out why!

▲ Figure 27.5 *Astronaut floating inside the International Space Station*

 **Activity 27.2** **What is the relationship between the extension of a spring and the applied force?**

 Activity video

 Safety
- Take care handling the weights so that you don't drop them.

Equipment needed

Spring

Light holder for weights

Weights measured in newtons

Metre stick

➡ Conducting the activity

1. Hang a spring from a clamp connected to a retort stand as shown in Figure 27.6.
2. Connect a light holder for weights to the end of the spring. The holder should have a pointer on one side.
3. Arrange a metre stick so that the pointer is directly opposite the zero on the metre stick.
4. Place a known weight on the holder.
5. Note and record in the table in your Student Activity Book both the value of the weight and the **extension** of the spring.

   Measure and note how far the pointer moved along the metre stick. This is the value of the extension. For example, when the first weight is added to the holder the pointer might move to the 4 cm mark: then the extension is 4 cm.
6. Place another weight on the holder with the first.
7. Note and record the value of the two weights and the extension of the spring.
8. Continue this procedure for several weights. Each time note and record the total weight and the extension.

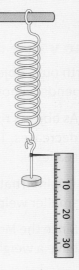

▲ Figure 27.6

The pattern and relationship

Draw a graph to illustrate your result using the graph paper in your Student Activity Book.

- Using the data you recorded, plot a graph with weight on the *x*-axis. Remember that weight is a force and is measured in newtons.
- Plot the values of extension on the *y*-axis. Extension is measured in centimetres.
- Examine the plotted points on the graph paper. You will notice that they form a straight line passing through the origin.

Because the points give a straight line through the origin it can be concluded that:

The extension of an elastic body (a spring) is directly proportional to the force causing the extension.

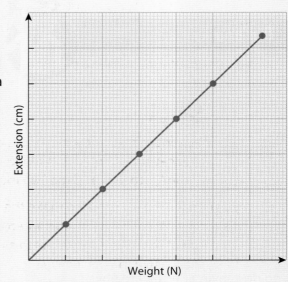

▲ Figure 27.7 *Extension plotted against weight*

Question

27.6 Find out what connection the scientist Robert Hooke (1635–1703) has to activity 27.2.

Sample calculation 3

David performed an experiment to investigate the relationship between the extension of a spring and the force (weight) that caused the extension. He recorded the following data:

Force (N)	3	6	9	12	15	18
Extension (cm)	2	4	6	8	10	10.2

Plot a graph on graph paper with force (weight) on the *x*-axis and extension on the *y*-axis. From the graph:

(a) Calculate the extension that a force of 4 N would cause

(b) Calculate the force needed to cause an extension of 7 cm.

Answer:

Graph:

(a) Go to 4 N on the *x*-axis. Draw a line vertically upwards from 4 N to the graph. Now move across horizontally to the *y*-axis. The extension value is approximately 2.6 cm.

(b) Go to 7 cm on the *y*-axis. Draw a line horizontally across to the graph. Now draw a line vertically down to the *x*-axis. The force value is approximately 10.5 N.

In this sample calculation the graph is not straight at the top. The spring has been stretched too far. This is because the spring has gone beyond its elastic limit.

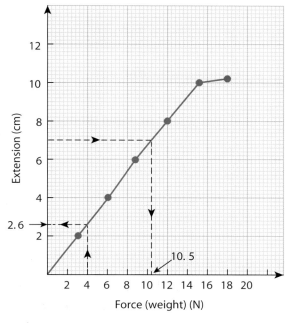

▲ **Figure 27.8** *Extension plotted against force*

What is the moment of a force?

Imagine a footballer taking a free kick. This is a good example of a force causing an object to move. The force was supplied by the footballer and the ball moved.

However, a good footballer can also make the ball spin as it moves through the air. Sometimes when a force is applied to an object the object will move in a circular manner. In Figure 27.10 a force is applied to a child's windmill. Force will make the plastic windmill spin around in a circular manner.

◀ **Figure 27.9** *Kicking a football may cause the ball to move forward and to spin*

If the force caused the blades to spin around several times, we would say that the force had a large turning effect. The turning effect is the spinning of the blades of the windmill. In scientific language we would say that the force had a large moment, so **moment of a force** simply refers to a force causing something to spin.

Did you know?

The moment of a force tells us how much spin or circular motion a force can cause.

▲ Figure 27.10 *The blades on a child's windmill spin round*

✏ Activity 27.3 How can we demonstrate the moment of a force?

 Equipment needed

An open classroom or cupboard door

Masking tape or some other removable marker

 Safety

- While standing around the classroom pay attention to your teacher's instructions and avoid bumping into somebody or tripping over school bags.
- Avoid an excessive force when pushing the door with your finger.
- Keep fingers away from the frame of the door in case the door slams shut causing injury to you or others.

➡ **Conducting the activity**

1. Using masking tape, mark positions 20 cm, 40 cm, 60 cm and 80 cm away from the hinge on the door.
2. With the door open push it at the 20 cm position using your finger. You are trying to close the door.
3. Repeat this step using the same finger at the other three positions you marked.
4. Record in words what force you think you needed to use to close the door. Write your descriptions in the table in your Student Activity Book.

? Questions

27.7 Explain the difference in the force needed to close the door in each of the four cases.

27.8 Outline the relationship between the force needed and the distance from the hinge.

27.9 Where on a door do you normally find the handle? Explain why.

> **27.10** Why did you use the same finger each time you pushed the door?
>
> **27.11** How could you measure the value of the force? (Hint: pull the door open with a newton balance.)

Levers

One of the main reasons that we study the moment of a force is to help us understand the **lever. A lever is any rigid body that is free to move about a fixed point** (in Figure 27.12 the fixed point is shown by the blue triangle and the lever is the bar). We'll start by looking at what levers can do.

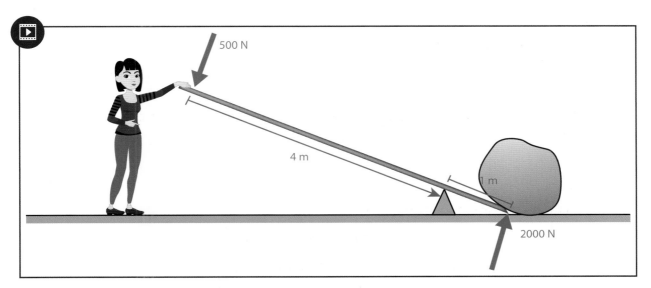

▲ **Figure 27.12** *The student can increase her strength by a factor of four*

In Figure 27.12 the student pushes down on the bar with a force of 500 N. However, the force on the large rock is 2000 N (see the explanation below). The student's force of 500 N on the 4 m length of bar is the same as the upward force of 2000 N on the rock. What happened here was:

smaller force × larger distance = larger force × smaller distance

$$500 \text{ N} \times 4 \text{ m} = 2000 \text{ N} \times 1 \text{ m}$$

$$2000 \text{ Nm} = 2000 \text{ Nm}$$

The student used her intelligence and knowledge to increase the effectiveness of her strength.

Sample calculation 4

In relation to the situation illustrated in Figure 27.12, answer the following questions.

(a) If the student applied a force of 700 N on the bar, calculate the force applied to the large rock.

(b) If the student wants to apply a force of 6000 N to the large rock, what force must she apply to the bar?

(c) If the 4 m length of bar were only 2 m long and the other 1 m length were changed to 80 cm, what force would be applied to the rock? The total length of the bar would now be 2 m and 80 cm long and the force applied to the bar would remain at 500 N.

Answer:

(a) force × distance to fixed point = force × distance from fixed point

$700 \times 4 = F \times 1$

$2800 \text{ N} = F$

(b) force × distance to fixed point = force × distance from fixed point

$F \times 4 = 6000 \times 1$

$4 F = 6000$

$F = 1500 \text{ N}$

(c) force × distance to fixed point = force × distance from fixed point

$500 \times 2 = F \times 0.8$

$1000 = 0.8 F$

$1250 \text{ N} = F$

Remember to change the 80 cm to m. The unit for distance must be the same on both sides of the equation!

Everyday use of a lever

Very few people could lift a car 15 cm off the ground to change a wheel if one of the tyres were flat.

However, with the correct lever, called a jack, this can easily be done.

What we see here is the application of a law of physics to assist people in everyday life.

You could consider a lever as a device to increase the effectiveness of a force. In many ways it is like a force amplifier.

▲ **Figure 27.13** *A heavy car can easily be raised using a lever*

? Questions

27.12 Use the internet to find six examples of the use of levers.

27.13 Within your group take 10 minutes to decide on the meaning of the words 'pressure, 'work' and 'power'. Make a note of your answers and see how they compare to the information that follows in this chapter.

What does pressure mean?

Pressure is a word that you meet regularly in normal conversation. You may be under pressure to finish homework. In sport you may put pressure on an opposing team. However, in science we are looking for the exact scientific meaning of pressure.

▲ Figure 27.14 *The weight of a brick will cause a force*

If you place a solid brick on a table the brick will put a force on the table. The weight of the brick is causing the force. The brick is also exerting a pressure on the part of the table it is touching. So how do we calculate this pressure?

Calculating pressure

? Question

27.14 **In your group, take 10 minutes to read and discuss the following.**

A group of students was testing a new machine for measuring pressure. Five bricks of different weights were placed on a horizontal surface. The areas of contact between the bricks and the horizontal surface were recorded. The following table has the data gathered. The students did not know the units for pressure.

Weight of a brick (N)	Area of contact (cm³)	Pressure
25	50	0.5
30	60	0.5
35	70	0.5
40	80	0.5
45	90	0.7

(a) What pattern do you notice in the data above?

(b) What might be the cause of any break in the pattern?

(c) From the data, work out a mathematical rule that would allow you to calculate the pressure value.

Does your mathematical rule agree with the following formula for calculating pressure?

$$\text{pressure} = \frac{\text{force}}{\text{area}}$$

Use the formula in this way:

1. First calculate the force that the brick puts on the table.

2. Then calculate the area of the brick in contact with the table.

3. Now divide the force by the area to find the pressure.

Units for pressure

Any of the following units may be used to measure pressure:

- N/cm² or N cm⁻²
- N/m² or N m⁻²
- Pascal (Pa), which is another way of saying N/m².

The unit you choose for measuring the pressure will depend on the information given.

Sample calculation 5

A force of 200 N acts on an area of 25 m². Calculate the pressure.

Answer:

$$\text{pressure} = \frac{\text{force}}{\text{area}} = \frac{200 \text{ N}}{25 \text{ m}^2} = 8 \text{ N m}^{-2}$$

Sample calculation 6

(a) Calculate the pressure on the ground due to a person of weight 500 N if they can balance themselves on the heel of a stiletto shoe. The area of the heel of the shoe is 1 cm².

(b) Calculate the pressure on the ground due to an elephant of weight 50 000 N. The elephant is balanced on one foot. The area of the elephant's foot is 400 cm².

▲ Figure 27.15 *How much pressure is there on a stiletto heel?*

Answer:

(a) $\text{pressure} = \dfrac{\text{force}}{\text{area}} = \dfrac{500 \text{ N}}{1 \text{ cm}^2} = 500 \text{ N/cm}^2$

(b) $\text{pressure} = \dfrac{\text{force}}{\text{area}} = \dfrac{50\ 000 \text{ N}}{400 \text{ cm}^2} = 125 \text{ N/cm}^2$

It may seem strange that the pressure of the person is four times greater than the pressure of the elephant. However, this is due to the very small area of the stiletto heel.

Did you know?

Stiletto heels can put dents in wooden floors, much to the annoyance of homeowners.

Changing pressure and the importance of understanding pressure

? Questions

27.15 Use the internet to research pressure using the following pointers. Present your findings as a slide presentation. Find out:

(a) How to increase and decrease values of pressure.

(b) How pressure changes as you go deeper in water and how this affects the design of a dam.

(c) Why an airplane is pressurised when flying at a high altitude.

(d) About values of pressure in space and the design of spacesuits.

27.16 Describe briefly how you would show that pressure increases with depth in a liquid.

What is the meaning of 'work'?

? Question

27.17 In your group take 10 minutes to read and discuss the following.

The data in the table below is part of a report prepared by a group of students.

Force (N)	Distance (m)	Work (J)
20	5	100
17.5	10	175
12	4	48
25	5	125
11	2.4	26.4

(a) What pattern do you notice in the data above?

(b) From the data, work out a mathematical rule that would allow you to calculate the work value.

Does your mathematical rule agree with the following formula for calculating work?

work = force × distance

Work is done if a force results in an object moving a distance. If you apply a force to an object and there is no movement, no work is done. If you push the wall of a house, the wall will not move. Therefore, your pushing force did no work on the wall of the house.

▲ **Figure 27.16** *The pushing force on a trolley is doing work*

▲ **Figure 27.17** *No work is done when pushing against a wall*

Unit of work

The unit we use to measure work is the joule, and the symbol is J.

Earlier in the chapter we saw that force is measured in newtons. You will remember that distance is measured in metres. Using the above meaning of work you could say that:

1 joule = 1 newton × 1 metre

1 J = 1 Nm

Animated Scientist Biography

Watch an Exploring Science animation to find out more about the scientist James Prescott Joule and his experiments.

▶ Figure 27.18 *James Prescott*

Sample calculation 7

A force of 10 N is being used to move an object a distance of 20 m. Calculate the work done.

Answer:

work = force × distance

= 10 N × 20 m

= 200 J

Sample calculation 8

Calculate the work done when a force of 15 N moves an object a distance of 40 cm.

Answer:

When calculating the work done it is important that the distance is measured in metres. In this question we change 40 cm to 0.4 m.

work = force × distance

= 15 N × 0.4 m

= 6 J

What is the meaning of 'power'?

When work is being done we often need to know how fast this happens. This is the idea of **power**.

Power is the rate at which work is done. The amount of work done in one second is the power.

$$\text{power} = \frac{\text{work done}}{\text{time taken}}$$

▲ Figure 27.19 *The watt unit of measurement for power was named after Scottish engineer James Watt*

⑦ Question

27.18 In your group take 10 minutes to read and discuss the following.

A student was sitting an exam and was presented with the following table of data.

Work done (J)	Time taken (s)	Power (W)
100	5	20
450	9	50
1000	125	8
625	25	25
196	10	19.6

(a) What pattern do you notice in the data above?

(b) What might be the cause of any break in the pattern?

(c) From the data, work out a mathematical rule that would allow you to calculate the power value.

Does your mathematical rule agree with the following formula for calculating power?

$$\text{power} = \frac{w}{t}$$

Unit for power

The unit we use to measure power is the **watt**, and the symbol is W.

Earlier in the chapter we saw that work is measured in joules. You will remember that time is measured in seconds. Using the above meaning of power you could say that:

$$1 \text{ watt} = \frac{1 \text{ joule}}{1 \text{ second}}$$

You will often see the unit kilowatt: 1 kW = 1000 W.

Sample calculation 9

A force of 10 N is being used to move an object a distance of 20 m in a time of 5 seconds.

Calculate:

(a) The work done

(b) The value of average power.

Answer:

(a) work done = force × distance

$$= 10 \text{ N} \times 20 \text{ m}$$

$$= 200 \text{ J}$$

(b) $\text{power} = \dfrac{\text{work}}{\text{time}}$

$$= \frac{200 \text{ J}}{5 \text{ s}}$$

$$= 40 \text{ W}$$

Summary questions

● 27.19 What are three things that a force can do?

● 27.20 What is the unit of force?

● 27.21 What are four different types of force?

● 27.22 Give a practical use of each of the four different forces that you named in question 27.21.

● 27.23 What causes friction between two surfaces?

● 27.24 List three examples of where friction is a useful force in everyday life.

● 27.25 List three examples of where friction is a nuisance in everyday life.

● 27.26 Lubricants are used to reduce friction. Give three examples of the use of lubricants.

● 27.27 What is pressure?

● 27.28 Give three different units for pressure.

● 27.29 Calculate the pressure when a force of 400 N acts on an area of 8 m^2.

● 27.30 What is the unit for work?

● 27.31 What is the unit for power?

● 27.32 Explain the difference between mass and weight.

● 27.33 What is the unit for weight?

● 27.34 What is the unit for mass?

● 27.35 Convert the following mass values to weight:

(a) 4.5 kg (b) 900 g (c) 70 g

● 27.36 Convert the following to mass values:

(a) 270 N (b) 16 N

● 27.37 A block has a weight of 12 N. Explain how the value of this weight could change even though the mass would remain the same.

● 27.38 Explain why the force of gravity is smaller on the Moon than on Earth.

● 27.39 An elephant can walk on a sandy beach quite easily. A cyclist would find it difficult to cycle on a sandy beach. Explain why.

● 27.40 Explain how we calculate the value of work done.

● 27.41 Calculate the work done when a force of 15 N moves an object 12 m.

● 27.42 Calculate the work done when a force of 90 N moves an object 80 cm.

● 27.43 Calculate the power when a force of 50 N moves an object 5 m in 10 seconds.

● 27.44 Erin performed an activity to investigate the relationship between the extension of a spring and the force that caused the extension. She recorded the following data.

Force (N)	2	4	6	8	10	12
Extension (cm)	1.5	3	4.5	6	7.5	9

Plot a graph on graph paper with force on the *x*-axis and extension on the *y*-axis. From the graph:

(a) Calculate the extension that a force of 7 N would cause

(b) Calculate the force needed to cause an extension of 4 cm.

Assessment questions

27.45 To calculate pressure we use the formula: **(15 marks)**

$$pressure = \frac{force}{area}$$

(a) Which of the following units could be used for pressure (there are two correct answers)?

Pascal   Newton   N cm^{-2} N m   Ohm

(b)

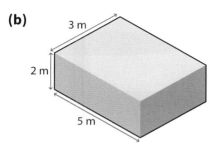

▲ Figure 27.20

The rectangular block has six sides.

   (i) Calculate the area of the side with the maximum surface area.

   (ii) Calculate the area of the side with the minimum surface area.

(c) The block has a weight of 60 000 N and it rests on a piece of ground that is smooth and horizontal. Explain why the pressure the block puts on the ground depends on which side is touching the ground.

(d) **(i)** Calculate the maximum pressure the block can put on the ground.

   (ii) Calculate the minimum pressure the block can put on the ground.

27.46 (a) The person shown in Figure 27.21 is pushing a trolley. Explain why he is doing work. **(30 marks)**

(b) The person applies a force of 200 N to the trolley as it moves a distance of 6 m in 4 s.

   (i) Calculate the work done by the person on the trolley.

   (ii) Calculate the power in this situation.

▲ Figure 27.21

(c) The person applies a 250 N force to the trolley and the work done is 200 J and the power in this situation is 250 W.

   (i) How far was the trolley moved?   **(ii)** How much time did this activity take?

(d) The four wheels on the trolley are identical and you can assume the area of contact between a wheel and the ground is 1 cm^2. The mass of the trolley and its contents is 20 kg and the trolley is stationary.

Calculate the pressure the trolley exerts on the ground.

(Hint: weight and mass are different.)

 Log on to **www.edcolearning.ie** for Additional Assessment Questions

CHAPTER 28

ENERGY

LO: PW2, PW6, PW7, PW8

What does 'energy' mean in science?

'**Energy**' is a word you probably use quite often in your everyday conversation. In science, it has a precise meaning, and that is:

Energy is the ability to do work.

Unit used for energy

The unit we use to measure energy is the joule (J), the same unit as used for work.

Work involves moving an object. Since energy is the ability to do work, then energy is the ability to make things move.

▲ Figure 28.1 *These basketball players are using energy*

Forms of energy

There are many different forms of energy. These include:

- **Kinetic energy:** energy that a body has because it is moving – for example a ball rolling along the ground

- **Potential energy:** energy that a body has because of its position relative to other bodies – for example a stationary object raised above ground level; changing the shape of an object can also involve potential energy – for example when you bend a ruler

- **Sound energy:** energy that is produced by a vibration – for example the sound produced by a guitar string vibrating after it is plucked

- **Heat energy:** energy that travels between a hot object and a cool object – for example when a spoon is placed in hot tea, heat travels from the tea to your fingers along the spoon

- **Chemical energy:** energy that is stored in food is a good example of chemical energy

- **Electrical energy:** energy that comes from the flow of electric charge – for example, electric current flowing along a copper wire

- **Solar energy:** energy that comes from the Sun

- **Nuclear energy:** energy produced from nuclear reactions – for example nuclear fission or nuclear fusion.

PHYSICAL WORLD

> **? Question**
>
> 28.1 By researching on the internet, prepare a short presentation on six different forms of energy. Your presentation might include:
>
> - A photograph (be guided by some of the photographs from this chapter)
>
> - A sentence that will explain what each form of energy is
>
> - Two examples of each form of energy.

Sample presentation:

▲ Figure 28.2 *Both the wave and the surfer have kinetic energy*

Kinetic energy:

Moving objects have kinetic energy

Examples:

- A car travelling along a road has kinetic energy.

- Waves crashing onto a beach have kinetic energy.

▲ Figure 28.3 *Energy in a spring*

▲ Figure 28.4 *A vibrating guitar string*

▲ Figure 28.5 *Heat energy, which can be detected by an alcohol thermometer*

▲ Figure 28.6 *Batteries store chemical energy*

▲ Figure 28.7 *An electric car uses electrical energy to make it run*

▲ Figure 28.8 *A nuclear power station*

> **?** **Question**
>
> **28.2** Outline the benefits and disadvantages of getting energy from:
>
> **(a)** Nuclear fission
>
> **(b)** Nuclear fusion.

The principle of conservation of energy

The amazing thing about energy is that it never goes away. Energy does not get used up. Energy changes from one form to another form. For example:

- The chemical energy stored in a battery can change to the sound energy you hear from your mobile phone

- The chemical energy in the food that we eat can change to kinetic energy when we move

- Nuclear energy can change to electrical energy. This electrical energy can change to sound energy, heat energy or kinetic energy in our homes.

The fact that energy never gets used up leads to a famous principle in physics. This principle is called the principle of conservation of energy:

Energy is neither created nor destroyed but can be converted from one form to another.

Wasted energy – a challenge to us all

We must reduce the energy we waste. While it is true that energy never gets used up, energy changes from useful forms to not so useful forms, so there is a very great need to avoid wasting useful forms of energy. This is what we mean when we talk about **energy conservation**.

What is the meaning of 'energy dissipation'?

Energy dissipation is when energy changes from a useful form to a not so useful form. For example, the food we eat provides the chemical energy we need to walk. When walking, our bodies produce heat energy, some of which passes into the air around us; we have no way of making use of this. Some of the original chemical energy has been dissipated.

In a very simple way you could refer to energy dissipation as a waste of useful energy.

▲ Figure 28.9 *Food gives us chemical energy*

> **? Question**
>
> 28.3 Create a poster to present to the class on one of the following:
>
> (a) Renewable forms of energy
>
> (b) Non-renewable forms of energy
>
> (c) How to improve the heat insulation in a house or apartment
>
> (d) How to reduce the energy needed for a public transport system
>
> (e) Reasons for and against a nuclear power station.
>
> When you have all presented your posters, vote for the best three to display.

Examples of energy changes

We'll look at some examples of energy changes and consider how much energy is dissipated.

Solar water heater

The energy from the Sun is referred to as solar energy. Solar energy can be used to heat water in specially designed glass pipes. This hot water is stored in a tank and can be used for baths, showers, washing clothes, etc., so you will use less electricity or natural gas to heat your water.

● The **energy change** that occurs is from solar energy to heat energy.

● A large amount of the solar energy is dissipated. However, with improvements in design more and more of the solar energy is changed to useful heat energy.

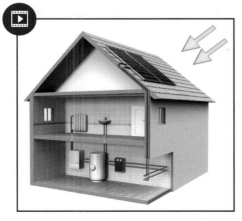

▲ Figure 28.10 *A solar panel connected to a hot-water system*

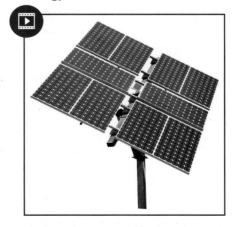

▲ Figure 28.11 *A solar panel*

The bicycle dynamo

A dynamo is a device for converting mechanical energy into electrical energy. Dynamos are often found built into the front wheel of a bicycle to power a light.

Here is a look at how we may convert energy:

- You get out of bed early on a day that you plan to cycle to school.

- You eat a good breakfast, or we could say you consume a lot of chemical energy.

- Some of this chemical energy will be changed to kinetic energy as you cycle. A certain amount of the chemical energy will be dissipated into the air as heat energy from your body.

- As the bicycle is moving, some of the kinetic energy will be changed to electrical energy by the dynamo. A certain amount of the kinetic energy will be dissipated as you try to cycle against the breeze.

- Some of the electrical energy will be converted into light energy in the bulb connected to the dynamo. A certain amount of the electrical energy will be dissipated as heat energy into the air as the bulb heats up.

chemical energy $\rightarrow$ kinetic energy $\rightarrow$ electrical energy $\rightarrow$ light energy

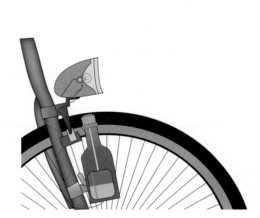

▲ Figure 28.12 *A bicycle dynamo*

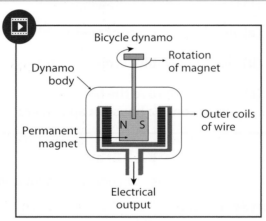

▲ Figure 28.13 *Inside a bicycle dynamo*

Sound energy

Activity 28.1 demonstrates what we have learned: that energy within a system (in this case sound energy) remains constant but is changed from one form to another form.

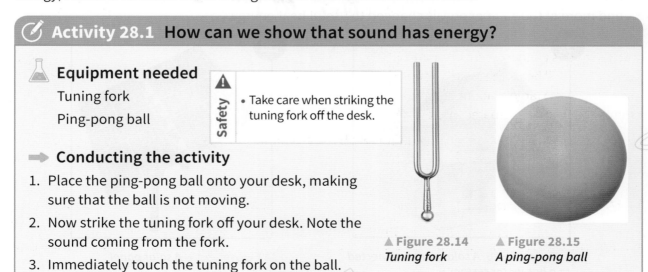

Activity 28.1 How can we show that sound has energy?

🧪 **Equipment needed**
Tuning fork
Ping-pong ball

⚠ Safety
- Take care when striking the tuning fork off the desk.

➡ **Conducting the activity**
1. Place the ping-pong ball onto your desk, making sure that the ball is not moving.
2. Now strike the tuning fork off your desk. Note the sound coming from the fork.
3. Immediately touch the tuning fork on the ball.

▲ Figure 28.14
Tuning fork

▲ Figure 28.15
A ping-pong ball

? Questions

28.4   At step 1, when the ball was not moving, what form of energy did it have?

28.5   What happened to the ball at step 3?

28.6   What form of energy did the ball have at step 3?

How sound travels

Picture two students at opposite ends of a classroom: Emma is talking and Naomi is listening. How exactly does the sound travel?

This is what happens:

- Emma's vocal cords vibrate

- The air molecules in Emma's mouth vibrate

- When Emma opens her mouth the vibration energy is passed on to the air molecules in the room, which vibrate

- The air molecules in Naomi's ear canal vibrate and knock against her ear drum

▲ Figure 28.16 *Sound travels across a classroom*

- The energy falling on Naomi's ear drum generates vibrations that allow her to hear Emma's voice.

In this example the energy started as a vibrating vocal cord, which is an example of kinetic energy. The energy stays in the form of kinetic energy but transfers like this:

---

the vocal cords → the air in Emma's mouth → the air in the room →
the air in Naomi's ear → the vibrating ear drum

You might ask: 'How did Emma's vocal cords produce so much energy to vibrate all the air in the room?'

In actual fact, Emma's vocal cords produced very little energy. Only a tiny fraction of this energy reached Naomi's ear, but she still hears the sound. You could say that a large amount of the sound energy was dissipated into the air.

Did you know?

The human ear is an amazing device. can detect sounds of extremely small energy. In science we say that the ear is very sensitive to energy.

Sound energy travels quite fast. It can travel about 340 metres in one second through air. We can write this speed as 340 ms^{-1}.

? Question

28.7   Is there sound in space? Explain your answer.

PHYSICAL WORLD

Sankey diagrams

Sankey diagrams are named after H R Sankey, a Tipperary-born engineer. He used them in 1898 to describe the energy **efficiency** of a steam engine.

Sankey diagrams show the flow of energy to and from a device.

In a Sankey diagram the width of each arrow represents the proportion of energy named.

Below are three Sankey diagrams to compare the energy flow to and from three different types of light source.

▲ **Figure 28.17** *Sankey created his diagrams to describe the energy efficiency of a steam engine*

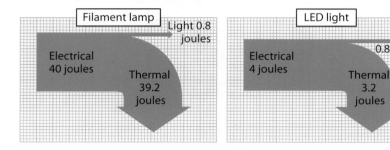
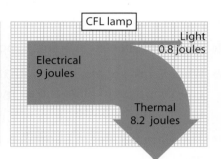

▲ **Figure 28.18** *Sankey diagrams*

Sample calculation

By using the information in Figure 28.18 compare the electrical energy that is put into each lamp with the amount of light energy produced.

Calculate the percentage of light energy produced in each case:

Filament lamp:

Electrical energy put in = 40 joules   light energy produced = 0.8 joules

Percentage = $\frac{0.8}{40} \times \frac{100}{1} = 2\%$

LED light:

Electrical energy put in = 4 joules   light energy produced = 0.8 joules

Percentage = $\frac{0.8}{4} \times \frac{100}{1} = 20\%$

Compact fluorescent lamp (CFL):

Electrical energy put in = 9 joules   light energy produced = 0.8 joules

Percentage = $\frac{0.8}{9} \times \frac{100}{1} = 8.9\%$

ⓘ Question

28.8 By researching on the internet, prepare a poster that shows a Sankey diagram of an electrical appliance that you may have in your home.

Activity 28.2   Can we design a device to transform energy from one form to another?

On a warm day an electric fan would help cool people indoors. How could we use solar energy to make the electricity operate the fan? The Sun, which is causing the room to be too warm, can be used to solve the problem. We will demonstrate this using a lamp.

Equipment needed

Several solar cells

Small electric motor with a fan attached

A study lamp

> **Safety**
> - Take care when handling the lamp as the bulb may get hot and should not be touched.
> - The lamp will be plugged into a socket and great care must be taken with all electrical devices.

The idea is that the light energy (similar to solar energy) will fall onto the solar cells and change to electrical energy. The electrical energy will operate the motor that rotates the fan.

Conducting the activity

Arrange the apparatus as indicated in Figure 28.19, with the solar cells connected to the electric motor, which is connected to a fan.

When the lamp is switched on you will observe the fan moving.

Energy transfer

The light energy from the lamp was converted to electrical energy in the solar cells, which was converted to kinetic energy in the moving fan.

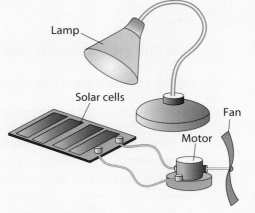

▲ Figure 28.19

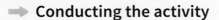 Questions

28.9   Declan decided to do activity 28.2 outdoors using sunlight instead of the study lamp. What, do you think, would happen to the rotation of the fan if:

(a) There was bright sunlight?

(b) A dark cloud blocked the sunlight for a few minutes?

(c) Declan stood in the shade of a tall building?

(d) Declan tried the activity at night-time when it was dark?

28.10   In the design of activity 28.2, some of the original light energy is dissipated. If we can reduce the amount of energy dissipated or lost we would improve the efficiency of our design. By working in small groups discuss the following:

(a) Not all of the light energy from the lamp falls on the solar cells. How might you get more of the light energy to shine on the solar cells?

(b) Solar cells can be joined together to make a cell with a bigger surface area. Is there any practical limit to how large the solar cell should be?

(c) What material might you use for the blades of the fan? Would you suggest a strong metal blade or a blade made from a light plastic?

? Questions

28.11 In your group take 10 minutes to examine the photograph in Figure 28.20, read the caption and discuss the following. Then present a short report to the class.

◀ Figure 28.20 *Workers generating electricity using stationary exercise bikes in a gym at a homeless shelter.*

(a) Describe the transformations that would occur in the situation depicted in the photograph.

(b) Could the idea shown by the photograph be extended to include all gyms?

(c) Would you consider it ethical that residents of a homeless shelter should be encouraged to generate electricity in this manner?

28.12 Ethics

Split into groups and prepare the following topics for a class discussion.

(a) Why should we try to conserve energy?

(b) Give examples of where people have wasted energy in the past.

(c) 'Ireland should have many more wind generators for electricity so that we can export electrical energy to other countries.' Do you agree with this statement? Give reasons to support your opinion.

Summary questions

28.13 Explain the term 'energy'.

28.14 Name eight different forms of energy.

28.15 For each of the eight forms of energy you named in the previous question give an example of how the energy can cause motion.

28.16 Describe how energy is wasted in:

(a) A car engine **(b)** A TV **(c)** A central heating boiler.

28.17 Would solar water heaters work better in Ireland or in Spain? Give two reasons in support of your answer.

28.18 Why are solar water heaters usually placed only on one side of the roof of a house?

28.19 We get chemical energy when we eat food. What kinds of food give more energy?

28.20 Describe the kind of weather that would cause a lot of heat energy to leave your body as you cycle.

28.21 The Sun is often regarded as the primary source of energy. What does this mean?

28.22 What problem might arise with solar water heaters in extremely cold weather?

28.23 What kind of light bulbs heat up only a little when they light up?

Assessment question

28.24 **Question from SEC Junior Cycle Science sample paper** (30 marks)

Sankey diagrams are named after H. Riall Sankey, a Tipperary-born engineer, following his 1898 description of the energy efficiency of a steam engine.

Sankey diagrams show the flow of energy to and from a device.

In a Sankey diagram, the width of each arrow represents the energy named.

The Sankey diagrams for a filament lamp and a compact fluorescent lamp (CFL) are shown below.

▲ Figure 28.21

(a) Examine figures **1** and **2** in Figure 28.22. Which lamp is more efficient? Justify your answer.

(b) Why is it important to improve the energy efficiency of household devices, such as lamps?

(c) A student is asked to investigate and compare the heat energy produced by filament lamps and CFLs.

Apart from the lamps themselves, name a piece of equipment that could be used during this investigation. Explain how this piece of equipment could be used during the investigation.

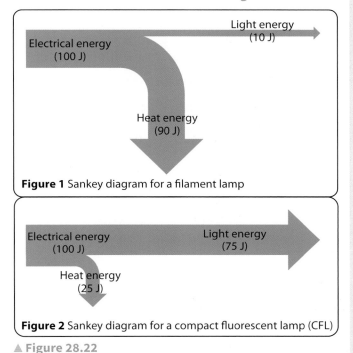

Figure 1 Sankey diagram for a filament lamp

Figure 2 Sankey diagram for a compact fluorescent lamp (CFL)

▲ Figure 28.22

(d) The energy conversions that happen in a CFL are described in the table below.

Write a new row of the table for another device which transforms energy from one form to another and which you designed as part of your studies in science.

Name of the device	Function of the device	Main useful energy conversion	Main loss of energy
Compact fluorescent lamp (CFL)	To provide artificial light	Electrical to light	Electrical to heat

(e) Sketch a Sankey diagram for the device you described in part **(d)**. Label each part of the diagram.

 Log on to **www.edcolearning.ie** for Additional Assessment Questions

Learning intentions

At the end of this chapter you will be able to:

✓ Explain why heat is a form of energy

✓ Use a thermometer to measure temperature, i.e. the hotness of a body

✓ Show by suitable activities that solids, liquids and gases expand when heated and contract when cooled

✓ Explain how heat sometimes changes a state instead of changing a temperature.

Keywords

⚬ heat
⚬ thermometer
⚬ temperature
⚬ expansion
⚬ contraction
⚬ conduction
⚬ convection
⚬ radiation
⚬ latent heat

How can we say that heat is a form of energy?

The evidence that heat is a form of energy is that heat can cause movement. Think of:

● Steam engines pulling trains

● Curtains moving when they are above a hot radiator.

Since heat is a form of energy, it is measured in joules.

As heat is a form of energy it can be converted into other forms. For example, in power stations oil and gas are burned to produce heat energy. This heat produces steam, which turns the blades of a turbine — kinetic energy. This turning of the blades produces electrical energy.

▲ Figure 29.1 *A steam engine is an example of heat energy causing motion*

⑦ Questions

29.1 List everyday examples of heat being converted into other forms of energy.

29.2 Electricity power stations burn oil and gas to produce heat to generate the electricity.

What other fuels can also be used?

29.3 In what way is heat energy beneficial to animals?

29.4 What forms of transport besides trains used steam engines in the past?

How do we measure the temperature of a substance?

We use a **thermometer** to measure hotness, or **temperature**.

▲ Figure 29.2 *Electrical thermometer*

▲ Figure 29.3 *Laboratory thermometer*

Note:
- Heat is a form of energy.
- Temperature is a measure of the hotness of a body.

? Questions

29.5 Use the internet to research and then prepare a poster on a comparison between two different types of thermometer. Be guided by the following suggestions:

- Include examples of types of thermometer: liquid in a glass thermometer, an electrical thermometer, a liquid crystal thermometer.

- Include pictures of your choices of thermometers.

- State the scientific principle on which the thermometer is based (for example, in a liquid in a glass thermometer the liquid expands when it gets hotter and it then rises up the glass tube).

- State where the thermometer would be used.

- Is the thermometer used in many situations or does it have a limited use?

- Is the thermometer expensive to buy?

- State how the thermometer is used to measure temperature.

- State the units used to measure temperature.

29.6 Research on the internet and prepare a short presentation on the following:

(a) The Celsius temperature scale.

(b) The Fahrenheit temperature scale.

(c) The Kelvin scale.

(d) Any easy method to change a temperature value from one scale to another scale.

(e) Why alcohol is safer to use than mercury in a thermometer.

Activity 29.1 What are the temperatures of everyday items?

Equipment needed

Laboratory thermometer

Cold tap water

Water that has been stored in a fridge

Ice from a freezer

Warm tap water

⚠ Safety
- Be careful not to spill water or ice on the floor to avoid the danger of somebody slipping.

➡ Conducting the activity

1. Measure and make a note in the table in your Student Activity Book of the temperature in degrees Celsius of each of the following:
   - ● Air temperature
   - ● Cold tap water
   - ● Ice from a freezer.
   - ● Warm tap water
   - ● Cold water from a fridge

2. Compare your results with those of other students in your class. Write their results in the table in your Student Activity Book.

> **(?) Questions**
>
> **29.7** Do your results and your classmates' results differ?
>
> **29.8** What might be the reason for any differences?
>
> **29.9** What is the normal range for human body temperature?

What is meant by expanding and contracting?

Heating causes expansion (when things get bigger) and cooling causes contraction (when things get smaller).

Activity 29.2 How does heating and cooling of solids affect their expansion and contraction?

Equipment needed

▶ **Activity video**

Retort stand

Metal ball and ring apparatus

Bunsen burner

Stopwatch or timer

Tongs

⚠ Safety
- Make sure you are aware of and follow all the recommended precautions when working with a Bunsen burner.
- Do not touch the metal ball after heating as it can get quite hot.

➡ Conducting the activity

1. Test to see that the metal ball fits through the ring at room temperature.

2. Using tongs to hold the metal ball, heat it over a Bunsen flame for 4 minutes.

3. Try to fit the metal ball through the ring now that it is heated.

4. Allow the metal ball to cool for about 10 minutes.

5. See if the metal ball fits through the ring now that it has cooled.

6. Record your results in the space provided in your Student Activity Book.

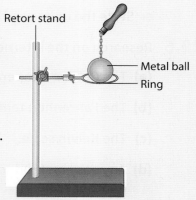

▲ **Figure 29.4** *Solids expand when heated and contract when cooled*

PHYSICAL WORLD

Did you know?

● The lowest temperature possible anywhere in the universe is –273.15°C. This is called absolute zero.

● –40° Celsius is the same temperature as –40° Fahrenheit.

 Activity 29.3 How does heating and cooling of liquids affect their expansion and contraction?

 **Activity video**

Equipment needed

Retort stand

Food dye

Round-bottomed flask

Bunsen burner

Glass tube

Stopwatch or timer

Water

Safety

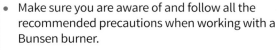
● Make sure you are aware of and follow all the recommended precautions when working with a Bunsen burner.
● Do not touch the round-bottomed flask after heating as it can get quite hot.

Conducting the activity

1. Totally fill a round-bottomed flask with water and add a few drops of food dye.

2. Insert a stopper with a glass tube into the top of the flask.

3. Hold the flask in place with clamps as shown in Figure 29.5.

4. Heat the flask with the Bunsen burner for a few minutes.

5. Watch the level of the coloured water in the glass tube as the water heats.

6. Turn off the Bunsen burner from under the flask.

7. Observe the level of water in the glass tube over the next 10 minutes.

8. Record your results in your Student Activity Book.

Note: the food dye does not affect the expansion or contraction. The purpose of the dye is to make it easier to see the water in the narrow glass tube.

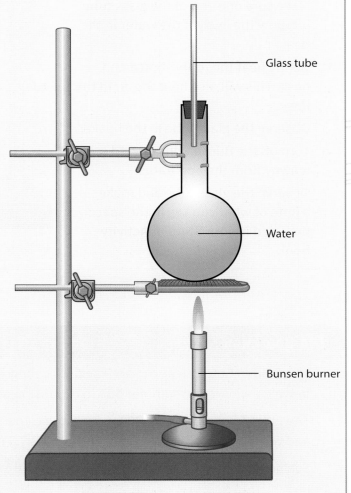

Glass tube

Water

Bunsen burner

▲ Figure 29.5 *The effect of heat on a liquid*

Activity 29.4 How does heating and cooling of gases affect their expansion and contraction?

Equipment needed

Retort stand

Water

Beaker

Round-bottomed flask

Bunsen burner

Glass tube

Stopwatch or timer

Safety

- Make sure you are aware of and follow all the recommended precautions when working with a Bunsen burner.
- Do not touch the round-bottomed flask after heating as it can get quite hot.

Conducting the activity

1. Insert a stopper with a glass tube into the top of the flask.

2. With a retort stand and a clamp, set up the arrangement as shown in Figure 29.6.

3. Make sure one end of the glass tube is below the level of the water in the beaker.

4. Gently heat the round-bottomed flask. This will also heat the air in the flask.

5. Observe the glass tube in the beaker.

6. Turn off the Bunsen burner and move it away from the apparatus.

7. Observe the glass tube and make a note of what you see in the space provided in your Student Activity Book.

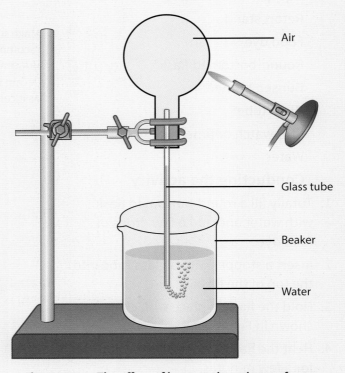

▲ Figure 29.6 *The effect of heat on the volume of a gas*

Did you know?

- The Golden Gate Bridge in San Francisco changes length by over 1 m between winter and summer due to expansion and contraction.

- The Eiffel Tower in Paris is 300 m high and is made of iron. Between summer and winter its height changes by as much as 7.5 cm.

- Sealed bottles or cans explode in fires.

- If you take an empty cold glass bottle and put a coin over the open neck and then wrap your hands around the bottle, after a while the coin will pop up.

▲ Figure 29.7 *The Golden Gate Bridge in San Francisco changes length depending on whether it is summer or winter*

▲ Figure 29.8 *The Eiffel Tower in Paris changes height depending on whether it is summer or winter*

⑦ Questions

29.10 Use the internet to research the unusual behaviour of water as it cools to just below 4°C and as it heats to just above 4°C.

29.11 Can you now explain why icebergs float on water?

29.12 Can you now explain why water pipes sometimes burst in very cold weather?

Heat transfer

There are three ways in which heat energy can be moved or transferred:

● **Conduction**   ● **Convection**   ● **Radiation.**

Conduction

Conduction is the movement of heat energy from one object to another object that is in direct contact and is at a lower temperature.

Conduction works really well in solids such as metals.

Example: a saucepan heating up on a hot hob.

▲ Figure 29.9 *A saucepan on a hob is heated by conduction*

Convection

Convection is the movement of heat energy within a liquid or gas.

Because particles within a liquid or gas can move, they can transfer the heat within that liquid or gas. This occurs when warmer areas in the liquid or gas rise and are replaced by cooler liquids or gas.

Example: water heating in a kettle.

Radiation

The hotter an object is the more heat energy that is emitted or released from the object.

No particles are needed to carry the heat. This form of heat energy (radiation) can move through a vacuum (a vacuum has no particles in it, like space in the solar system).

Example: the Sun releasing heat energy into space.

▲ Figure 29.10 *Water is heated in a kettle by convection*

What do we mean by latent heat?

When you heat an object you expect the temperature of the object to rise. However, this does not always happen. Look at the situation in Figure 29.11.

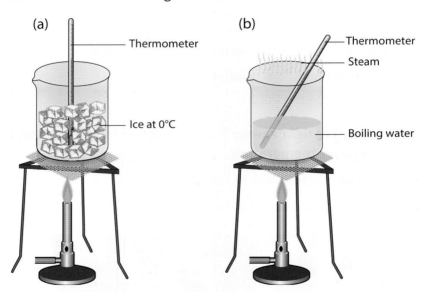

▲ Figure 29.11 *(a) When you heat a beaker of ice, the temperature does not rise until all the ice has melted; (b) when you heat a beaker of boiling water, the temperature does not change*

When you slowly heat a beaker of ice you will notice that the temperature does not rise at first. The temperature remains at 0°C for several minutes until the last piece of ice has melted.

When you heat a beaker of boiling water you will notice that the temperature does not rise. The temperature remains at 100°C.

What happens to the heat energy? Heat energy cannot just disappear! In the situations shown in Figure 29.11 the heat changes the state of the ice and of the boiling water. **When heat changes a state instead of the temperature we call it latent heat.**

The role of perspiration

When we exercise vigorously we perspire or sweat. This causes small droplets of liquid to form on our skin. Heat then leaves the body to evaporate this liquid, or to change its state to a gas. Perspiration is the body's natural way to cool down.

Did you know?

Unlike a human perspiration system, a dog's body cools itself mainly through an evaporation system that involves the dog's tongue. Although a dog's body does have sweat glands, the dog's body is cooled off mainly through its tongue. Dogs must never be left in a car on sunny days, because they can die very quickly from overheating.

▲ **Figure 29.12** *Dogs should never be left in a hot car*

✐ Activity 29.5 **How can we show that heating something may not change the temperature?**

 Equipment needed

12-V power supply	Stirrer
Electrical leads	Beaker
Thermometer	Ice cubes
Heating coil	Joulemeter

Safety
* The power supply unit may be plugged into a socket. Take care with all electrical appliances.

➡ **Conducting the activity**

1. Set up the apparatus as indicated in Figure 29.13.

2. Note the temperature on the thermometer as the ice starts to melt.

3. Turn on the electricity and the joulemeter will indicate how much electrical energy is being supplied to the melting ice.

4. What do you notice about the temperature reading on the thermometer as the electrical energy is being supplied?

5. Record your results in the space provided in your Student Activity Book.

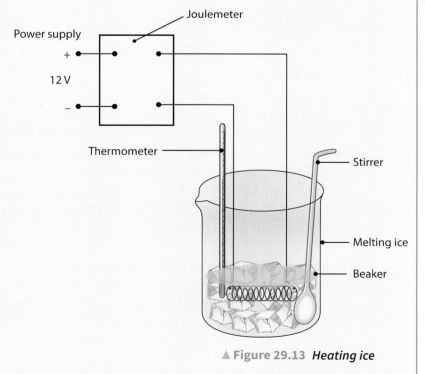

▲ **Figure 29.13** *Heating ice*

Summary questions

● 29.13 Name two liquids suitable for laboratory thermometers.

● 29.14 Explain the benefit of using a dye to colour the liquid in a thermometer.

● 29.15 What was the benefit of using a dye to colour the water in activity 29.3?

● 29.16 Give one reason for using an electrical thermometer rather than a glass thermometer with liquid in it.

● 29.17 **(a)** Explain why a metal ball was used in activity 29.2 instead of a wooden ball.
(b) Name five metals that would be suitable for this activity.

● 29.18 Give five examples of objects that do not transfer heat very well.

● 29.19 What name is given to objects/substances that do not conduct heat well?

● 29.20 What is the meaning of latent heat?

● 29.21 Explain why water is not suitable for use in a thermometer.

● 29.22 In activity 29.4 the water passed up into the glass tube when the air was cooled. Explain why this happened.

Assessment questions

29.23 Copy the paragraph and fill in the missing words from the list of five words provided. **(15 marks)**

hotter   radiation   energy   thermometer   convection

Heat is a form of _____. Heat can travel by three methods, conduction, _____ and by _____. We measure the hotness of an object using a _____. Heat energy normally travels from a _____ object to a cooler object.

29.24 Copy the paragraph and fill in the missing words from the list of five words provided. **(15 marks)**

gases   contract   thermometer   degree Celsius   longer

A solid, like a copper sphere will expand when heated and _____ when cooled. Like solids, liquids and _____ behave in a similar way. The length of a metal bridge will often be _____ in the summer compared to winter. A laboratory _____ depends on the expansion of liquids in order to measure temperature. The temperature of a body is measured in a unit called the _____.

29.25 A student performed an activity in which a hollow glass tube contained a red liquid and the tube was tied to a ruler with elastic bands. The glass tube and ruler were placed in a beaker of water, as illustrated in Figure 29.14. A laboratory thermometer was placed in the beaker of water to measure its temperature. A stirrer was also included in the arrangement. The beaker of water was slowly heated. As the **(30 marks)** water got hotter the red liquid started to rise up the tube. The student recorded values of water temperature and length of the column of red liquid.

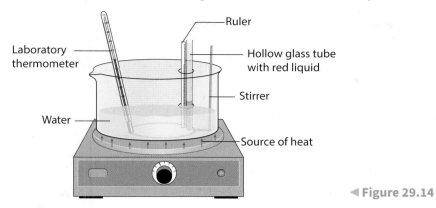

◀ Figure 29.14

The following data was recorded.

Temperature of water (°C)	10	20	30	40	50	60
Length of column of red liquid in glass tube (cm)	7	8	9	10	11	12

(a) Name a suitable source of heat in this activity and a precaution to be taken with this heat source.

(b) Suggest a reason for using a stirrer.

(c) Using the recorded data, plot a graph with temperature on the *x*-axis and length of red liquid on the *y*-axis.

(d) Use the graph to determine the length of the red liquid at a temperature of 45°C.

(e) What conclusion could you draw about the relationship between length of the red liquid and the temperature?

29.26 A student was reading a report of an activity in which ice at a temperature **(45 marks)** of –20°C was placed in a beaker and heated slowly until it eventually turned into boiling water at a temperature of 100°C.

The temperature was recorded at intervals of 1 minute.

The data recorded is as follows.

Time (min)	0	1	2	3	4	5	6	7	8
Temperature (°C)	–20	0	0	20	40	60	80	100	100

(a) Draw and label a diagram of a suitable experimental arrangement for this activity.

(b) Give two precautions that would be necessary with this activity to avoid causing harm or injury.

(c) Draw a graph of the data provided. Plot time on the *x*-axis and temperature on the *y*-axis.

(d) From the graph determine what the temperature was after 5 minutes and 30 seconds.

(e) The graph becomes horizontal (level) twice.

   (i) Explain why this happens.

   (ii) What is the scientific name for what is happening when the graph is horizontal?

PowerPoint summary   Weblinks

CHAPTER 30

ELECTRICITY – CURRENT ELECTRICITY

LO: PW1, PW2, PW3

Learning intentions

At the end of this chapter you will be able to:

✓ Correctly use the terms current, potential difference and resistance when talking about electricity

✓ Measure current, potential difference and resistance

✓ Describe the relationship between the current and potential difference for electricity flowing in a circuit

✓ Recognise the symbols used for various objects that are commonly used in the study of electricity

✓ Do simple calculations involving current, potential difference and resistance.

Keywords

- electrons
- battery
- current
- conventional current
- ammeter
- potential difference
- voltage
- voltmeter
- resistance
- ohmmeter
- lamp
- switch
- filament bulb

What is electrical current?

The wire in Figure 30.1 is made of a metal such as copper. In this piece of copper wire each atom has one or more loosely held **electrons** that are free to move within the wire. If you connect a **battery** across the ends of the wire these free electrons move along the wire.

The electrons move from the negative terminal of the battery towards the positive terminal of the battery. **This movement of electrons is called current.**

Electricity was discovered before the electron was discovered. In the early days when scientists first studied electricity they agreed that current was the flow of positive charge from the positive terminal of a battery to the negative terminal of the battery. Today this is called **conventional current**.

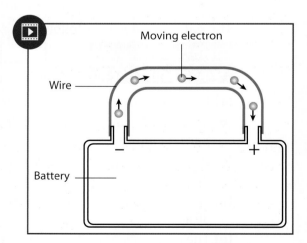

▲ Figure 30.1 *Current electricity is the flow of electrons along a wire*

Although there is some historical confusion, just try to remember this:

- Current electricity is actually the flow of negative electrons from the negative terminal to the positive terminal of a battery. See Figure 30.1.

- However, because of a historical agreement, we say that current flows from the positive terminal to the negative terminal of a battery. See Figure 30.2.

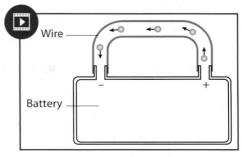

▲ Figure 30.2 *Conventional current in a circuit*

Measuring current

Unit for current

Current is measured in amperes (A). These are often shortened to amps.

Current is measured with an **ammeter**.

What is voltage (potential difference)?

A chemical reaction happens inside a battery. The result of this reaction is that excess electrons build up on the negative terminal of the battery. The reaction also causes a loss of electrons at the positive terminal of the battery.

When you join a conducting wire (a wire through which an electric current can pass) from one terminal to the other, the excess electrons flow from the negative terminal to the positive terminal.

The battery gives the electrons the ability to move. Another word for this ability is 'potential'. We therefore say that **the battery has a potential difference between the positive and the negative terminals**.

Very often potential difference is called voltage.

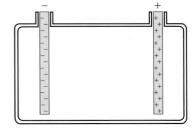

▲ Figure 30.3 *A battery showing excess electrons at the negative terminal*

Measuring voltage

Unit for voltage (potential difference)

Voltage is measured in volts (V).

Voltage is measured with a **voltmeter**.

To help you remember

Figure 30.4 shows a positive charge leaving the battery with a box full of voltage. He uses up a little bit of this voltage to get to the lamp. He uses up most of the voltage to light the lamp. He has just enough voltage left to get back to the battery. At the battery he fills up his box with voltage again.

Notice that in Figure 30.4 we let the current flow in the direction agreed by the early scientists.

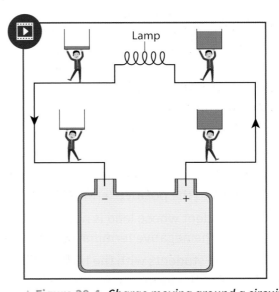

▲ Figure 30.4 *Charge moving around a circuit*

Just remember:

- Whatever current leaves the battery, the same current returns to the battery.

- Voltage gets used up as the current flows around the circuit.

What is the difference between current and voltage?

- **Current is a measure of the number of electrons flowing along the wire.**
- **Voltage is a measure of the ability of the electrons to do a particular task.**

To help you remember

Imagine that you have organised a football match between five players from sixth year and 40 players from junior infants.

- The sixth years have a small number of players but are individually very capable at football. Their team would be small current but high voltage.
- The junior infant team has a large number of players but individually they would not be very capable. Their team would be high current but low voltage.

What is resistance?

Electrons find it easier to flow along some conducting materials than others. We say that some materials are better conductors than others. However, all conductors try to oppose the moving electrons. **The opposition to the flow of electrons is called resistance.**

Metals such as silver and copper are good conductors of electricity and have a low resistance.

Carbon is not as good a conductor and we say that carbon has a higher resistance.

Measuring resistance

Unit for resistance

Resistance is measured in the ohm. The symbol for the ohm is a Greek letter called 'omega' (Ω).

Resistance is measured with an **ohmmeter**.

Activity 30.1   How can we demonstrate an electrical circuit?

Equipment needed

Electrical lead for each student	Bulb
Low voltage battery	Clips

 Safety
- As the whole class has to stand around the room, follow the teacher's instructions and avoid bumping into other students or tripping over school bags.

Conducting the activity

1. Each student has an electrical lead.
2. Join your lead to the leads of the students on either side of you, so that when everyone does this the leads are joined all around the class.
3. The student with the battery unclips the lead from his or her neighbour's lead and joins it instead to the positive terminal of the battery.
4. The student whose lead is not now joined to another lead on one side attaches the loose end to the negative terminal of the battery.
5. The two students with the bulb unclip their leads and one student attaches the loose end to one of the terminals on the bulb and the second student attaches the loose end of their lead to the other terminal of the bulb.

   The bulb should light up as long as all the other leads are attached to each other and there is no break in the circuit.

What symbols are used in electricity?

When you perform activities to do with electricity you use objects such as batteries, lamps, switches and resistors. Diagrams of equipment used normally have a symbol for those objects rather than a picture of the object itself. Figure 30.5 shows the symbols you are most likely to come across.

All the symbols in Figure 30.5 are in the *Formulae and Tables* booklet used in all state exams.

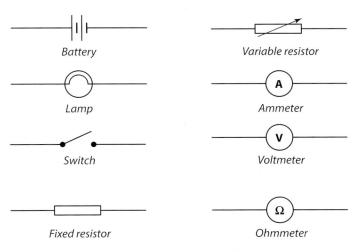

Battery

Variable resistor

Lamp

Ammeter

Switch

Voltmeter

Fixed resistor

Ohmmeter

▲ **Figure 30.5** *Symbols used for electricity*

How do we measure current and voltage?

Figure 30.6 shows an ammeter, which is used to measure current. When it is connected into a circuit the needle moves on the scale for you to read the amount of current.

Figure 30.7 shows a voltmeter, which is used to measure voltage (potential difference). When it is connected into a circuit the needle moves on the scale for you to read the amount of voltage.

Figure 30.8 shows a multimeter. This is a digital meter and does not have a moving needle. By adjusting the settings it can be used to measure current, voltage and resistance. It is really a combination of an ammeter, a voltmeter and an ohmmeter.

▲ **Figure 30.6** *An analogue ammeter*

▲ **Figure 30.7** *An analog voltmeter*

▲ **Figure 30.8** *A digital multimeter*

② Question

30.1 Use the internet to research the **difference between analogue instruments and digital instruments**. Present your findings in the form of a poster. Pay particular attention to:

● Which type of instrument was used first

● Which type of instrument might be more expensive to buy.

✐ Activity 30.2   How do we measure current?

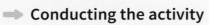

🧪 Equipment needed

12 V power supply with a variable output

Switch

Ammeter

12 V filament bulb

Electrical leads

| ⚠ **Safety** | ● Take care not to drop the ammeter as it may break, leaving the parts with sharp edges. |

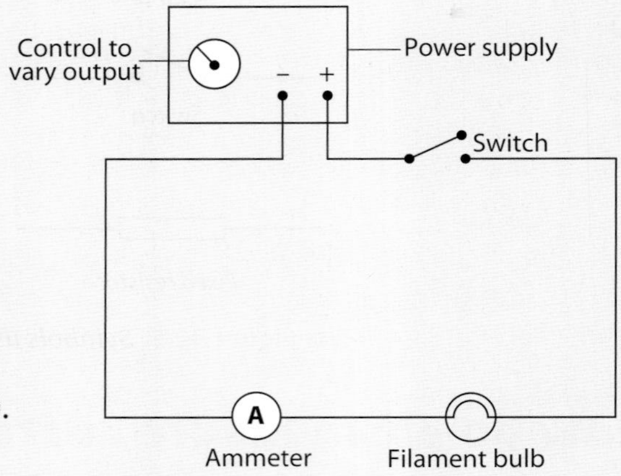

Control to vary output — Power supply

− +

Switch

➡ Conducting the activity

1. Set up the equipment as indicated in Figure 30.9.
2. Close the switch.
3. Vary the output from the power supply.
4. Record your observations in the space provided in your Student Activity Book and answer the questions below.

A

Ammeter   Filament bulb

▲ **Figure 30.9** *Circuit diagram to show measurement of current*

② Questions

30.2 As you varied the output from the power supply what did you notice about the bulb?

30.3 As you varied the output from the power supply what did you notice about the reading on the ammeter?

30.4 Did you notice any pattern about the reading on the ammeter and the brightness of the bulb?

30.5 Would it make any difference if you put the ammeter on the other side of the filament bulb?

Activity 30.3 How do we measure voltage?

 Equipment needed

12 V power supply with a variable output

Switch

Voltmeter

12 V filament bulb

Electrical leads

➡ **Conducting the activity**

1. Set up the apparatus as indicated in Figure 30.10.

2. Close the switch.

3. Vary the output from the power supply.

4. Record your observations in the space provided in your Student Activity Book and answer the questions below.

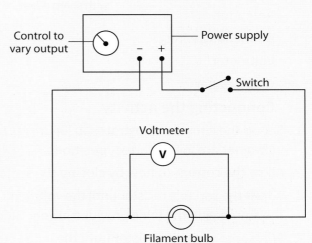

▲ **Figure 30.10** *Circuit diagram to show measurement of voltage*

(?) **Questions**

30.6   As you varied the output from the power supply what did you notice about the bulb?

30.7   As you varied the output from the power supply what did you notice about the reading on the voltmeter?

30.8   Did you notice any pattern about the reading on the voltmeter and the brightness of the bulb?

30.9   Would it make any difference if you put the voltmeter on the side of the filament bulb where you put the ammeter in activity 30.2?

30.10 Find out the terms used for the difference in how the ammeter is connected in Figure 30.9 and how the voltmeter is connected in the circuit in Figure 30.10.

Activity 30.4 How can we see the relationship between current and voltage?

Equipment needed

6-V battery

Resistor

Switch

Variable resistor

Ammeter

Connecting wires

Voltmeter

Graph paper

⚠ Safety
- Take care not to drop the ammeter or voltmeter as they may break, leaving the parts with sharp edges.

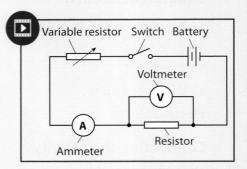

▲ **Figure 30.11** *Circuit diagram to show the relationship between current and voltage*

Conducting the activity

1. Set up the circuit as illustrated in Figure 30.11. Take great care that the ammeter and voltmeter are in the correct positions.

2. Allow the current to flow by closing the switch to complete the circuit.

3. Adjust the variable resistor until the voltmeter reads 1 volt. Now record the current reading on the ammeter in the table provided in your Student Activity Book.

4. Adjust the variable resistor until the voltmeter reads 2 volts. Now record the current reading on the ammeter in your table.

5. Repeat this procedure for 3 volts, 4 volts, 5 volts and 6 volts.

6. Using the graph paper in your Student Activity Book, draw a graph of the data collected with Voltage on the *y*-axis and Current on the *x*-axis.

Result

The graph should be a straight line passing through the origin as shown in Figure 30.12.

Conclusion

Because the graph is a straight line through the origin, we conclude that the voltage is directly proportional to the current.

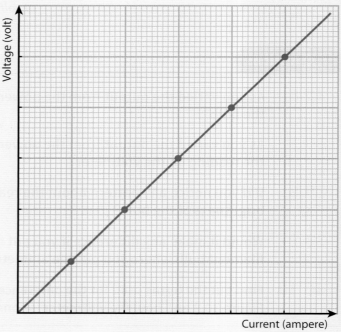

▲ **Figure 30.12** *A graph to show voltage plotted against current*

? Question

30.11 Research Georg Ohm on the internet and prepare a short biography of him. Present your work in the form of a poster.

▲ Figure 30.13 *Georg Ohm*

Did you know?

Scientist Georg Simon Ohm discovered the relationship between current and voltage (potential difference).

Note: The resistor used in activity 30.4 usually has a low resistance, i.e. it is quite a good conductor. The temperature of this resistor should stay constant. For this reason the resistor is sometimes placed in a liquid to prevent it from getting hot. A loosely coiled piece of nichrome wire (this wire resists the flow of electricity, which causes the electrical energy to be converted into heat) works well here as the resistor. The wire is coiled to keep it compact, as shown in Figure 30.14.

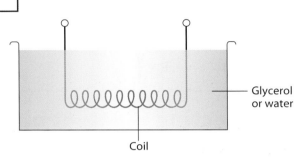

Glycerol or water

Coil

▲ Figure 30.14 *Keeping the resistor at a fixed temperature*

Calculations

From activity 30.4 we found that voltage is directly proportional to current. However, when we write this law as a mathematical equation we get:

$$\frac{V}{I} = R$$

where:

V = voltage (potential difference)

I = current

R = resistance

A triangle makes this equation easy for us:

$$\frac{V}{I \times R}$$

- To calculate the value of voltage, put your finger over V. This will show you that you have to multiply I and R (V = I × R).
- To calculate the value of current, put your finger over I. This will show you that you have to divide V by R $\left(I = \frac{V}{R}\right)$.
- To calculate the value of resistance, put your finger over R. This will show you that you have to divide V by I $\left(R = \frac{V}{I}\right)$.

Sample calculation 1

Calculate the voltage across a resistor of resistance 10 Ω if the current flowing through it is 2 amperes.

Answer: $V = I \times R$ $V = 2 \times 10$ $V = 20$ volts

Sample calculation 2

Calculate the current flowing through a resistor of 20 Ω when the voltage across it is 6 volts.

Answer: $I = \dfrac{V}{R}$ $I = \dfrac{6}{20}$ $I = 0.3$ amperes

Sample calculation 3

Calculate the resistance of a resistor when a voltage of 12 volts causes a current of 0.2 amperes to flow.

Answer: $R = \dfrac{V}{I}$ $R = \dfrac{12}{0.2}$ $R = 60$ ohms

Connecting filament bulbs in series and in parallel

A student has been asked to connect three filament bulbs together and realises that this could be done in more than one way.

Two options that are available is to connect the bulbs in series or to connect the bulbs in parallel.

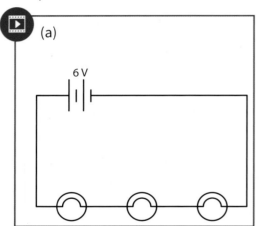
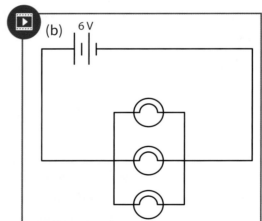

▲ **Figure 30.15** *Three bulbs connected in series (a) and three bulbs connected in parallel (b)*

Summary questions

- 30.12 **(a)** Name the unit for current.
  - **(b)** What is the symbol for the unit for current?
  - **(c)** What is used to measure current?
- 30.13 **(a)** Name the unit for voltage.
  - **(b)** What is the symbol for the unit for voltage?
  - **(c)** What is used to measure voltage?
  - **(d)** What is the other term used for voltage?

30.14 **(a)** Name the unit for resistance.

(b) What is the symbol for the unit for resistance?

(c) What is used to measure resistance?

30.15 Draw the symbol used for each of the following:

(a) Battery **(e)** Variable resistor

(b) Lamp **(f)** Ammeter

(c) Switch **(g)** Voltmeter

(d) Fixed resistor **(h)** Ohmmeter

30.16 Complete the following sentences.

(a) When current leaves the battery the _____ _____ returns to the battery.

(b) Voltage gets _____ _____ as current flows around the circuit.

30.17 Calculate the voltage across a resistor of resistance 5 Ω if the current flowing through it is 3 amperes.

30.18 Calculate the voltage across a resistance of 240 Ω if the current flowing through it is 0.05 amperes.

30.19 Calculate the current flowing through a resistor of 30 Ω when the voltage across it is 12 volts.

30.20 Calculate the current flowing through a resistor of 2000 Ω when the voltage across it is 12 volts.

30.21 Calculate the resistance of a resistor when a voltage of 6 volts causes a current of 2 amperes to flow.

30.22 Calculate the resistance of a resistor when a voltage of 240 volts causes a current of 0.2 amperes to flow.

30.23 Draw a circuit diagram to show three bulbs connected in parallel to a battery as in Figure 30.15b. Now add a switch to the diagram so that all three bulbs may be turned off and on at the same time.

30.24 Draw a circuit diagram to show three bulbs connected in parallel to a battery as in Figure 30.15b. Now add three switches to the diagram so that each bulb may be turned on and off independently of the others.

30.25 Are the bulbs in your home connected in series or in parallel?

Assessment questions

30.26 (a) Copy this diagram and label the various pieces of equipment. **(15 marks)**

(b) Give a precaution to be taken with:

(i) The power supply

(ii) The filament bulb

(iii) The ammeter.

(c) A student found that as the current increased the brightness of the filament bulb increased. Draw a sketch of a graph to show this relationship, with brightness on the *y*-axis and current on the *x*-axis.

You can ignore the units when drawing the graph.

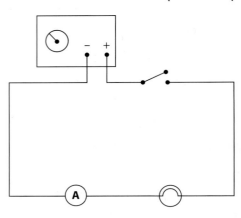

▲ Figure 30.16

30.27 A student carried out an activity to investigate the relationship between current and voltage for an unknown component. Several different values of voltage were used. The values of the voltage and corresponding values of current were recorded by the student: **(30 marks)**

Voltage (V)	Current (A)
1	0.3
2	0.6
3	0.8
4	0.95
5	1.0
6	1.0

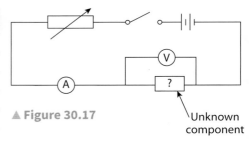

▲ Figure 30.17 Unknown component

(a) Give one precaution a student should take in this activity.

(b) Copy and label all parts of the diagram of the experimental arrangement.

(c) Draw a graph of the data with current on the *y*-axis and voltage on the *x*-axis.

(d) By using the formula $\text{resistance} = \dfrac{\text{voltage}}{\text{current}}$

calculate the resistance of the unknown component for all six values of voltage.

(e) Is there any pattern in the values of the resistance?

30.28 A student carried out an activity to investigate the relationship between the current and voltage for an unknown component. Several different values of voltage were used. The values of the voltage and corresponding values of current were recorded by the student: **(30 marks)**

(a) Give one precaution a student should take in this activity.

(b) Copy the circuit diagram of the experimental arrangement and label the symbol for the variable resistor.

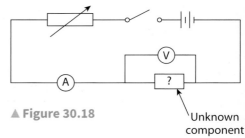

▲ Figure 30.18 Unknown component

(c) Draw a graph of the data with current on the *y*-axis and voltage on the *x*-axis.

(d) By using the formula **resistance** = $\dfrac{\text{voltage}}{\text{current}}$

calculate the resistance of the unknown component for all six values of voltage.

(e) (i) Is there any pattern in the values of the resistance?

(ii) Comment on the shape of the graph.

Voltage (V)	Current (A)
1	0.3
2	0.6
3	0.9
4	1.2
5	1.5
6	1.8

30.29 **Question from SEC Junior Cycle Science sample paper** (15 marks)

Copy and complete the table below for the instruments shown.

In each case, state what physical quantity the instrument measures. Also state the unit used for that measurement.

(Some parts of the table are already completed for you.)

Metre stick

Stopwatch

Graduated cylinder

Thermometer

Newton meter

Ohmmeter

▲ **Figure 30.19**

Instrument	Quantity measured	Unit
Metre stick		
Stopwatch		
Graduated cylinder		
Thermometer		
Newton meter		Newton (N)
Ohmmeter	Resistance	Ohm (Ω)

 Log on to **www.edcolearning.ie** for Additional Assessment Questions

PowerPoint summary **Weblinks**

CHAPTER 31

ISSUES THAT ARISE FROM GENERATION AND USE OF ELECTRICITY

LO: PW2, PW3, PW4, PW7, PW8

Learning intentions

At the end of this chapter you will be able to:

✓ Identify the different ways of generating electrical energy

✓ List good points and bad points relating to the different ways of generating electrical energy

✓ Do simple calculations on electrical power

✓ Understand the unit of energy that is used for electricity in the home

✓ Research and discuss how we use electrical energy and how our actions today may affect future generations.

Keywords

⚬ fossil fuels
⚬ nuclear fuels
⚬ geothermal energy
⚬ solar cells
⚬ wire coil
⚬ magnet
⚬ turbine generator
⚬ electrical power
⚬ watt
⚬ kilowatt-hours
⚬ sustainable

How is electricity generated?

Generating electricity

Electricity is generated from some of the following sources:

- **Fossil fuels**
- **Nuclear fuels**
- Wind
- Moving water
- **Geothermal energy**
- **Solar cells**.

Energy from fossil fuels

The main fossil fuels used are:

- Coal
- Oil
- Natural gas.

They are fuels because they release heat energy when they are burned.

Did you know?

Fossil fuels are so called because they were formed from the remains of organisms living millions of years ago.

Activity 31.1   How can we generate electricity?

 Equipment needed

About 1 metre of insulated copper wire

Pencil

Different types of magnet

Digital multimeter

Safety
⚠ • Take care not to drop the magnets as they can be quite heavy and may trip someone.

➡ **Conducting the activity**

1. Wrap the wire around the pencil and leave about 10 cm of the wire unwrapped at both ends. You now have a copper **wire coil**.

2. Connect the two free ends of the wire to the terminals of the multimeter.

3. Turn the dial of the multimeter so that it will read millivolts.

4. Move one of the **magnets** back and forth near the wire wrapped around the pencil.

5. Note in the space provided in your Student Activity Book what you observe from the multimeter.

6. Repeat steps 4 and 5 using different magnets.

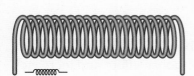

▲ Figure 31.1 *Copper wire coil*

▲ Figure 31.2 *Magnets*

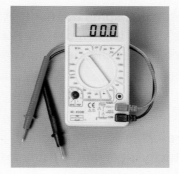

▲ Figure 31.3 *Digital multimeter*

? Questions

31.1   What do you notice on the multimeter if you move the magnet faster?

31.2   What do you notice on the multimeter if you use a stronger magnet?

31.3   Does using a magnet of a different shape make any difference?

31.4   Would using a longer piece of wire make any difference?

31.5   What do you notice if you move the wire instead of the magnet?

31.6   The insulation used for copper wire may be varnish, which is a type of clear paint. Why, do you think, would this type of wire be helpful in the above experiment?

PHYSICAL WORLD

Did you know?

The fossil fuels generate electricity by changing energy from one form to another form, like this:

Coal, oil and gas are stores of chemical energy.
↓
When burned they release heat energy.
↓
The heat energy boils water to make steam.
↓
The moving steam has kinetic energy, which turns the blades of a turbine generator.
↓
The turbine spins the magnet near the coil of wire in the generator, which makes the electrical energy.

▲ **Figure 31.4** *Coal-burning electrical plant*

Points to note about fossil fuels:

- At present most of the world's electricity is generated using fossil fuels
- Their supply is limited and they will eventually run out
- Fossil fuels release carbon dioxide when they burn, which adds to the greenhouse effect and increases global warming (see chapter 41)
- Coal and oil release sulfur dioxide gas when they burn, which causes breathing problems for living creatures and contributes to acid rain.

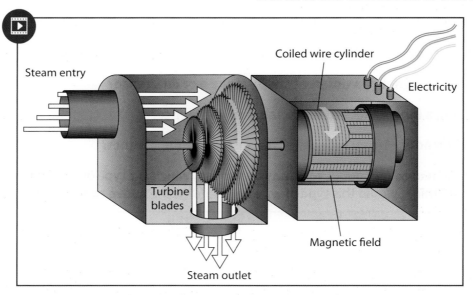

▲ **Figure 31.5** *A turbine generator*

? Question

31.7 Using the internet for research, prepare a short slide presentation on four of the different ways that electricity is generated. Your presentation might include:

- A photograph
- A brief explanation as to how the electrical energy is generated
- Two points to note about that particular method of generating electricity.

(Hint: read about how electricity is generated from fossil fuels before you start your presentation.)

Energy from solar cells

Activity 31.2 How can we generate electricity from **solar cells**?

 Equipment needed

Solar cells   Study lamp   Multimeter

Safety
- Take care when handling the lamp as the bulb may get hot and should not be touched.
- The lamp will be plugged into a socket and great care must be taken with all electrical devices.

➡ **Conducting the activity**

1. Set up the equipment as shown in Figure 31.6.
2. Switch on the lamp and allow the light to fall onto the solar cells.
3. Turn the dial of the multimeter so that it reads millivolts.
4. Note and record the reading on the multimeter.
5. Move the lamp nearer the solar cells.
6. Note any differences to the reading on the multimeter.
7. Cover some of the solar cells with a piece of paper. You have now reduced the area of the solar cells that is exposed to the light.
8. Note the reading on the multimeter in your Student Activity Book.

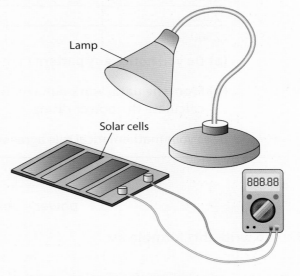

▲ Figure 31.6 *Generating electricity from solar cells*

? Questions

Use the internet to find out:

31.8 What percentage of electrical energy is generated in Ireland by each of the individual methods listed on page 354 (fossil fuels, nuclear fuels, wind, moving water, geothermal, solar).

31.9 What percentage of electrical energy is generated in the world by each of the individual methods from question 31.8?

31.10 Write a brief account of how you think each of the individual methods of generating electricity will be used in 20 years' time. Which methods do you think will be more popular and which will be less popular?

What is electrical power?

As with other words we have looked at, 'power' has a very precise meaning in the physical world. Note the following:

- **Electrical power** is the amount of electrical energy changed to other forms of energy in one second

- The unit for electrical power is the **watt** (W)
- Sometimes you see a unit called the kilowatt (kW), which is 1000 watts.

? Question

31.11 Read the following and then answer the questions below.

A research scientist was investigating the performance of electric kettles by connecting them to power supplies of different voltage values. In each trial he noted the value of the voltage and the value of the current flowing through the kettle; he also recorded the power rating of each kettle:

Power rating (W)	Voltage (V)	Current (A)
1200	120	10
1500	150	10
1800	180	10
2000	250	8
2200	110	20
2500	125	20

(a) Do you notice any pattern in the data the scientist recorded?

(b) From the data, work out a mathematical rule that would allow you to calculate the power rating.

Does your mathematical rule agree with the following formula for calculating a power?

---

power = voltage × current

We can write this formula as:

$$P = V \times I$$

Where:

P = power

V = voltage (potential difference)

I = current.

We can rewrite this as a triangle to help solve other calculations:

$$\frac{P}{V \times I}$$

Note: This maths formula is used only for questions on electricity. Try not to confuse this with the formula for power, on page 318.

② Questions

31.12 When you buy an electrical appliance the power is usually written on it.

How do the following values compare to what you have at home?

(a) An 11-watt energy-saving bulb

(b) A 900-watt microwave oven

(c) A 2500-watt electric kettle

(d) A 110-watt flat-screen TV

What do you notice about the heat output of appliances that have a higher power rating?

Note: be very careful with electrical appliances at home. Examine them only when they are unplugged from the socket. Hot appliances should be allowed to cool before being examined.

Sample calculation 1

Calculate the power used by an electrical appliance that consumes 2 amperes of current when connected to a 230-volt supply.

Answer:

$$P = V \times I$$
$$P = 230 \times 2$$
$$P = 460 \text{ watts}$$

Sample calculation 2

Calculate the current used by an electric kettle rated 2300 watts when it is plugged into the socket at home, which gives 230 volts.

Answer:

$$\text{Rearrange } P = V \times I \text{ to get } I = \frac{P}{V}$$
$$\text{Therefore } I = \frac{2300}{230}$$
$$I = 10 \text{ amperes}$$

Sample calculation 3

Calculate the voltage (potential difference) applied when a 24-watt car bulb uses a current of 2 amperes.

Answer:

$$\text{Rearrange } P = V \times I \text{ to get } V = \frac{P}{I}$$
$$\text{Therefore } V = \frac{24}{2}$$
$$V = 12 \text{ volts}$$

What is the unit of electrical energy?

We saw in previous chapters that the unit of energy is the joule. This unit would not be very suitable for calculating the electrical energy used in our homes as the joule is a very small amount of energy. So electricity supply companies use a different unit for energy: the **kilowatt-hour** (kWh).

The kilowatt-hour is the energy used when 1 kilowatt of power is used for 1 hour.

Note: the kilowatt-hour is often called the unit of electricity.

The price of 1 kWh can vary just like the price of most items. However, an average price would be about 18 cents for 1 kWh.

Power rating of electrical appliances

Most electrical appliances will have their power rating written on them. The power rating can be given in watts or in kilowatts. When you want to calculate the cost of using an appliance you must always work with kilowatts.

To help you convert to kilowatts, remember to divide the power in watts by 1000.

$$500 \text{ watts} = \frac{500}{1000} = 0.5 \text{ kW}$$

$$75 \text{ watts} = \frac{75}{1000} = 0.075 \text{ kW}$$

Sample calculation 4

An electrical kettle has a power rating of 2 kW. The kettle is used to boil water for a total of 2 hours each day for a full week. Calculate:

(a) The number of units of electricity used in the week

(b) The total cost if 1 kWh costs 18 cents.

Answer:
(a) Number of units = number of kW × total number of hours

$$= 2 \times (2 \times 7)$$

$$= 28 \text{ kWh}$$

(b) Cost = number of kWh × cost per unit

$$= 28 \times 18 \text{ cents}$$

$$= 504 \text{ cents}$$

$$= €5.04$$

▲ Figure 31.7 *An electric kettle has a power rating of 2 kWh*

Sample calculation 5

A family goes away on holiday for exactly 2 weeks. An 11 W bulb is left on for the full 2 weeks. Calculate:

(a) The number of units of electricity used in the 2 weeks

(b) The total cost if 1 kWh costs 18 cents.

Answer:

(a) Remember: $11\ W = \dfrac{11}{1000}\ kW = 0.011\ kW$

Number of units = number of kW × total number of hours

$$= 0.011 \times (24 \times 14)$$

$$= 3.696\ kWh$$

(b) Cost = number of kWh × cost per unit

$$= 3.696 \times 18$$

$$= 66.528\ cents$$

$$= 67\ cents\ (rounded\ to\ the\ nearest\ cent)$$

Were you surprised by the cost of lighting the bulb for a full fortnight?

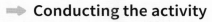

Activity 31.3 How can we estimate the cost of electricity in our homes for a week?

Equipment needed

Various electrical appliances in your home

A recent electricity bill from your home
(don't bring this into class as it is private to your family)

Safety
- Unplug any appliance before you examine it.
- Allow any hot appliance to cool down before you examine it.

➡ **Conducting the activity**

1. In the table in your Student Activity Book, make a list of 10 electrical appliances you have at home.

2. Beside each appliance on your list write down the power rating, taking care to unplug any appliance before you examine it. (The power rating will be written on the appliance.) Let any hot appliance cool before you examine it.

3. Make an estimate of the number of hours that each appliance is used in a week.

4. Calculate the total number of kilowatt-hours for all these appliances for the week.

5. Find out the cost of one kilowatt-hour (one unit) from a recent electricity bill in your home.

6. Calculate the total cost of using all these appliances for the week.

Questions

31.13 How does your estimated cost compare with your bill?

31.14 How much time is covered by your bill at home? Was it one week, one month or longer?

31.15 Give some reasons why your estimated bill and your actual bill might be quite different.

How can we reduce consumption of electrical energy?

Many people in the world benefit from electrical energy. In some cases this benefit is very obvious. However, in order to conserve energy and keep costs down, we need to know how much electrical energy is used in the world and what it is used for.

Question

31.16 Use the internet to find out factual information on the following:

(a) Which household appliances in the home use most electrical energy

(b) How much electrical energy different industries use

(c) How much electrical energy has been used in Ireland in different periods in the last 50 years

(d) How much electrical energy is used in different countries.

Ethical issues and sustainability

Sustainable development is development that meets the needs of the present without compromising the ability of future generations to meet their own needs.

Question

31.17 By working in small groups, discuss the following issues.

(a) What can we do in school to be responsible with our use of electrical energy?

(b) What can we do at home to be responsible with our use of electrical energy?

(c) What can the people of Ireland do to be responsible with their use of electrical energy?

(d) What steps do world leaders need to take to help future generations meet their energy needs?

Summary questions

31.18 Name six different ways of generating electricity used in the world today.

31.19 Name three fossil fuels.

31.20 Explain why some fuels are called fossil fuels.

31.21 Some of the following statements are true and some are false. Copy out the ones that are true.

(a) A stationary magnet beside a stationary coil of wire may generate electricity.

(b) A moving magnet beside a stationary coil of wire may generate electricity.

(c) A stationary magnet beside a moving coil of wire may generate electricity.

(d) A moving magnet beside a coil of wire moving in the opposite direction may generate electricity.

31.22 Look carefully at Figure 31.8.

Regarding the activity illustrated in this figure, some of the following statements are true and some are false. Copy out the ones that are true.

(a) When the lamp is off and stationary, electricity may be generated.

(b) When the lamp is off and moving, electricity may be generated.

(c) When the lamp is on and stationary, electricity may be generated.

(d) When the lamp is on and moving, electricity may be generated.

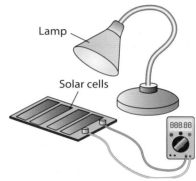
▲ Figure 31.8

31.23 Calculate the power used by an electrical appliance that consumes 10 amperes of current when connected to a 230-volt supply.

31.24 Calculate the power used by an electrical appliance that consumes 0.25 amperes of current when connected to a 230-volt supply.

31.25 Calculate the current used by an electric kettle rated 2760 watts when it is plugged into the socket at home, which gives 230 volts.

31.26 Calculate the current used by an electric kettle rated 1840 watts when it is plugged into the socket at home, which gives 230 volts.

31.27 Calculate the voltage applied when an 18-watt car bulb uses a current of 1.5 amperes.

31.28 Calculate the voltage applied when a 14-watt living-room bulb uses a current of 0.06 amperes.

31.29 An electrical kettle has a power rating of 2500 W. The kettle is used to boil water for a total of 3 hours each day for a full week. Calculate:

(a) The number of units of electricity used in the week

(b) The total cost if 1 kWh costs 18 cents.

31.30 A family goes away on holiday for exactly 2 weeks. A 500 W garden security light bulb is left on for the full 2 weeks. Calculate:

(a) The number of units of electricity used in the 2 weeks

(b) The total cost if 1 kWh costs 18 cents.

Log on to **www.edcolearning.ie** for Additional Summary Questions

PHYSICAL WORLD

Assessment questions

31.31 Copy the paragraph and fill in the missing words from the list of five words provided. **(15 marks)**

| water | magnet | kinetic | chemical | burned |

Coal, oil and gas are stores of _____ energy. When _____ they release heat energy. The heat energy boils _____ to make steam. The moving steam has _____ energy, which turns the blades of a turbine. The turbine spins the _____ near the coil of wire in the generator, which makes the electrical energy.

31.32 Copy the table and fill in the missing values. **(15 marks)**

Power (watt)	Voltage (volt)	Current (ampere)
1000	250	
	230	10
100		0.5
	6	0.05
12	6	
0.288		0.008

31.33 A student generated electricity by shining light from a lamp onto a solar cell as shown in Figure 31.8 on page 363. **(30 marks)**

(a) Give a precaution to be taken here regarding the lamp.

(b) Name the device connected to the solar cells that measures the voltage generated.

(c) The student used five different solar cells of the same type but of different surface areas. She recorded the following data:

Surface area of solar cells (cm²)	Voltage recorded (V)
40	0.2
80	0.4
120	0.6
160	0.8
200	1.0

(d) Draw a graph of the above data by plotting voltage on the y-axis and surface area on the x-axis.

(e) From your graph calculate the voltage generated by a solar cell of surface area 100 cm².

(f) From this activity, what conclusion can you make about the relationship between surface area of a solar cell and the voltage generated?

31.34 Question from Junior Cycle Science exam paper (30 marks)

Electrical energy is one of the most important types of energy that we use in our daily lives. An electrical appliance has a power rating which tells you how much electricity it uses.

The table below shows the power rating of some common household appliances and the forms of energy that are produced in the appliances.

Appliance	Power rating (W)	Forms of energy produced	Current used (A)
Coffee maker	1380	Heat, Sound	6
Television	115	Heat, Light, Sound	0.5
Kitchen blender	345	Heat, Kinetic, Sound	1.5
Dishwasher	2300	Heat, Kinetic, Sound	10

(a) Which appliance listed in the table uses the most electrical energy?

(b) Select one of the appliances from the table above and name a useful form of energy produced when the appliance is being used.

For the appliance you have selected, name an unwanted form of energy produced.

For the appliance you have selected, calculate the voltage applied across the appliance.

Include the unit for your answer.

(c) What pattern, if any, exists between the power rating of the appliance and the current used?

Sustainability issues arise from the generation and consumption of electricity.

(d) What do you understand by the term sustainability?

(e) Suggest one way in which we can reduce how much electrical energy we use.

(f) Electrical energy can be produced using renewable and non-renewable sources.

Identify **two** renewable sources of energy from the list below.

Oil   Solar   Natural gas   Wind

Log on to **www.edcolearning.ie** for Additional Assessment Questions

PowerPoint summary   Weblinks

CHAPTER 32

ELECTRONICS

LO: PW2, PW5

Learning intentions

At the end of this chapter you will be able to:

✓ Identify the symbols for a buzzer, a diode, a light-emitting diode (LED) and a light-dependent resistor (LDR)

✓ Explain that when a diode is forward biased it can conduct electricity

✓ Explain that when a diode is reverse biased it cannot conduct electricity

✓ Explain that LEDs can emit light when a current flows through them

✓ Explain that an LDR can have its resistance changed simply by shining light on it

✓ Investigate how diodes, LEDs and LDRs work.

Keywords

🔑 buzzer
🔑 diode
🔑 forward bias
🔑 reverse bias
🔑 light-emitting diode (LED)
🔑 light-dependent resistor (LDR)
🔑 resistor

▲ Figure 32.1 *The electrical unit in a washing machine heats the water and rotates the clothes*

Circuits

An electrical circuit will mainly change electrical energy into other forms of energy, usually heat, light or movement. An electronic circuit can process information and make a decision.

In a washing machine the electrical circuit will heat the water and rotate the clothes. The control panel is an electronic circuit, used to select and control temperature and time settings and it turns on an indicator light when the clothes are washed.

? Question

32.1 Make a list of five electrical appliances you have at home that contain both electrical and electronic circuits. For each appliance give one example of what the electrical circuit is used for and one example of what the electronic circuit is used for.

Present your findings in the form of a poster.

What electronic components will we use?

You will remember that we listed the devices that are used in electrical circuits in chapter 30. The list comprised: battery, filament bulb, switch, resistor, variable resistor, ammeter, voltmeter and ohmmeter. Here, we will look at some electronic devices, namely:

- Buzzer
- Diode
- Light-emitting diode (LED)
- Light-dependent resistor (LDR).

What is a buzzer?

A buzzer is a device that converts electrical energy to sound energy. It makes a buzzing sound when an electric current passes through it. Its symbol is shown in Figure 32.2.

▲ Figure 32.2 *The symbol used for a buzzer*

What is a diode?

A diode is a device that allows an electric current to flow in one direction only. The symbol used for the diode is shown in Figure 32.3.

▲ Figure 32.3 *The symbol used for a diode*

---

⑦ **Question**

32.2 By comparing the symbol in Figure 32.3 and the photograph of the diode in Figure 32.4, can you tell if the right-hand side of the diode in the photograph corresponds to the right-hand side of the diode symbol?

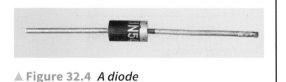

▲ Figure 32.4 *A diode*

🖊 **Activity 32.1   What happens when a diode and a bulb are connected to a battery?**

🧪 **Equipment needed**

1.5-V battery	Small bulb
Diode	Connecting wires

⚠ **Safety**
- Take care not to let the bulb fall as it could break into very sharp pieces.

➡ **Conducting the activity**

1. Connect the diode and the bulb to the battery as shown in Figure 32.5.
2. Note in the space provided in your Student Activity Book what happens to the bulb.
3. Disconnect the diode, turn it around the other way and connect it in the circuit again.
4. Record what happens to the bulb.

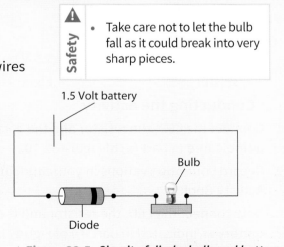

1.5 Volt battery

Bulb

Diode

▲ Figure 32.5 *Circuit of diode, bulb and battery*

To help you remember ...

If you look at the symbol for the diode it looks like parts of the letters P (for positive) and N (for negative) have been squashed together.

▲ Figure 32.6 *The symbol for a diode*

Forward bias: P is positive and N is negative

The diode allows current to flow if the P terminal is connected to the positive of the battery and the N terminal is connected to the negative of the battery.

When the diode allows current to flow we say that the diode conducts. We also say that the diode is in **forward bias**.

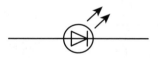

▲ Figure 32.7 *Current flows in the circuit (forward bias)*

Reverse bias: N is positive and P is negative

The diode will not allow current to flow if the P terminal is connected to the negative of the battery and the N terminal is connected to the positive of the battery.

When the diode does not allow current to flow we say that the diode does not conduct. We also say that the diode is in **reverse bias**.

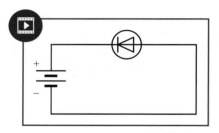

▲ Figure 32.8 *Current does not flow (reverse bias)*

> **Did you know?**
>
> Diodes can change between being forward biased and reverse biased many millions of times each second. This is the basic idea behind modern digital electronics.

What is a light-emitting diode (LED)?

Some diodes can give out light when current flows through them. They are called light-emitting diodes and the abbreviation used is LED. The symbol for the LED is shown in Figure 32.9.

▲ Figure 32.9 *Symbol for the LED*

✎ Activity 32.2 When does an LED emit light?

🧪 **Equipment needed**

An LED   1.5-V battery
A resistor   Electrical leads

➡ **Conducting the activity**

1. Connect the LED, the resistor and the battery as indicated in part (a) of Figure 32.10.

2. Record your observations in your Student Activity Book.

3. Now connect the LED, the resistor and the battery as indicated in part (b) of Figure 32.10.

4. Record your observations in your Student Activity Book and answer the questions on the next page.

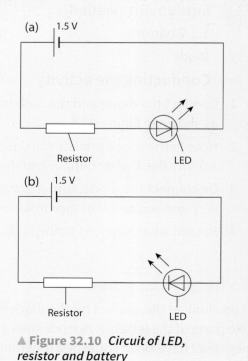

▲ Figure 32.10 *Circuit of LED, resistor and battery*

? Questions

32.3 Under what condition will the LED emit light?

32.4 Under what condition will the LED not emit light?

32.5 What are the terms used for when an LED will emit light and when it will not emit light?

Why does an LED need a resistor?

An LED uses only a very small current when it is emitting light. In fact, the LED uses much less current than a bulb.

If a large current flows through an LED it will most likely burn out. The LED will no longer work. To prevent damage to the LED, we always have a resistor connected in series to limit the current, as you can see from Figure 32.11.

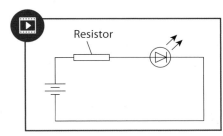

▲ **Figure 32.11** *The circuit for an LED, including a resistor to limit the current*

? Question

32.6 **(a)** On your own, on a sheet of paper draw circuit diagrams including a battery, a resistor and an LED to show:

  (i) An LED that is lighting

  (ii) An LED that is not lighting.

(b) Give a brief explanation of why the LED does or does not light.

(c) In pairs compare your answer to that of your fellow student.

Did you know?

The Nobel Prize in Physics 2014 was awarded jointly to Isamu Akasaki, Hiroshi Amano and Shuji Nakamura 'for the invention of efficient blue light-emitting diodes which has enabled bright and energy-saving white light sources'.

? Question

32.7 Each person from a group of four should select one of the following topics for internet research.

Each student should present a poster project to the class on one of the following:

(a) The history of the diode before 1960

(b) The history of the diode after 1960

(c) The history of the LED and examples of where LEDs are used in the home

(d) The reason for awarding the 2014 Nobel Prize in Physics to Isamu Akasaki, Hiroshi Amano and Shuji Nakamura.

What is a light-dependent resistor (LDR)?

The light-dependent resistor (LDR) is a resistor whose value of resistance can change. The value of the resistance will change as the intensity or brightness of the light falling on it changes.

Using an LDR you can arrange for an electrical appliance to be controlled by light. In fact some appliances can be switched on or switched off simply by shining light on the LDR connected to them. Public street lights are an example of this.

The symbol for the LDR is shown in Figure 32.12.

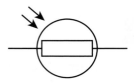

▲ Figure 32.12 *The symbol for the LDR*

▲ Figure 32.13 *A light-dependent resistor*

🖉 Activity 32.3 What factor controls the resistance of an LDR and the current flowing through it?

🧪 Equipment needed

An LDR

Digital ohmmeter (multimeter)

6-V battery

Filament bulb

Electrical leads

Switch

> **Safety**
> • Take care not to drop the 6-V battery as it is quite heavy.
> • Take care not to let the bulb fall as it could break into very sharp pieces.

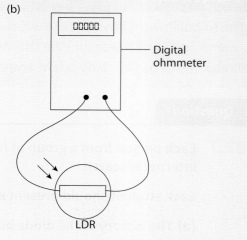

▲ Figure 32.14 *Circuit to show resistance of an LDR*

➡ Conducting the activity

1. Connect the 6-V battery, the LDR, the switch and the filament bulb as indicated in part (a) of Figure 32.14.

2. Close the switch and record your observations.

3. Now cover the LDR with your hand. Record your observations in the space provided in your Student Activity Book.

4. Now connect the LDR directly to the digital ohmmeter as indicated in part (b) of Figure 32.14.

5. Record the value of the resistance.

6. Now cover the LDR with your hand. Record the value of the resistance.

Answer the questions on the next page.

32.8 What happened to the light from the filament bulb when you covered the LDR with your hand?

32.9 What can you conclude about the current flowing through an LDR when it is covered and doesn't get light from the room?

32.10 What was the difference in the resistance of the LDR when it was covered and when it was not covered?

32.11 Use the internet to find three examples of where LDRs are used in everyday situations.

 Activity 32.4 **How can we set up a circuit to choose between a high-frequency buzzer and a low-frequency buzzer?**

Equipment needed

6-V battery   High-frequency buzzer
Low-frequency buzzer   2 diodes
Resistor   Connecting wires

 Safety
• Take care not to drop the 6-V battery as it is quite heavy.

Conducting the activity

1. Connect the terminals of the battery so that A is connected to the positive terminal and B to the negative terminal, as shown in Figure 32.15.
2. The high-frequency buzzer will sound. Explain why in the space provided in your Student Activity Book.
3. The low-frequency buzzer is silent. Explain why.
4. Now connect the terminals of the battery so that A is connected to the negative terminal and B to the positive terminal.
5. The low-frequency buzzer will sound. Explain why.
6. The high-frequency buzzer is silent. Explain why.

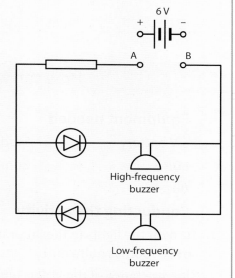

▲ Figure 32.15 *High-frequency and low-frequency buzzers*

Did you know?

By using three different LEDs, the first could emit red light, the second green light and the third blue light. You can then combine the three colours to get the type of light we get from ordinary bulbs. We call this light white light. This idea gives us bulbs that use very little energy and won the Nobel Prize in Physics for the three scientists mentioned previously.

Activity 32.5 How can we choose which LED will emit light?

 Equipment needed

6-V battery   2 resistors   LED emitting red light

2 switches   LED emitting green light   Connecting wires

➡️ **Conducting the activity**

1. Set up one circuit as shown in Figure 32.16.

2. Close switch A and keep switch B open. Write down your observations and explain why this happened in the space provided in your Student Activity Book.

3. Close switch B and keep switch A open. Write down your observations and explain why this happened.

4. Close both switches. Write down your observations and explain why this happened.

⚠️ Safety
- Take care not to drop the 6-V battery as it is quite heavy.

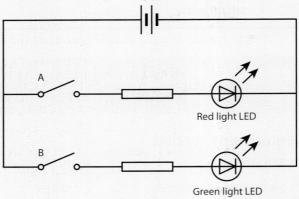

▲ **Figure 32.16** *Changing from a red light to a green light*

Activity 32.6 How can we activate a buzzer by switching on a light?

Equipment needed

6-V battery   Study lamp

LDR   Connecting wires

Buzzer

⚠️ Safety
- Take care not to drop the 6-V battery as it is quite heavy.
- The bulb may get hot and should not be touched.
- The lamp will be plugged into a socket and great care must be taken with all electrical devices.

➡️ **Conducting the activity**

1. Turn off the lights in the laboratory so the room is quite dim.

2. The resistance of the LDR is high because of the dim light and only a very small current flows through the buzzer. There is no sound from the buzzer.

3. Switch on the study lamp so that bright light shines on the LDR.

4. The resistance of the LDR is now low, allowing a greater current to flow through the buzzer.

5. You can now hear sound from the buzzer.

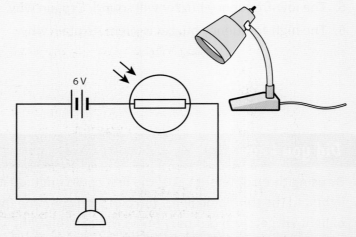

▲ **Figure 32.17** *Activating a buzzer by switching on a light*

PHYSICAL WORLD

Summary questions

32.12 (a) What do the letters LED stand for?

  (b) Draw the symbol for the LED.

32.13 Name the three scientists who won the Nobel Prize in Physics in 2014.

32.14 What do the letters LDR stand for?

32.15 Draw the symbol for the LDR.

32.16 What is the difference between an electrical circuit and an electronic circuit?

32.17 What happens when electricity passes through a buzzer?

32.18 What is a diode used for?

32.19 Draw the symbol for a diode.

32.20 What is the meaning of a diode in forward bias?

32.21 What is the meaning of a diode in reverse bias?

32.22 Draw a simple circuit diagram to show a battery connected to a diode in forward bias.

32.23 Draw a simple circuit diagram to show a battery connected to a diode in reverse bias.

32.24 A student wanted to connect an LED to a battery and was advised to put a resistor in the circuit. Explain the reason for the resistor.

32.25 Draw a simple circuit diagram of a battery, resistor and LED connected together so that the LED emits light.

32.26 Draw a simple circuit diagram of a battery, resistor and LED connected together so that the LED does not emit light.

32.27 What happens to the resistance of an LDR when bright light shines on it?

32.28 Name one practical use for an LDR.

Assessment questions

32.29   (15 marks)

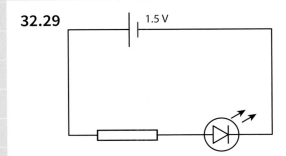

▲ Figure 32.18

Copy the following paragraph and fill in the missing words from the list of five words provided.

forward   current   reverse   light   battery

In the above circuit diagram a resistor, an LED and a _____ are shown connected together. The resistor is used to limit the _____, to prevent the LED burning out. The LED emits _____ when current flows through it. When an LED emits light we say it is in _____ bias. If the terminals of the LED are switched around, no light is emitted and the LED is in _____ bias.

32.30 Question from Junior Cycle Science exam paper (30 marks)

When green light is shone into a red solution, such as blood, some of the light is absorbed, some is reflected and some passes straight through.

A student set up the apparatus shown below to investigate the relationship between the concentration of a red solution and how much green light passes through it.

On one side of the test tube of red solution, green light was emitted from a light-emitting diode (LED).

On the other side of the test tube, a light-dependent resistor (LDR) was used to detect how much green light passed through the solution.

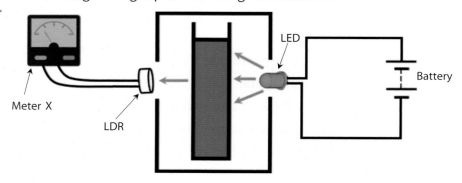

▲ Figure 32.19

The student made different concentrations of a solution of red food dye by varying the number of drops of dye added to 20 cm³ of water. The resistance of the LDR was then determined using meter **X**. The following results were obtained.

Number of drops of food colouring	0	1	2	3	4	5	6	7	8
Resistance (Ω)	1.0	1.5	2.0	2.5	3.0	3.5	4.0	4.5	5.0

(a) Draw a graph of the results obtained.

(b) State one conclusion which is supported by the results.

(c) Name meter **X**, which was used to determine the resistance of the LDR.

(d) Name a piece of equipment the student could have used to accurately measure 20 cm³ of water.

(e) A smart watch uses a green LED to measure a person's pulse by shining green light into the red blood in the person's wrist.

Describe one other technological application of physics that is used in everyday life.

(f) The chamber of the heart marked **X** pumps blood around the body and generates a pulse.

Name chamber **X**.

Explain why some of the tubes connected to the heart are coloured red and some of them are coloured blue.

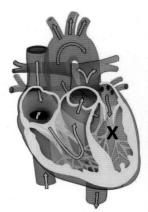

▲ Figure 32.20

 Log on to **www.edcolearning.ie** for Additional Assessment Questions

PowerPoint summary   Weblinks

IMPACT OF MODERN PHYSICS ON SOCIETY

CHAPTER 33

LO: PW4

What is digital electronics?

We saw in chapter 32 that a diode could control the direction in which a current could flow. Based on this idea, many other **digital electronic** devices were developed in the second half of the twentieth century. Indeed, in the last 25 years huge improvements have been made in the performance of these devices.

Sounds entering our ears can be represented by a wave, as shown in Figure 33.1. This type of wave is an **analog signal**, represented in the diagram in Figure 33.2. A **digital signal** is different, as you can see in Figure 33.3.

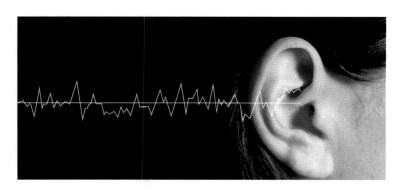

▲ Figure 33.1 *We hear analog signals*

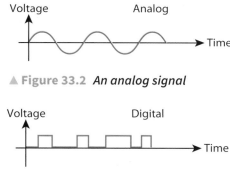

▲ Figure 33.2 *An analog signal*

▲ Figure 33.3 *A digital signal*

Digital signals, as you can see from the figures, are not smooth like analog signals. Digital signals are simple 'true-false' or 'on-off' statements to represent information. Because digital devices recognise only one of two possible signals, they are less affected by unwanted electronic signals.

The mathematics for digital electronics is based on the work of George Boole, who was the first professor of mathematics in Cork University, from 1849 to 1864.

Digital electronics has had a great impact on **society**. You might call it an electronics revolution.

To help us to discuss and research how digital electronics has affected the world, we will examine the technology associated with telecommunications and the internet. We will look at how science, the environment and society in general have been affected by these technologies.

? Question

33.1 By using the internet, research the life and work of George Boole. Present your findings in the form of a poster.

What is meant by 'telecommunications'?

Keeping in touch by telephone has become easier, cheaper and more reliable in recent years. We will consider some short statements on how the following have been affected by new forms of **telecommunications**:

- Science
- Environment
- Society.

Once you have looked at these topics, you will form groups to research and discuss issues relating to them.

▲ Figure 33.4 *Optical fibres have replaced old cables for phones and are much more efficient*

▲ Figure 33.5 *Antique telephone*

Science

The popularity of mobile phones has resulted in a greater need for people to be skilled in electronics and computing. Many courses in electronics are offered by universities and third-level colleges. More people today understand and appreciate the wonders of this area of science.

Environment

Many modern electronic devices become outdated very quickly. Outdated devices are dumped or recycled and newer devices are manufactured. Earth's natural resources are being used up in the manufacturing process and the waste causes a problem in the **environment**.

The problem has also led to a greater awareness of the need to recycle. The copper in old wiring is very often recycled.

▲ Figure 33.6 *Soldering equipment and electronic parts*

Society

Instead of walking or cycling to a friend's house, people today choose to text or use social media from the comfort of home. Are people becoming lazier? How will this lack of exercise affect a person's health as they get older?

Many young adults move to foreign countries after they finish their education. With the improvement in communications technology they can keep in contact with their parents and friends back home on a regular basis. This is very comforting to the young person abroad and to the family at home.

▲ Figure 33.7 *Much material is recycled, like these speakers*

▲ Figure 33.8 *Is the ease with which we can keep in touch with people making us lazy?*

? Question

Topics for discussion and research

33.2 **(a)** In your group, discuss the following topics (i)–(ix). One person from each group should record and present the group's views to the rest of the class.

(b) At home do some research on the same nine topics. Back in class, discuss these same topics again. This time you will have the benefit of having done some research. Is there a difference in the views of the groups on the various topics?

(i) Third-level colleges provide many courses on digital electronics and computer-related studies. Is this having a negative impact on more traditional areas of study such as languages, history, geography, and so on?

(ii) Will the study of digital electronics have a negative impact on the study of the biological sciences?

(iii) Is the education system producing too many people interested in electronics and computer studies?

(iv) People spend more time indoors using devices than in previous years. Has this made people less aware of their natural environment?

(v) Is the electronics industry a major cause of pollution in the environment?

(vi) What parts of an out-of-date mobile phone can be recycled?

(vii) Some parents keep in contact with their children using mobile phones. Is this good for children? Are children safer today because of mobile phones?

(viii) How are parents affected when their adult children move abroad to work? Has the improvements in technology made this easier for the parents?

(ix) Modern technology has enabled us to find information quickly. Do we really need instant access to information?

What is the internet?

The **internet** is a vast, world-wide network of computers all connected together.

> ? **Question**
>
> **33.3** Explain the difference between the internet and the world wide web.

A quick look at Table 33.1 will show how the internet has influenced the lives of people.

Table 33.1 Numbers of people using the internet

At the end of the year	Number of people using the internet
1995	16 million
1999	248 million
2003	719 million
2006	1093 million
2009	1802 million
2012	2497 million
2015	3366 million
2019	4536 million
Present year	?

> ? **Questions**
>
> **33.4** What do you predict will be the figure in the last row of the table?
>
> **33.5** Research the number of people using the internet worldwide this year. How close was your estimate?

Consider the following short statements on how the internet has affected each of the following:

● Science   ● Environment   ● Society.

Once you have looked at these, you will form groups to research and discuss topics.

Science

The internet gives access to an amazing library, with an almost endless supply of information. The study of science has been greatly facilitated by the internet: you can find information and share information with others so easily. You can study the historical development of science as well as keeping up to date with recent discoveries.

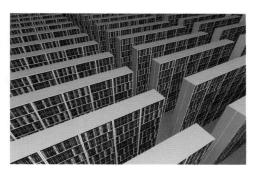

▲ Figure 33.9 *The internet is like an infinite library*

Environment

The internet has made it very easy to learn about what is happening all around the world. An example of a benefit of this is the idea of renting bicycles to travel around a city: one city started this, and in a short time cities all around the world were copying this clever idea. This had resulted in cities being less polluted and commuters becoming fitter.

▲ Figure 33.10 *Dublin bikes*

Society

Many tasks are made easier because of the internet. You can book a holiday, order a book and buy clothes on the internet. However, the people who worked for the holiday company, the book shop and the clothes shop may have lost their jobs. Has the internet been good for society?

▲ Figure 33.11 *Internet shopping affects bricks-and-mortar shops and livelihoods*

? Questions

Topics for discussion and research

33.6 **(a)** In your group, discuss the following topics (i)–(x). One person from each group should record and present the group's views to the rest of the class.

(b) At home do some research on the same ten topics. Back in class, discuss these same topics again. This time you will have the benefit of having done some research. Is there a difference in the views of the groups on the various topics?

(i) Has the internet helped students to be skilled at research on a computer but less capable at performing activities in a laboratory with their own hands?

(ii) What do you use the internet for? What is the most common use of the internet among students in your class?

(iii) Has the internet allowed students from some poorer countries to compete with students from wealthier countries?

(iv) New discoveries are being made at a very rapid rate. Will these new ideas make the science you learn in school totally out of date?

(v) In the past people lived in cities to find a good job. However, with the internet you can live far away from a city and work online. Will this be good for the environment?

(vi) When you use the internet a certain amount of electrical energy is needed to power this. Is the energy consumption of the internet a cause of concern for the environment?

(vii) Has the internet made people more aware of the need to protect our environment for future generations?

(viii) What kinds of jobs have people lost because of the internet?

(ix) Do people work less hard than before because of the internet? Do people have more free time to relax? Is this good for society?

(x) Internet bullying (often referred to as cyber bullying) is a major problem all around the world. What can be done to help prevent this bullying?

33.7 Class discussion:

You have now discussed several topics based on how the internet has affected our lives. For this you used the internet itself as a source of information.

(a) How reliable is the information on the internet?

(b) Is it possible to tell if the information is biased?

(c) Could the information be out of date?

(d) Who is responsible for keeping information up to date?

Summary questions

33.8 Sketch a graph to show an analog signal with voltage on the y-axis and time on the x-axis.

33.9 Sketch a graph to show a digital signal with voltage on the y-axis and time on the x-axis.

33.10 With regards to Professor George Boole:

(a) What subject was he a professor of?

(b) Name the university in which he worked.

33.11 What is the meaning of the word 'telecommunications'?

● **33.12** Give an example of how science has benefitted from modern telecommunications.

● **33.13** Has modern telecommunications been good or bad for the environment? Justify your answer.

● **33.14** Give an example of how the internet has had a direct benefit to the environment.

● **33.15** **(a)** Give an example of how the internet has benefitted society in general.

   (b) Give an example of how the internet has been bad for society in general.

● **33.16** **(a)** Give an example of how modern telecommunications has been good for society in general.

   (b) Give an example of how modern telecommunications has been bad for society in general.

● **33.17** The internet gives access to a vast library. Give two examples of how the internet is better than a school library or a local library. Give two examples of how it is worse.

Assessment questions

33.18 Many new technologies have been developed in the last 200 years. **(15 marks)** Telecommunication technologies are good examples of this. Being able to communicate across the Atlantic shows the progress that has been made in this area. The telegraph was invented in 1837 and it enabled the first transmission of signals using electrical methods.

In 1866, Valentia Island in Kerry and Newfoundland in Canada were connected by the first successful transatlantic cable. Instead of taking weeks to send a message across the Atlantic by ship, electrical signals could be transmitted in seconds.

The first television signal was sent across the Atlantic in 1962. The signal was transmitted using microwaves and the Telstar communications satellite, which was in Medium Earth orbit. This is an orbit above Earth at a height of more than 2000 kilometres. Signals were transmitted from Maine in the USA to Brittany in France for 20 minutes during each orbit of 2.6-hours.

Towards the end of the 20th century, several cables were laid across the Atlantic, and communication of signals using optical fibres had arrived. In 2015, the Hibernia Express optical cable, which connects Cork and London to Halifax and New York, was completed. Data transmission across the Atlantic has never been so fast, with the signal from New York to London taking just 29 milliseconds to arrive!

(a) When was the telegraph invented?

(b) Name the two parts of the world connected by the first successful transatlantic cable in 1866.

(c) Name the type of wave used for transmitting the first TV signal.

(d) What kind of cables were laid across the Atlantic and used for communication in the late twentieth century?

(e) How many seconds is 29 milliseconds? (Hint: it is less than 1 second.)

33.19 Rock music became very popular in the 1960s. At this time, many musicians **(15 marks)** changed from using acoustic guitars to electric guitars. The science behind these two instruments is very different.

The frequency of the musical note played by the guitar depends on the length of the string and the tension in the string, among other factors.

In the electric guitar the strings are made of steel. There is a small bar magnet under each string. The purpose of the magnet is to magnetise the steel string. The magnet has a coil of wire wrapped around it.

When the string is plucked, it vibrates. The string is now like a vibrating, or moving, magnet. A voltage is made in the coil wrapped around the bar magnet, which causes a current to flow in the coil. The signal is amplified and sent to a set of speakers.

Jimi Hendrix was a musician who was very famous for playing the electric guitar. He made use of the fact that further control over the music could be achieved by having coils of different numbers of turns.

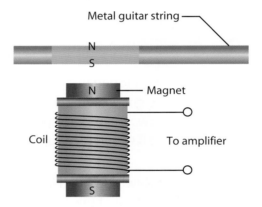

▲ **Figure 33.12** *A string on an electric guitar*

(a) Name the two different types of guitar.

(b) Name the type of energy of a vibrating guitar string.

(c) Not all metals can be made into magnets. Name the metal used for the guitar string.

(d) What causes the electrical current to flow in the coil?

(e) What energy change occurs in a speaker?

PowerPoint summary   Weblinks

EARTH AND SPACE

LEARNING OUTCOMES: LO

ES1. Students should be able to describe the relationships between various celestial objects including moons, asteroids, comets, planets, stars, solar systems, galaxies and space

ES2. Students should be able to explore a scientific model to illustrate the origin of the universe

ES3. Students should be able to interpret data to compare the Earth with other planets and moons in the solar system, with respect to properties including mass, gravity, size, and composition

ES4. Students should be able to develop and use a model of the Earth-Sun-Moon system to describe predictable phenomena observable on Earth, including seasons, lunar phases, and eclipses of the Sun and the Moon

ES5. Students should be able to describe the cycling of matter, including that of carbon and water, associating it with biological and atmospheric phenomena

ES6. Students should be able to research different energy sources; formulate and communicate an informed view of ways that current and future energy needs on Earth can be met

ES7. Students should be able to illustrate how earth processes and human factors influence Earth's climate, evaluate effects of climate change and initiatives that attempt to address those effects

ES8. Students should be able to examine some of the current hazards and benefits of space exploration and discuss the future role and implications of space exploration in society

CHAPTER 34

THE BIG BANG – HOW OUR UNIVERSE BEGAN

LO: ES2

Learning intentions

At the end of this chapter you will be able to:

✓ Explore a scientific model to illustrate the origin of the universe

✓ Outline the Big Bang theory

✓ Explain the term 'singularity'.

Keywords

🗝 galaxies
🗝 solar system
🗝 astronomer
🗝 expanding universe
🗝 singularity
🗝 gravity

What is in the universe?

Our universe is a vast area of space within which we find all the galaxies, stars and solar systems that make up the universe as we know it.

Was there a beginning to the universe?

How did our universe begin? Where did it all start? What was there at the very beginning? These are some of the questions that humans have asked in their desire to discover the origins of the universe.

People have always had more questions than answers on this subject. The limits of our technology meant there was a complete lack of evidence for scientists to work with previously. These questions about the creation of the universe remained unanswered until discoveries in astronomy and physics led scientists to determine that there was a beginning to our universe.

? Questions

34.1 Find a simple explanation of a 'galaxy'. Write your answer in your copy, together with a note of the source of your answer.

34.2 Name three stars that you know of.

34.3 What is a solar system?

▶️ **Animated Scientist Biography**

Watch an Exploring Science animation to find out more about Stephen Hawking and his theories about the beginning of the universe.

▶ Figure 34.1 *Stephen Hawking*

? Question

34.4 Find out and write a paragraph explaining what is meant by:

(a) The study of astronomy

(b) The study of physics.

Activity 34.1 How can we explore our knowledge about the origins of the universe?

Divide into groups of six. Within each group work in pairs.

Each pair should select one of three **astronomers**: Copernicus, Kepler or Galileo, and conduct some research on them. Or you may decide to research an astronomer of your own choosing.

From your research, answer the following.

(a) Explain the term 'astronomer'.

(b) Create a biography on the life of your selected astronomer.

(c) Outline the main theories that they had about the universe.

(d) Explore and compare any inaccuracies or flaws in their ideas or theories of the universe to modern-day knowledge.

(e) Each pair must now present their findings to the other members within the group.

▲ **Figure 34.2** *Illustration representing the beginning of the universe*

▲ **Figure 34.3** *Illustration representing the expanding universe*

In 1929, US astronomer Edwin Hubble discovered that the universe is expanding. This means that all objects in the universe are moving away from each other. Trying to imagine something on this scale is a very difficult concept for people to grasp. Here is a simple task that may demonstrate the **expanding universe**.

Activity 34.2 How can we visualise how the universe is expanding?

 Equipment needed

White (or pale) balloons   Black marker pen
Ruler   Length of string

 Safety Take care when blowing up the balloons that they do not burst.

➡ **Conducting the activity**

1. Blow up your balloon to a small size – no more than half of its maximum size.

2. Randomly mark about ten dots on your balloon with the marker pen. These represent galaxies. Give them numbers so you can identify them for the next part of the activity.

3. Let about half the air out of your balloon.

4. Use the ruler to measure how far apart the galaxies (the dots), are from each other and record this in the table in your Student Activity Book.

5. Blow up your balloon as large as you can without bursting it.

6. Look at where the dots representing your galaxies are now located.

7. Use a piece of string to measure how far apart the galaxies now are from each other. You will do this by holding the string on one dot and stretching it to the next dot, holding the length or marking the string with a pen, and then measuring the length of string you used with a ruler. Use one galaxy as a starting point for your measurement.

8. Record your results in your table.

9. Repeat the measurements between several of the dots to record how each dot has moved away from others.

? Question

34.5 In activity 34.2, why did you use a ruler for your first measurements (at step 4) and a piece of string for your second measurement (at step 7)?

Hubble noted that not only was the universe expanding, it was expanding at a great rate. **Hubble's discovery became known as Hubble's Law**.

Hubble's Law: Galaxies are moving away from each other. The farther away a galaxy is, the faster the galaxy is moving away from us.

Animated Scientist Biography

Watch this animation to find out more about Edwin Hubble and his work.

▶ Figure 34.4 *Edwin Hubble, US astronomer*

Why is the Hubble Space Telescope so important?

The Hubble Space Telescope, which was launched by NASA in 1990, is named after Edwin Hubble. The Hubble Space Telescope is extremely important for furthering our knowledge of space.

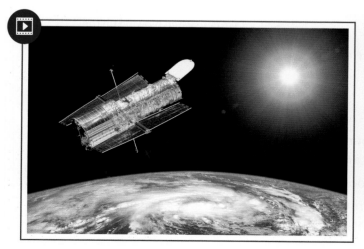

▲ Figure 34.5 *The Hubble Space Telescope*

▲ Figure 34.6 *An image taken from the Hubble Space Telescope*

THE BIG BANG – HOW OUR UNIVERSE BEGAN

Normally when we look into space we are looking through telescopes that are located on Earth. The images that we see are distorted or changed by Earth's atmosphere. This can affect what we see. The Hubble Space Telescope is out in space, orbiting at a height of 569 km above Earth. Therefore, Earth's atmosphere does not affect the images the telescope receives from space.

> **(?) Question**
>
> **34.6** Research the main discoveries that scientists have made about the universe using information provided by the Hubble Space Telescope.
>
> In your research identify four key discoveries that have been made with the help of the Hubble Space Telescope in relation to any object, planet or galaxy that is located in our universe.

Was there really a Big Bang?

The term 'bang' suggests that there was an explosion of some form. But this is not actually what happened at the start of the universe.

A starting point

Edwin Hubble concluded that there must have been a single moment when the entire universe was held within a single zone. This was the beginning of the universe, which Hubble's observations put at around 13.8 billion years ago. Scientists call this single zone, in that single moment, the **singularity**.

Singularity: a zone that is very, very small, very, very dense and very, very hot.

The Big Bang

The singularity was a region so intensely hot that the normal particles of matter – particles that occur in atoms – did not exist.

Within a single moment (some scientists believe this time frame to be as short as one second) this intensely hot singularity expanded rapidly. This is what we term the Big Bang.

In the first few moments after the Big Bang the universe was so hot that we cannot imagine a level of temperature that great.

BIG BANG THEORY

EXPANDING AND COOLING UNIVERSE

4 ~9 BILLION YEARS LATER FORMATION OF THE SOLAR SYSTEM AND EARTH

3 ~300 MILLION YEARS LATER BEGINNING FORMATION OF THE STARS AND GALAXIES

2 ~380 000 YEARS LATER ELECTRONS AND NUCLEI COMBINED INTO ATOMS

1 FIRST SECONDS AFTER BIG BANG BIRTH OF SUBATOMIC PARTICLES

~13.8 BILLION YEARS AGO BIG BANG

▲ Figure 34.7 *Evolution of the universe*

After the Big Bang

As the universe continued to expand it began to cool. The now cooler temperature allowed particles to exist. It was now also cool enough for light to begin to travel through the universe.

Did you know?

Where did this singularity, this point in space, actually come from? What was this singularity? Did this singularity actually appear out of nowhere? Scientists do not know!

How did matter form?

Gravity is a force that pulls particles together. We will be looking again at gravity when we learn about the planets. This force of gravity, which was originally present within the singularity, allowed the particles to form matter. This matter came together and formed into the stars, the planets and all other known structures in the universe. We will be looking at all of these structures in the following chapters.

Large groups of stars formed into the galaxies and our universe came into existence.

✏ Activity 34.3   How can we research information to support the Big Bang theory?

➡ **Conducting the activity**

Research the main scientific evidence that supports the Big Bang theory. In your research make notes about:

(a) The scientists who discovered this evidence

(b) How that evidence supports the theory of the Big Bang.

Did you know?

If the universe were represented by a sandy beach, a single star would be equal to one grain of sand on the entire beach.

▲ Figure 34.8 *Ripples of light radiation from the Big Bang*

The Big Bang theory is only one of the explanations for the formation of the universe. It is how scientists have tried to explain how the universe developed from a single moment. It is amazing to think that we are living on a planet that is orbiting a dazzling star. This star, the Sun, is one of billions of other stars that are part of our galaxy.

Our galaxy is also one of many other galaxies that make up the universe. The exact answer to how our universe began is still unknown. Scientists continue to look for an explanation for the origin of our universe.

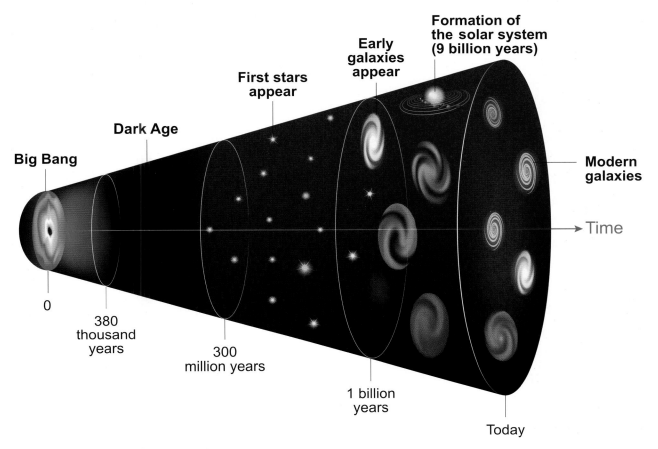

▲ Figure 34.9 *The universe expanding ever since the Big Bang*

Summary questions

- 34.7 Explain what is meant by the Big Bang. When did the Big Bang happen?
- 34.8 Explain the words 'astronomy' and 'astronomer'.
- 34.9 Outline Hubble's Law.
- 34.10 Explain the term 'singularity'.
- 34.11 Describe why telescopes on Earth can receive distorted images of objects in space.
- 34.12 Write out the sequence of events of the Big Bang.
- 34.13 From your research, list the main scientific discoveries that support the theory of the Big Bang.
- 34.14 Explain why telescopes in space provide better information than telescopes on Earth.

Assessment questions

34.15 Copy and complete the following paragraph using words from the list given. **(15 marks)**

| galaxies | expanded | singularity | million | gravity |
| matter | dense | particles | billion | stars | moon |

The Big Bang took place 13.8 _____ years ago. A _____, that was very hot, very _____ and very small _____ rapidly. No _____ existed within the singularity. This singularity _____ and this is what we call the Big Bang. As the universe _____ it began to cool and _____ began to form. The force of _____ pulled the particles together to form the _____ and stars began to form. Our universe came into existence.

34.16 In your copy, state 'True' or 'False' for each of the following statements. **(15 marks)**

(a) The universe is made up of stars, galaxies, solar systems.

(b) The universe is collapsing at a rapid rate.

(c) A singularity is very cold, dense and small.

(d) Gravity pulled particles together to form matter.

(e) As the universe expanded it cooled.

(f) Within the singularity there was matter.

(g) There was light before the Big Bang.

(h) The Big Bang took place 13.8 billion years ago.

34.17 The 'Big Bang' theory is one theory that attempts to explain the origin of the universe. **(30 marks)**

The graphs A, B and C in Figure 34.10 show how the size of the universe may have changed with time.

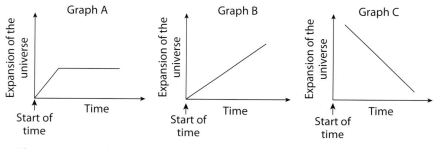

▲ **Figure 34.10**

Answer the following questions in relation to the graphs in Figure 34.10.

(a) Which graph would the Big Bang theory suggest is correct?

(b) Outline three reasons for your answer to (a).

(c) Describe the main events that took place during and after the Big Bang, beginning with the singularity.

PowerPoint summary   Weblinks

GALAXIES, STARS AND THE SOLAR SYSTEM

CHAPTER 35

LO: ES1, ES3

Learning intentions

At the end of this chapter you will be able to:

✓ Identify the type of reactions that take place in a star

✓ Describe the life cycle of a star

✓ Classify the objects that are located within the Solar System

✓ Interpret data to compare Earth with the other planets and moons in the Solar System, with respect to properties, including mass, gravity, size and composition

✓ Describe the relationship between various celestial objects including planets, stars, solar systems, galaxies and space.

Keywords

- star
- luminous
- nuclear fusion
- supernova
- nebula
- red giant
- white dwarf
- terrestrial
- planetoid
- jovian
- galaxy
- solar system
- planet
- main sequence

What are stars?

When you look up at the sky on a clear night, are you amazed by the stars that exist there, shining brightly? Do you ever wonder what a **star** is and how it was formed?

A star is an object made up of gas. It is luminous, which means it is a light source, and this is a result of nuclear reactions.

What are nuclear reactions?

Nuclear reactions that take place in a star occur between two hydrogen atoms. The nucleus of one hydrogen atom fuses with the nucleus of another hydrogen atom, forming a completely new element called helium.

▲ Figure 35.1 *Nuclear fusion reactions*

It is the conversion of hydrogen to helium in nuclear fusion that releases the heat and light that causes our stars to shine (be luminous). The heat and light released are forms of energy.

◀ **Figure 35.2** *Light energy from the Sun*

Does a star last forever?

Some stars have only a small amount of matter; some stars have a large amount of matter. Every star is different and every star is at a different stage in its life cycle. A life cycle is a series of changes that an object goes through in its life.

Some stars have already died, because they have run out of hydrogen.

Some stars explode during the process of dying, dramatically releasing a dazzling amount of light that may be seen throughout the universe in what is called a **supernova**.

Some stars appear small and are called dwarfs. A small star may be around 200 000 km across – about the same size as the planet Jupiter.

The life cycle of a star has four phases:

● Phase 1 – formation

● Phase 2 – the stable period

● Phase 3 – the red giant

● Phase 4 – the white dwarf.

Phase 1: formation

There are large gas clouds in space, called nebulae (singular nebula). The attractive forces of gravity of the gas particles cause these gases to collapse and come together.

As temperature and pressure within the cloud increase, the gases begin to spin rapidly, which causes the nuclei of elements to join together (i.e. nuclear fusion reactions take place) and a star is born.

▲ **Figure 35.3** *Stages in the life of a star*

▲ **Figure 35.4** *A supernova in space*

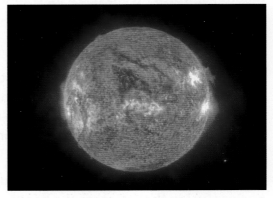

▲ **Figure 35.5** *A main sequence star*

Phase 2: the stable period

Over billions of years the star becomes stable. We call such a star a main sequence star.

A star spends the majority of its life as a main sequence star. It is in this phase that the star is using up all its available resource of hydrogen in nuclear reactions to emit heat and light energy.

A main sequence star balances between:

● Its own gravity trying to shrink it

● The heat energy that it is producing trying to make it expand.

The star in this form will continue to glow for billions of years. Our own sun is in this phase of its life.

Phase 3: the red giant

When the star has used up all its supplies of hydrogen in its core, it begins burning helium on its outer parts. This causes the star to release more heat. As a result, the outer part of the star expands. The star now becomes a huge structure, **and is known as a red giant**.

Phase 4: the white dwarf

Once the red giant has turned all the hydrogen that it contains both in its core and on its surface to helium – this may take from 5 to 10 billion years, depending on the size of the star – it **condenses and collapses in on itself, forming a tiny, but very dense, star called a white dwarf**.

A white dwarf has only about one-quarter of its original mass left. The white dwarf will produce less and less light until eventually it produces no more light.

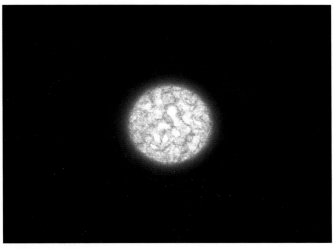

▲ **Figure 35.6** *A white dwarf*

> ### ✎ Activity 35.1 How can we illustrate the celestial events of a black hole and a supernova?
>
> There are many celestial events (events that take place in astronomy) that take place during the 'death' of a star. In groups or pairs, research the series of events that lead to:
>
> **(a)** A black hole   **(b)** A supernova.

Is that a star I see?

Stars emit light. That light takes time to travel through the vacuum of space to Earth until we can see it. So as we look at the night sky we are in reality looking back in time – possibly millions of years. When we see a star in the sky, the light that we see coming from that star is light from the past that has travelled through space to where we can see it now.

▲ **Figure 35.7** *Stargazing*

Did you know?

The 'twinkle' from the stars is a result of turbulence in Earth's atmosphere.

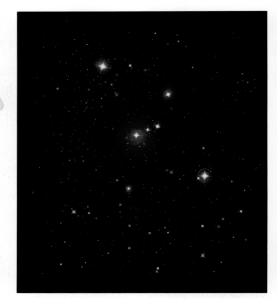

► **Figure 35.8** *The Orion constellation – a pattern of stars that we can see in the night sky from the Northern Hemisphere*

Now that we know how stars are formed, we will look at their role within the universe.

What is in the universe?

It is mind-boggling to think about how many galaxies are in the universe, and how many stars are in each galaxy. It is fascinating to wonder whether there is life in other galaxies. Many science-fiction stories have been written imagining what those life forms would be like.

We'll start with our own tiny spot in the universe.

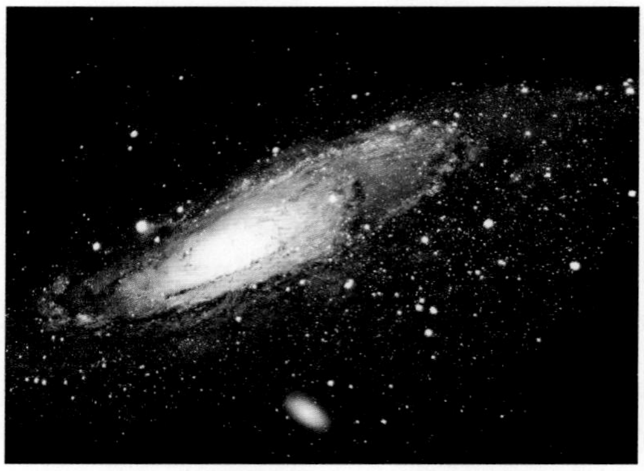

▲ **Figure 35.9** *The Milky Way – Earth's galaxy*

Galaxies

A galaxy is a collection of millions or billions of stars, along with gas and dust, all held together by gravitational forces.

There are billions of galaxies in the universe. Some galaxies are small, with only a few million stars. Other galaxies have 400 billion stars, or more.

Galaxies are constantly moving away from each other.

Earth is in the Milky Way galaxy. This galaxy is spiral-shaped, which is the most common galaxy shape in the universe.

Our solar system

Our solar system is made up of the Sun and the planets (including Earth) that orbit around it.

The Sun (which is a star) is one of billions of stars that make up the Milky Way galaxy.

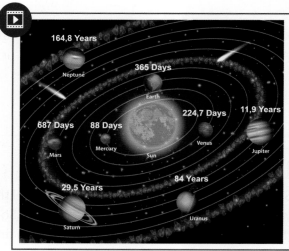

▲ **Figure 35.10** *The eight planets in our solar system and their orbit time around the Sun*

Before we look at planets, we need to explain gravity.

Gravity is a force a planet and other bodies have that 'pulls' objects towards their centres. Gravity has been around since the very beginning of the universe.

Check back to chapter 34 to read about the Big Bang and the role gravity had in the formation of the universe.

Gravity attracts objects towards each other. Earth has gravity. When you jump up it is gravity that 'pulls' you down. In fact, any object that has mass has gravity; the bigger the mass the greater the gravity, the smaller the mass the lower the gravity.

Therefore, the gravity of the Sun holds the planets in their orbit around the Sun. This is because the Sun has a greater mass and a greater gravity than the planets. And it is gravity that maintains the orbit of the Moon around Earth for that same reason.

▲ **Figure 35.11** *An astronaut 'weightless' in space*

Distance also has an impact on how much gravity we experience. As you move out into space, away from a planet or a moon, the effect of that force of gravity becomes less and less. That is why astronauts experience micro-gravity in space and are said to be 'weightless'.

The closer to a body you get, for example Earth, the stronger the pull of gravity.

When an object is located on a body with a mass, example Earth, gravity can often be termed as 'surface gravity'. We measure gravity in metres per second squared, m/s^2.

? Question

35.2 An astronaut in space is 'weightless'. Has the astronaut the same mass in space as on Earth? Explain your answer.

Planets

To be called a 'planet' three conditions must be met:

1. The object must orbit a star, such as our sun

2. The object must be big enough to allow its own gravity to pull it inwards to make it look like a sphere (rounded)

3. The object must be big enough for its own gravity to move other objects around the same size out of its way in its orbit around the Sun.

Within our solar system there are three types of planet:

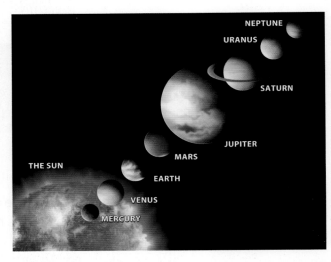

▲ **Figure 35.12** *How the planets line up within our solar system*

- Terrestrial planets
- Jovian planets
- Dwarf planets, or planetoids.

We will look at these types of planet in relation to the solar system, although there are many other planets in the universe.

Did you know?

A good way to remember the celestial bodies is to use this trick:

My	Very	Easy	Method	Just	Speeds	Up	Naming	[Planets]
Mercury	Venus	Earth	Mars	Jupiter	Saturn	Uranus	Neptune	[Pluto]

Terrestrial planets

The solar system's **terrestrial** (rocky) planets are:

- Mercury
- Venus
- Earth
- Mars.

These orbit closest to the Sun and are known as the inner planets. They are composed mainly of rock and metal.

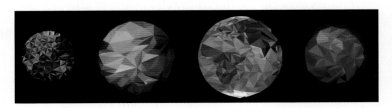

▲ **Figure 35.13** *Illustration of the terrestrial planets of the solar system: Mercury, Venus, Earth and Mars*

Jovian planets

'**Jovian**' means 'Jupiter like'. The Jovian planets are the gas giants in our solar system:

- Jupiter
- Uranus
- Saturn
- Neptune.

These planets are mostly composed of helium and hydrogen. They are very large and have rings around them.

▲ **Figure 35.14** *Jupiter*

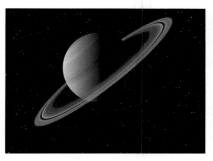

▲ Figure 35.15 *Saturn*

▲ Figure 35.16 *Uranus, taken from the Hubble Space Telescope*

▲ Figure 35.17 *Neptune*

Did you know?

Jupiter has the biggest ocean of any planet. It is 40 000 km deep. That is as deep as Earth is round! (The circumference of Earth is 40 075 km.)

Planetoids

A **planetoid** is a 'dwarf' planet. These are objects that are:

- Too large to be asteroids (which are rocky bodies located in our solar system)
- Too small to be planets.

Our solar system has one planetoid: Pluto.

▲ Figure 35.18 *Pluto*

How do planets orbit?

The planets orbit around the Sun. That is why we have a 'solar system'. The Sun is a very large object and as a result has a very large gravity. The Sun's gravity 'pulls' planets towards it. At the same time the planets are always trying to pull away from the Sun out into space. But the Sun's gravity keeps each of the planets in a curved orbit.

▲ Figure 35.19 *Planets aligned with the Sun in the solar system*

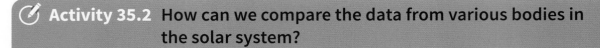

Activity 35.2 How can we compare the data from various bodies in the solar system?

➡ **Conducting the activity**

Table 35.1 compares two planets in our solar system and Earth's moon, to Earth. Read the information in the table and answer the questions below.

Table 35.1

Feature	Venus	Earth's moon	Earth	Mars
Diameter (km)	12.104	3474.2	12 742	6779
Acceleration due to gravity (m/s^2)	8.87	1.62	9.81	3.71
Average temperature (°C)	462	127, when Sun's rays strike the Moon	14.6	−60
Atmosphere – main constituents	Carbon dioxide, nitrogen 96.5%, argon, water vapour	Little to no atmosphere	Oxygen, nitrogen, carbon dioxide, water – in all three states, gas, liquid and solid	Carbon dioxide, nitrogen, polar water (a combination of water ice and carbon dioxide ice)
Number of moons	0	0	1	2

⑦ Questions

35.3 Looking at the information in Table 35.1, identify and explain two pieces of data that indicate why life exists on Earth.

35.4 What, do you think, are the reasons for the temperature on Venus being so high.

35.5 Compare the gravity on Venus, Mars and the Moon to that on Earth. Outline what you think you would experience if you were standing on those planets and on the Moon.

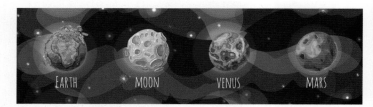

▲ **Figure 35.20**

35.6 If life was to exist on any other planet or moon in the table, select and explain two pieces of data to outline reasons why you think life may be possible there.

Table 35.2 contains data about the planets and moons within our solar system that were not included in Table 35.1. Read the information in the table and answer the questions below.

Table 35.2

Planet/ moon	Diameter (km)	Time to orbit sun (days)	Mass (kg)	Surface gravity (m/s²)	Surface temperature (°C)	Number of moons	Atmosphere
Mercury	4879	88	3.285×10^{23}	3.72	173	0	Traces of O_2, H, He
Jupiter	142 984	4331	1.889×10^{27}	24.92	−145	79	H_2, He, NH_3
Ganymede – one of Jupiter's moons	5262.4	--------	1.48×10^{23}	1.428	−163	0	Trace O_2, H_2
Saturn	120 536	10,747	5.683×10^{26}	10.44	−178	53 confirmed 9 to be confirmed	H_2, He
Titan – one of Saturn's moons	5149.24	-------	1.35×10^{23}	1.352	−179	0	N_2
Uranus	51 118	30 589	8.681×10^{25}	8.87	−224	27	H_2, He
Neptune	49 528	59 800	1.024×10^{26}	11.15	−214	14	N_2

O_2 – oxygen, H – hydrogen, N_2 – nitrogen, H_2 – hydrogen gas, He – helium, NH_3 – ammonia

? Questions

35.7 Compare the surface gravity of each planet in Table 35.2 to Earth's surface gravity of 9.81m/s², listing each planet and moon's gravity, starting with the greatest gravity.

35.8 List the three planets and/or moons, with:

(a) The highest diameter and temperature

(b) The lowest diameter and temperature.

(c) In your opinion is there a link between diameter of an object and its gravity? Explain your answer.

35.9 Explain, using the data on temperature and composition of their atmosphere, why life does not exist on any of the planets or moon named above.

35.10 Explain the link between the orbit time of the planets around the Sun and each planet's orbit position (where it is located) in the solar system. Refer to Figure 35.10 on page 394.

Is there more than one moon?

Moons are objects that are found revolving around planets in our Solar System. Some planets, such as Earth, have one moon. Other planets have more than one moon – Jupiter, for example, has 79 moons! We will be looking at our moon and other moons in more detail in chapter 37.

Are there other life forms in the solar system?

Earth is unique within the solar system as it has been able to sustain life. Earth has a suitable temperature, gravity and an atmosphere containing the correct gases that allow all living organisms to exist.

Summary questions

- 35.11 Outline how a star produces light and heat.
- 35.12 Explain the term 'nebulae'.
- 35.13 What type of nuclear reactions take place in a star?
- 35.14 List the four phases in the life cycle of a star.
- 35.15 In what phase of its life cycle is our sun?
- 35.16 Explain the term 'galaxy'.
- 35.17 Explain what objects are found within our solar system.
- 35.18 Outline the three conditions that classify an object as a planet.
- 35.19 Name the two types of planets in our solar system.
- 35.20 List the planets found within each of the categories named is question 35.19.
- 35.21 Explain the term 'gravity'.
- 35.22 Why are astronauts said to be 'weightless' in space?
- 35.23 Describe the following words: terrestrial, jovian and planetoid.

Assessment questions

35.24 Our Solar System contains eight planets, listed below. Place the planets in the correct order, in terms of their orbit location, from the Sun. **(15 marks)**

Earth   Neptune   Jupiter   Mercury   Saturn   Venus   Uranus   Mars

SUN

35.25 Copy and complete the paragraph below using the following words: **(15 marks)**

mass   gravity   smaller   weightlessness   greater   lower   attracts   force

Any body that has a _____ has _____. Gravity is a _____ that _____ one body to another. The _____ the _____ the greater the force of gravity. The lower the _____ the _____ the force of gravity. Astronauts in space experience _____ as they are farther away from Earth's pull of _____.

35.26 Look at the data in the table on the right. Earth is given the number 1 **(30 marks)** in terms of its distance from the Sun, its gravity and its diameter. Venus and Mars are compared to this figure. Answer the questions below using information within the table.

(a) Give two reasons each, for both Mars and Venus, why life may not exist on those planets.

(b) Using the comparison of the planets' diameter and gravity, outline for each planet how their diameter may be linked to their gravity.

Feature	Venus	Earth	Mars
Distance from the Sun compared with Earth's distance	0.7	1	1.5
Diameter compared with Earth's diameter	0.95	1	0.53
Acceleration due to gravity compared with Earth's gravity	0.9	1	0.4
Average temperature	462°C	14.6°C	−60°C

35.27 How can we calculate the force of weight on each planet? **(45 marks)**

Each planet has its own gravity. To calculate the force of weight you multiply mass by gravity (weight = mass × acceleration due to gravity). Weight is a force, so we measure it in Newtons (N).

Using the following table of the mass and the gravity of each planet, calculate the weight of a 50-kilogram (50 kg) object on each planet. Once you have done this, answer the questions below.

Planet	Acceleration due to gravity (m/s^2)	Mass of the body (kg)	Weight on the planet – Newtons (N)
Mercury	3.72	50	
Venus	8.87	50	
Earth	9.81	50	
Mars	3.8	50	
Jupiter	24.92	50	
Saturn	10.44	50	
Uranus	8.87	50	
Neptune	11.15	50	

(a) Describe what you would experience if you were standing on Mercury in comparison to Jupiter. Justify your answer using data from the table above.

(b) List the planets in order, based on their surface gravity, starting with the lowest gravity.

(c) Explain, using your knowledge of gravity, the reasons for the difference in the force of weight being experienced on the planets.

(d) Outline why a person's mass does not change, no matter what planet they are on, but their weight does.

PowerPoint summary   Weblinks

EARTH AND SPACE

CHAPTER 36

COMETS, ASTEROIDS AND METEORS

LO: ES1

Learning intentions

At the end of this chapter you will be able to:

✓ Describe the relationship between various celestial objects including comets, asteroids and meteors

✓ Explain how a comet is formed

✓ Distinguish between the terms 'meteoroid', 'meteor' and 'meteorite'

✓ Explain the difference(s) between a comet, an asteroid and a meteor

✓ Identify the locations of comets and asteroids within the solar system.

Keywords

🔑 comets
🔑 asteroids
🔑 meteors
🔑 meteoroid
🔑 meteorite

What other small objects are in our sky?

Apart from the Sun and the planets there are many other objects within our solar system.

We can look in the night sky and observe a vast array of spectacular cosmic structures (structures related to the universe). People used to consider them 'mythical' objects, but what exactly are they and where in space do they come from?

What are comets?

Comets are probably the most ancient objects within our solar system and may hold the key to how our solar system was formed 4.6 billion years ago.

Comets are termed by scientists as giant dirty snowballs. They are composed of frozen gases, rocks and dust.

Comets have an icy existence as they were formed and continue to be located a great distance from the heat energy of the Sun.

▲ Figure 36.1 *The Great Comet of 1811*

Comets originate from two areas of our solar system.

- **The Kuiper Belt:** The region containing the belt is beyond the orbit of the planet Neptune. Comets that originated here are termed short-period comets. This is because their orbit around the Sun takes around 200 years or less.

- **The Oort Cloud:** This 'cloud' surrounds the outer limits of the solar system and it contains trillions of comets. Comets that are located here are termed long-period comets, as their orbit around the Sun can take from 200 years to 30 million years!

▲ Figure 36.2 *Kuiper Belt objects*

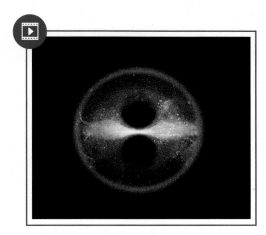

▲ Figure 36.3 *Oort cloud*

▲ Figure 36.4 *A comet*

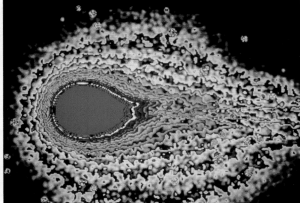

▲ Figure 36.5 *A computer image of Comet de Vico*

Comets look like solid objects until their orbit brings them close to the Sun. Then the Sun's heat energy evaporates the comet's ice. This sends dust and gases out into space, which form into a giant glowing head with a long tail. The tail can stretch out for millions of miles behind the comet.

There can be two tails behind a comet: one composed of rocks and dust, the other composed of gas. The tails of a comet always stretch away from the Sun.

Comets do not support life. It is possible that they brought water and other compounds to Earth.

▲ Figure 36.6 *A comet and its tails*

▲ Figure 36.7 *Comet Ikeya-Seki orbiting the Sun showing the tails of the comet stretching away from its head*

② Question

36.1 What are the differences between a comet and a planet?

Did you know?

Comet dust particles fall continuously to Earth at a rate of one billion dust particles per second. We cannot see this comet dust; however, scientists have found the dust preserved in the ice and snow in Antarctica.

The Rosetta mission

History was made on 12 November 2014 when the Rosetta mission, a joint mission between the European Space Agency (ESA) and National Aerodynamics and Space Administration (NASA), landed the Philae space probe on a moving comet. The Rosetta spacecraft travelled 6.4 billion km to land on the comet 67P/Churyumov-Gerasimenko, which was travelling at a speed of 135 000 km an hour. Data was sent back to Earth that will help us to understand more about comets.

After arriving successfully at its destination, the Philae lander continued to send data and images back to Earth, increasing our knowledge of comets. The Rosetta mission concluded on 30 September 2016, with the Philae lander sending its final Tweet on 6 September: 'Thank you all for being part of the journey! #GoodbyePhilae'.

▲ Figure 36.8 *Rosetta space probe*

? Question

36.2 In groups, research, using the internet or books from your school library, one of the 'great' comets. Present your findings in a report format. Use the following topics to assist your research.

(a) Explain the word 'comet'.

(b) Name three famous 'great' comets that have been seen from Earth.

(c) Note for each of the three comets you have listed in (b) above:

(i) The person, or persons, who discovered it

(ii) The year that each comet was discovered

(iii) The time span for its orbit around the Sun

(iv) The last appearance of the comet as seen from Earth

(v) The year of its predicted reappearance.

(d) Briefly outline why scientists have linked the extinction of the dinosaurs with a collision by a comet.

What are asteroids?

Apart from comets there are other small objects that exist within our solar system. These objects are termed **asteroids**.

Asteroids are small, rocky structures that have no air and no atmosphere.

Asteroids are located in the solar system's asteroid belt, which lies between Mars and Jupiter.

Asteroids can often collide with each other, which can knock them out of their asteroid belt and send them off on a different journey within the solar system. This different journey can sometimes bring them close to Earth.

Even though scientists believe that there are millions of asteroids within the asteroid belt, their total mass is less than the mass of Earth's moon.

Scientists are trying to learn more about asteroids. If there was an asteroid collision with Earth – which is a very rare event in Earth's history – it could bring about global destruction. Scientists believe that it was either a comet or an asteroid collision with Earth that caused the extinction of the dinosaurs.

▲ **Figure 36.9** *Scientists think it is likely that it was an asteroid or a comet colliding with Earth that killed the dinosaurs*

▲ **Figure 36.10** *The impact of an asteroid on Earth*

? Question

36.3 Find out the possible explanation that scientists have given for the formation of the asteroid belt.

▲ **Figure 36.11** *Image of the solar system planetoid, Pluto*

Asteroids vary greatly in size.

- Some are small at about 10 m in diameter. These are known as **meteors**.

- Some are large at about 100 km in diameter. These are known as planetoids.

Did you *know?*

The space station that orbits Earth is protected from meteor collisions. One example of the protection is that the windows are made of a specially reinforced glass.

Asteroids may appear to be small bodies but they have been, and continue to be, very dangerous structures that can do untold damage to Earth.

✎ Activity 36.1   How can we gather information to explain asteroid collisions with Earth?

➡ Conducting the activity

There have been many asteroid events on Earth. One of the most famous events took place in Russia.

On 15 February 2013, an asteroid disintegrated in the air above the town of Chelyabinsk. There was no advance warning. Many buildings were damaged in the event.

In groups or pairs, research this event using the internet and your school library and present your findings to the class as a slide presentation.

In your research:

- Describe the sequence of events that took place from when the asteroid entered Earth's atmosphere to its actual disintegration in the air

- Describe what happened to the surrounding area

- Identify what scientists, studying these events, have learned about the asteroids.

Asteroids can be assigned other names depending on where they are in the sky and whether or not they impact Earth. Use the following task to identify these other names for asteroids and clearly identify the difference between them.

Questions

36.4 Research what the following terms mean. Clearly distinguish between each of these words.

    (a) Meteoroid   **(b)** Meteor   **(c) Meteorite.**

36.5 What was the largest known meteorite to have been found on Earth? State the location of the meteorite's impact and its composition.

Scientists from NASA are currently studying the two largest asteroids within the asteroid belt, Ceres and Vesta. They are trying to gain a better understanding of these rocky worlds and hopefully find clues to the formation of the early solar system. NASA's project is called the Dawn Mission; the space probe was launched on 27 September 2007.

Asteroid Ceres

Ceres is the largest asteroid in the belt. It is a massive 950 km in diameter. On 22 January 2014 the European Space Agency announced that Ceres contained water. This is evident from the water vapour that was erupting into space from the asteroid.

NASA's Dawn Mission began its study of Ceres when it arrived at the asteroid in April 2015.

Asteroid Vesta

Vesta is the second-largest asteroid. It is 530 km in diameter and has a surface three times more reflective than our own moon. It is the only asteroid visible from Earth with the naked eye.

The Dawn Mission studied Vesta from July 2011 to September 2012.

▲ **Figure 36.12** *NASA Dawn Mission Spacecraft encountering the asteroid Ceres*

▲ **Figure 36.13** *A comparison of Ceres (in the centre) to Earth (left) and the Moon (right)*

▲ **Figure 36.14** *Image from the Dawn Mission of approaching dawn over the north pole of the asteroid Vesta*

▲ **Figure 36.15** *Ceres and Vesta in comparison to Europe*

Summary questions

- 36.6 Describe the structure of a comet.
- 36.7 Name the two areas in the solar system from which comets originate.
- 36.8 Explain which way the comets' tails stretch.
- 36.9 Identify the location of the asteroid belt in the solar system.
- 36.10 Name the two largest asteroids within the solar system.
- 36.11 Explain the difference between 'short-period' and 'long-period' comets.
- 36.12 Outline how comets' tails are formed.
- 36.13 Describe the structure of an asteroid.
- 36.14 Explain the difference between a planetoid and a meteor.
- 36.15 Distinguish between a meteor, a meteoroid and a meteorite.

Assessment questions

36.16 State 'True' or 'False' for each of the following statements.　　　**(15 marks)**

   (a) Asteroids are located in orbits around the Sun.

   (b) The Oort Cloud and Kuiper Belt contain asteroids.

   (c) Comets are composed of frozen gas, dust and rocks.

   (d) An asteroid's atmosphere is made up of oxygen and carbon dioxide.

   (e) A comet's tail stretches away from the Sun.

   (f) Comets can have more than one tail.

   (g) Comets do not support life.

   (h) The asteroid Vesta is the largest known asteroid in the solar system.

36.17　　　　　　　　　　　　　　　　　　　　　　　　　　　　　**(15 marks)**

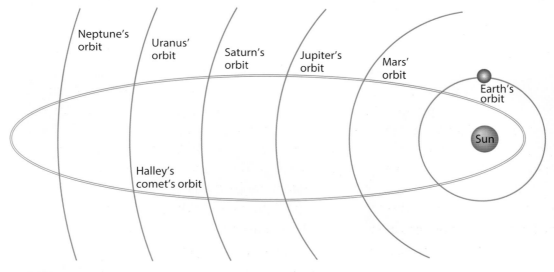

▲ Figure 36.16

Figure 36.16 on page 408 shows the orbit around the Sun of Halley's comet. Halley's comet was last observed from Earth in 1986, and the comet's projected return is approximately 75 years before we will be able to see it again in our night sky.

Answer the questions below with reference to Figure 36.16.

(a) Describe the differences between the orbits around the Sun of Halley's comet and the planets within the solar system.

(b) Identify the next possible year when we will observe the return of Halley's comet to our night sky.

(c) Outline three differences, in terms of atmosphere, life and structure; between Earth and a comet.

36.18 Read the information below on an asteroid impact that took place in the Tunguska Forest in Siberia, Russia, in 1908. Answer the questions related to the article. **(30 marks)**

It is 7.13am on June 30th 1908. An enormous blast is witnessed over the Tunguska Forest, Siberia in Russia. Massive shockwaves were registered on the seismic register – a measure of earthquake vibrations in the Earth's crust – and it was felt as far away as London, England, with many parts of Europe experiencing a night sky that glowed brighter than any daytime light levels. There were reports in parts of Asia, where 'daylight was seen at midnight!'.

A 5-10 km radial impact, from the event, took place with 80 million trees being flattened and reindeer being reduced to charred, burned bodies. But there was no crater from the impact! Trees in the area of the explosion were upright. Scientists feel that this was due to the very fast moving shock waves from the structure bursting apart.

▲ Figure 36.17

So, what happened in this remote part of Russia, and more importantly what structure appeared to collide with Earth?

Many theories were put forward as to what happened in the Tunguska Forest. However, in 2013 a group of scientists finally gave a probable cause for this cosmic event.

It is now widely accepted that a comet or, more than likely, an asteroid of approximate mass of 220 million pounds (120 feet across) and travelling at a speed of 33, 500 miles per hour detonated over the forest with the strength of 185 Hiroshima atomic bombs. The combination of heat, with temperatures of 24, 700 degrees celsius, and pressure resulted in the structure detonating above the forest. Dust from the explosion was sent into higher altitudes which reflected light far beyond the horizon. This resulted in countries far away experiencing very bright light during night time hours.

(a) Explain why the trees at the centre of the blast remained upright.

(b) Outline the reasons behind a 'bright night time' being experienced.

(c) From your research on the Chelyabinsk asteroid occurrence in Activity 36.1, outline three similarities between the two asteroid events.

EARTH AND SPACE

(d) Explore what this event has taught scientists about asteroid impacts and collisions with Earth's atmosphere. Use information form the article above.

(e) Describe a series of events, from your knowledge of comets and asteroids, and the outcome, for Earth, of a comet or large asteroid colliding with Earth.

36.19 Answer the multiple-choice questions below by stating A, B, C or D for the correct answer. **(45 marks)**

(a) Most of the asteroids are located between the orbits of:

A Venus and Earth

B Earth and Mars

C Mars and Jupiter

D Jupiter and Saturn.

(b) If you saw a shooting star in the night sky and you saw that it collided with the ground on Earth, which object could you possibly pick up from the impact site?

A Asteroid

B Meteor

C Meteorite

D Meteoroid

(c) Select from the list below the order of a piece of debris as it passes from space down through Earth's atmosphere to the surface.

A Meteorite – meteor – meteoroid

B Meteor – meteorite – meteoroid

C Meteoroid – meteor – meteorite

D Meteor – meteoroid – meteorite

(d) The belt between Mars and Jupiter contains which celestial objects?

A Comets

B Asteroids

C Meteors

D Stars

(e) These objects are sometimes called 'shooting stars'.

A Asteroids   B Comets   C Meteors

(f) The tail of a comet usually stretches:

A Toward the Sun

B Toward Earth

C Away from the Sun

D Away from Earth.

(g) Sometimes I am called a 'dirty snowball'. I am invisible except when near the Sun. What am I?

A An asteroid

B A star

C A meteoroid

D A comet

PowerPoint summary   Weblinks

TO THE MOON AND BEYOND

CHAPTER 37

LO: ES1, ES3

Learning intentions

At the end of this chapter you will be able to:

✓ Explain the effect the Moon has on Earth

✓ Provide key data about the Moon

✓ Compare Earth to moons within the solar system.

Keywords

- gravitational
- rotation
- revolve
- satellite
- atmosphere
- reflect
- moon
- tides
- non-luminous

What is Earth's relationship with the Moon?

The Moon is our nearest neighbour in space. It is a constant in our everyday lives – it is always there and we are used to seeing it (unless it is very cloudy). The Moon affects a lot of what happens on Earth every day.

The Moon is the second brightest object in our sky after the Sun.

Scientists believe that it is the Moon that has made our planet stable. This has occurred due to the Moon's own **gravitational** forces which, through time, slowed down the **rotation** of Earth.

▲ Figure 37.1 *The full moon in the night sky*

▲ Figure 37.2 *Earth, Sun and Moon*

▲ Figure 37.3 *Earth and the Moon*

▲ Figure 37.4 *'Earth rising' from Apollo 8*

The stability that the Moon has given Earth has ensured that it is a habitable planet, a planet that can support life. Without the Moon, Earth would spin on a much greater axis tilt causing much greater extremes in Earth's climate.

But what exactly are moons? And more importantly, what effect do they have on the planet around which they **revolve**?

In terms of space:

- **Any object that orbits a sun is called a planet.**
- **Any object that orbits another world, apart from a sun, is termed a moon.**

The Moon is also known as a **satellite** of Earth.

▲ Figure 37.5 *The Moon's surface*

> ### ⑦ Question
>
> **37.1** Explain what you understand by the term 'satellite' in relation to the Moon.

How was the Moon formed?

- The Moon was probably formed when a large object, about the size of the planet Mars, collided with Earth.

- This impact ejected material from Earth into orbit; this material fused together and formed the Moon.

- The formation of the Moon took place at approximately the same time as the solar system was formed: around 4.6 billion years ago.

▲ Figure 37.6 *Illustration of the formation of the Moon*

Can we see the far side of the Moon?

From Earth we can observe only one side of the Moon.

▲ Figure 37.7 *The far side of the Moon*

- It takes the Moon approximately 28 days to **revolve** around our planet. **The revolution of the Moon is the Moon's orbit around Earth.**

- During this time the Moon is **rotating** on its own axis.

- This means that the Moon is turning around on itself in one complete circle at the same time as going completely around Earth once.

- As both of these movements by the Moon – the rotating and the revolving – are synchronised (that is, they are taking place at the same time) we see only one side of the Moon.

- This means that the time taken for the Moon to rotate on its own axis once is the same as the time it takes to revolve around Earth once.

In fact, because of movements of the Moon we can sometimes see as much as 59% of its surface.

 Activity 37.1 **How can we demonstrate that we see only one side of the Moon?**

Equipment needed

Small ball about the size of a tennis ball

Larger ball, the size of a football or a basketball

Black marker

Safety
- Take care always when moving around the science room.

Conducting the activity

1. Take the small ball and place a black dot or mark on its surface. This ball represents the Moon.

2. Now take the larger ball to represent Earth.

3. Begin moving the tennis ball around the larger ball. As you do this you must ensure that the black dot on the smaller ball is facing the larger ball at all times.

4. Do step 3 again to make sure you see what is happening.

5. Write your results in your Student Activity Book.

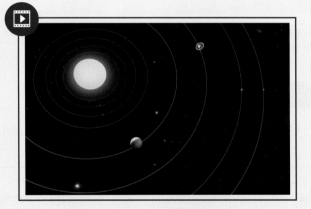
▲ Figure 37.8 *Orbits of Earth and Moon around the Sun*

Questions

37.2 As you were turning the ball around, what did you notice was happening to it?

37.3 Did you have to change your grip of the small ball in any way?

37.4 The side of the Moon that we do not see used to be called the 'dark' side of the Moon. The correct word is the 'far' side of the Moon. Why, do you think, did scientists change the wording for this side of the Moon?

Key facts about the Moon

- The distance from Earth to the Moon is 384 400 km.

- The Moon has no **atmosphere** and its force of **gravity is about one-sixth** of that of Earth.

- The Moon cannot produce its own light. As a result, the Moon is described as **non-luminous**. **It can only reflect the light that falls on it from the Sun.**

Did you know?

Only 12 people have walked on the Moon and all of them have been American.

▲ **Figure 37.9** *A man's footprint on the Moon with Earth in the background*

▲ **Figure 37.10** *Astronaut Buzz Aldrin on the Moon, Apollo 11*

? Question

37.5 Find out how scientists have been able to measure so accurately the distance from Earth to the Moon.

? Question

37.6 (a) Name some famous landmarks on Earth's moon.

(b) Outline how each landmark was given its name.

▲ **Figure 37.11** *The Moon reflecting light off its surface*

Tides

The Moon also has effects on patterns that take place on Earth. One of those patterns are the tides. As the planet spins on its own axis (turns around on itself) the water on Earth is kept at the same level. This is because the Earth's gravitational force 'pulls' the water inwards towards the centre of Earth.

However, the Moon disrupts this 'pull' inward. How? The Moon has its own gravity, and the gravitational force of the moon 'pulls' on the water on Earth. This results in our daily tides.

What are tides?

Tides are regular rises and falls in sea level as well as the horizontal flow of water – the tide coming in and going out. Tides take place twice a day, resulting in two high tides and two low tides.

The side of Earth closet to the Moon will experience the high tide, due to the additional gravitational pull of the Moon.

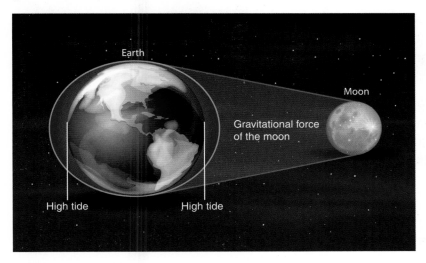

▲ Figure 37.12 *Tides*

> **? Question**
>
> **37.7** Look at Figure 37.12. Research and describe why there is a high tide – the 'bulge' on <u>both</u> sides of the Earth in the picture?

✏ Activity 37.2 How can we compare a spring tide and a neap tide?

There are different types of tide. Research, using your school library or the internet, the following types of tide and answer the questions below with reference to Figure 37.13.

- Spring tide
- Neap tide

> **? Questions**
>
> **(a)** Explain the flow of water and the height of the water, for both these types of tides.
>
> **(b)** Explain the role of the Sun *and* the Moon in spring and neap tides.

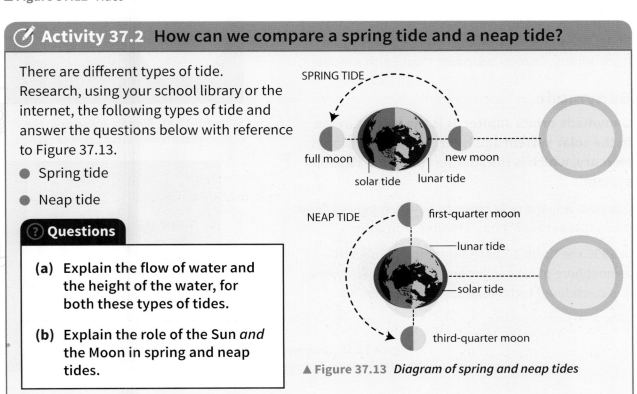

▲ Figure 37.13 *Diagram of spring and neap tides*

Are there other moons in the solar system?

We will look at the following five moons in the solar system:

- Titan
- Europa
- Ganymede
- Io
- Phobos.

Did you know?

There are 175 confirmed moons within the solar system. Each of these moons orbits (revolves around) a planet within the solar system.

Titan

Titan orbits Saturn. It is the only moon within the solar system to have an atmosphere almost fully made up of nitrogen gas (98.4%). Titan's atmosphere is so thick that telescopes cannot see the surface when they are looking at it. Special telescopes and cameras had to be developed to see through Titan's thick atmosphere.

NASA has discovered that Titan looks more like Earth than any other structure in space we know about. It has geological features of lakes and valleys. The big difference is that all flowing liquids on Titan's surface are composed of toxic methane.

▲ **Figure 37.14** *Titan and its atmosphere*

Europa

Europa orbits Jupiter. It is a frozen moon with its surface covered by ice 62 km deep. Scientists believe that there may be liquid oceans underneath Europa's icy exterior. This may be due to its core being warmed by the changing gravitational pull from Jupiter. Europa is smaller than Earth's moon.

Ganymede

Ganymede orbits Jupiter. It is the largest moon in the solar system and is larger than the planet Mercury, which is the smallest planet in the solar system.

Ganymede is the only moon to have a magnetic field. It has this because it has a molten iron core.

In 1996 the Hubble Space Telescope found a thin atmosphere of oxygen around Ganymede. However, it is considered too thin to support any life.

▲ **Figure 37.15** *Europa, taken from the Galileo global navigation satellite system*

▶ **Figure 37.16** *Ganymede, taken from the Voyager 1 space probe*

Io

Io orbits Jupiter. It is similar in size to our own moon. However, **Io is the most violently volcanic moon in the solar system**, with over 400 active volcanoes on its surface.

Phobos

Phobos, which **is one of the two moons that orbit Mars, is a very lumpy and dark moon**. Even though Phobos is only 18 km wide it **suffers extreme ranges of temperature**, ranging from –4°C on its sunlit side to –112°C on the side facing away from the Sun. This is because the surface on Phobos is mostly dust, which cannot retain the heat that it receives from the Sun.

▲ Figure 37.17 *Io, one of Jupiter's moons*

▲ Figure 37.18 *Phobos (on the right) orbits Mars*

Summary questions

- 37.8   What do we call an object that orbits a sun?
- 37.9   What do we call an object that orbits a planet?
- 37.10 How long does it take the Moon to revolve around Earth?
- 37.11 What is the distance from Earth to the Moon?
- 37.12 The Moon cannot produce light. What term describes this feature?
- 37.13 Name three moons in the solar system.
- 37.14 Name the largest moon in our solar system.
- 37.15 For the moons named in your answer to question 37.14, name the planets that they are in orbit around.
- 37.16 Which moon in the solar system do scientists think looks most like Earth?
- 37.17 Explain how the Moon was possibly formed.
- 37.18 Describe how tides occur, in terms of the Earth, Sun and Moon.

Assessment questions

37.19 The table below contains data comparing moons within the solar system **(45 marks)** to Earth. Study the information given and answer the questions that follow.

Structure	Gravity (m/s²)	Diameter (km)	Temperature (°C)	Composition of the atmosphere
Earth	9.81	12 742	−25 to 45	Nitrogen gas, oxygen gas, carbon dioxide gas, water in the form of solid, liquid, and gas
Earth's moon	1.62	3474.2	127 to −173	Traces of sodium and potassium
Europa	1.315	3121.6	40 to −220	Oxygen within water vapour
Titan	1.352	5149.5	−179	Nitrogen gas
Ganymede	1.428	5262.4	147 to −193	Extremely thin oxygen level
Io	1.796	3642.2	1649 (at the volcanoes), −130 (at the ice caps)	Collapsible atmosphere of sulfur dioxide
Phobos	0.0057	18	−4 to −112	No atmosphere

(a) Comparing the data above, list the moons in increasing order of their gravity.

(b) Create another list of moons above in increasing order of their diameter.

(c) Analyse your lists of gravity and diameter. Do you notice any pattern? What conclusion can you draw from this pattern in relation to gravity and the diameter of a structure?

(d) Select the moons with the lowest gravity and the highest gravity. Describe what a person from Earth would experience if they were to stand on each of those two moons.

(e) Using the information within the table, select which moon you think could possibly support life. Give two reasons for your answer using the data given.

37.20 **Question from Junior Cycle Science exam paper** **(45 marks)**

The planet Jupiter is the largest planet in our solar system and is described as a "gas giant". Jupiter has four large moons and many smaller ones.

These large moons were discovered in 1610 by Italian scientist Galileo Galilei.

Data about the size and density of the four large moons of Jupiter are given in the table below.

Moon of Jupiter	Diameter (km)	Density (g/cm³)
Io	3640	3.53
Europa	3120	3.01
Ganymede	5270	1.94
Callisto	4820	1.83

Io   Europa   Ganymede   Callisto

▲ Figure 37.19

Data about the size and density of some other objects in our solar system are given in the table below.

Object	Diameter (km)	Density (g/cm³)
Mercury	4880	5.43
Earth	12700	5.51
Earth's Moon	3470	3.34
Mars	6780	3.93
Jupiter	140000	1.33
The Sun	139000000	1.41

The densities of four materials commonly found in planets and moons are given in the table below right.

(a) A solid of mass 12 g has a volume of 1.5 cm³.
Calculate the density of the material.
Hence identify the material as either water, granite, basalt or iron.

Material	Density (g/cm³)
Water	1.0
Granite	2.8
Basalt	3.0
Iron	8.0

(b) Granite and basalt are found in the Earth's crust. Use the data given in the tables to state whether or not it is likely that all of the Earth is made of these rocks. Justify your answer.

(c) Use the data given for Jupiter and Earth to explain why Jupiter is described as a "gas giant".

(d) Callisto is a moon and Mercury, of similar size, is a planet.
What is the difference between a moon and a planet?

(e) Galileo's discovery of the moons of Jupiter changed our understanding of Earth and space.
Describe another example of how our scientific understanding changed over time.

(f) Scientists estimate that our solar system began to form about 4.6 billion years ago.
Scientists also estimate that our universe formed 13.8 billion years ago.
Describe two things that scientists believe happened during the early formation of the universe – before the formation of solar systems.

Log on to **www.edcolearning.ie** for Additional Assessment Questions

PowerPoint summary   Weblinks

CHAPTER 38

EARTH, SUN AND MOON – IT'S ALL RELATIVE

Learning intentions

At the end of this chapter you will be able to:

✓ Develop a model of the Earth-Sun-Moon system

✓ Explain the lunar phases of the Moon

✓ Illustrate how the relative positions of the Sun, Earth and the Moon result in the phases of the Moon as seen from Earth

✓ Describe how the occurrence of the seasons is directly related to the tilted revolution of Earth

✓ Examine how the processes of a lunar eclipse and a solar eclipse occur.

Keywords

○— lunar
○— waxing
○— crescent
○— gibbous
○— waning
○— seasons
○— axis
○— eclipse
○— umbra
○— totality
○— penumbra

What is the relationship between bodies found within the solar system?

The Sun, Earth and the Moon are all bodies that exist within the solar system. Each of these bodies is a different structure.

● The Sun is a star.

● Earth is a planet.

● The Moon is a satellite of Earth.

They are quite different in terms of their structures. In this chapter we will be looking at their relationship with each other and what results from that relationship.

The relationship between Earth, the Sun and the Moon is based on their positions relative to one another.

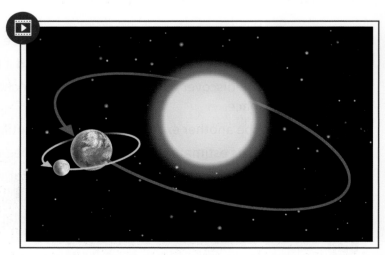

▲ Figure 38.1 *The relative orbits of Earth, the Sun and the Moon*

Activity 38.1 How can we develop and use a model of the Earth-Sun-Moon system?

Equipment needed

Tennis ball

String

Ruler

Scissors

Blue modelling clay

White modelling compound

Aeroboard

Ping pong ball

Cocktail sticks

Safety
- Be careful when using the scissors and when using the cocktail sticks.

Conducting the activity

1. The tennis ball represents the Sun, the blue modelling clay represents the Earth and the white modelling clay represents the Moon.

2. Take a piece of the blue modelling clay and roll it in the palm of your hand to the size of a ping pong ball, using the actual ping pong ball as a size comparison. You have now a model of Earth.

3. Using the string, starting at one point in the middle of the modelling clay of Earth, go all the way around the middle of the Earth until you come back to the starting point of the string and cut it.

4. Place the resulting piece of string along the length of a ruler – this measurement represents the circumference of Earth.

5. Divide the length of the string by 4, because the Moon is approximately one-quarter the size of the Earth, and cut a new piece of string to match this length. This represents the circumference of the Moon. Make a ball using the white modelling clay with a circumference to match this piece of string.

6. Place a cocktail stick into the bottom of each of your Earth and Moon models.

7. Insert the other end of the cocktail stick, with your models on top, into the aeroboard.

8. Place the Sun – the tennis ball – on one side of the model.

9. You now have a model that you can use in this chapter.

10. Document this activity in the space provided in your Student Activity Book.

What is the lunar cycle?

We will look first at changes in the appearance of the Moon in our night sky. This cycle is called the lunar cycle. *Luna* is the Latin term for the Moon, and therefore **any phenomena related to the Moon is described as 'lunar'.**

Did you know?

The word 'lunatic' is from the Latin term for 'moonstruck'. People used to believe that if the moonlight struck them when they were asleep they would become mad (i.e. a 'lunatic').

When we view the Moon from Earth it seems to change its shape and appearance from night to night.

These changes in the Moon's appearance are called the **phases of the Moon**.

The phases of the Moon

Each phase relates to the point that the Moon is in relation to Earth and how much sunlight is being reflected off the Moon at that particular time.

Phase 1: the new moon

During this phase, Earth, the Sun and the Moon are approximately in a straight line with each other. The Moon is between Earth and the Sun. From Earth we cannot see the Moon, as the Sun's light is striking the side of the Moon facing away from Earth.

> ? **Question**
>
> **38.1** Investigate the difference between the words 'revolving' and 'rotating' (see chapter 37, page 413).

Phase 2: the waxing crescent

The term waxing means 'growing'. This phase is due to the increasing levels of sunlight falling onto the Moon and being reflected off its surface. As a result we can now see more of the Moon, **but only a portion, which is called a crescent**. At this time we are seeing less than half of the Moon.

Phase 3: the first quarter moon

On day 7 of the lunar cycle we can see exactly half of one side of the Moon, i.e. a quarter; the other half of the illuminated moon is still in shadow.

Phase 4: the waxing gibbous

During this phase, more of the surface of the Moon becomes visible as more and more light from the Sun strikes it. **The term gibbous means a moon that is in between a half-moon and a full moon.**

▲ Figure 38.2 *The first quarter moon*

Phase 5: the full moon

▲ Figure 38.3 *The full moon*

On day 14 of the lunar cycle, Earth, the Sun and the Moon are again in an approximate line. But now the Moon is on the opposite side of Earth. The side of the Moon, facing Earth, is now completely sunlit due to the Sun's light rays being fully reflected off it. This means that we can now see a fully illuminated side of the Moon.

Phase 6: the waning gibbous

During this phase, a complete moon is no longer visible due to decreased levels of light from the Sun now striking the Moon and being reflected off it. The term **waning** means shrinking, or getting smaller.

▶ Figure 38.4 *The lunar cycle*

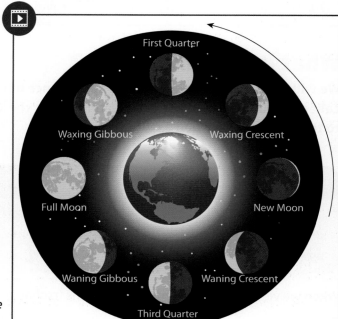

First Quarter

Waxing Gibbous

Waxing Crescent

Full Moon

New Moon

Waning Gibbous

Waning Crescent

Third Quarter

Phase 7: the third quarter

On day 21 of the lunar cycle, we can see half of the illuminated side of the moon.

Phase 8: the waning crescent

During this phase, we can see only part of the Moon – a crescent. This phase occurs just before another new moon, when the whole cycle starts again.

? Questions

38.2 Why, do you think, does the Moon not shine as brightly in the daytime as it does during the night? Discuss this with a classmate.

38.3 Can everybody on Earth see the same phase of the Moon at the same time? Give a reason for your answer.

✎ Activity 38.2 How can we create our own lunar guides for a month?

➡ **Conducting the activity**

1. Use the grid provided in your Student Activity Book, or make a grid in your copy containing a box for each day of the month you are studying.

2. For each night for one month observe and draw the Moon phase in the night sky for that particular date.

3. Sketch a diagram of what you have seen into the box in the grid that corresponds to that date in the month.

4. If you are unable to see the Moon due to weather conditions, check the internet, the daily paper or Met Éireann to find the phase of the Moon for that date.

What are the seasons?

There are other events that occur as a direct result of Earth revolving through space. The **seasons** that we experience during a calendar year are directly linked to the movement of Earth around the Sun.

Seasons are times in the year when we experience changes in our weather. The seasons result in our environment experiencing warmer or cooler temperatures and also affect the number of daylight hours that we experience.

▲ **Figure 38.5** *A representation of the seasons on one tree*

Many people think that we experience summer because we are closer to the heat energy of the Sun and winter because we are farther away from the Sun's energy. This is completely inaccurate.

In fact, we are closest to the Sun during winter and farthest away during summer.

? Question

38.4 Investigate the actual distance that Earth is from the Sun in winter and in summer.

So if it is not Earth's proximity or closeness to the Sun that cause our seasons, what is the factor that determines them?

> **? Question**
>
> **38.5** Examine Figures 38.6 and 38.7 and explain why when it is winter in Ireland it is summer in Australia. Note the angled/tilted position of the Earth in your answer.

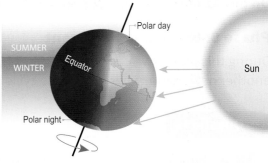

▲ **Figure 38.6** *Earth's axial tilt rotation showing seasons*

How does Earth rotate?

Earth rotates on an axis. The axis is an imaginary line that goes directly down the middle of Earth. Earth spins around this axis. It is the rotation of Earth on its axis that allows us to experience day and night. Not only does Earth rotate on its axis, **it actually rotates on a tilted axis of 23.5°**. As Earth completes its revolution around the Sun, the part of Earth that is tilted towards the Sun will experience summer and the part of Earth tilted away from the Sun will experience winter.

The tilted rotation of Earth has another effect: the angle at which the Sun's rays strike Earth.

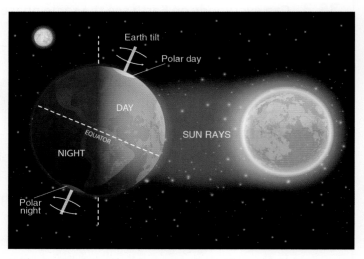

▲ **Figure 38.7** *Earth spins around an axis*

- The bigger the angle (e.g. 90°), when the Sun is at its highest point in the sky shining light directly down on the Earth over a small area during the summer, the greater and more direct the level of heat energy. This gives warmer temperatures.

- The smaller the angle (e.g. 26°), when the Sun is lower in the sky and the Sun's light is spread over a much wider area in winter, the less direct the level of heat energy. This gives us cooler and colder temperatures.

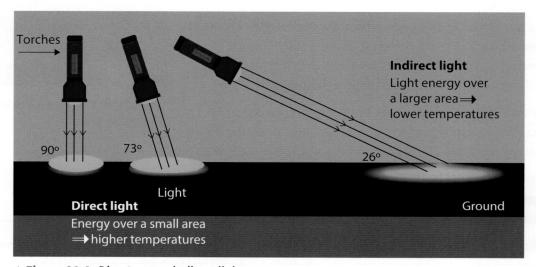

▲ **Figure 38.8** *Direct versus indirect light*

Activity 38.3 **How can we investigate Earth's tilt?**

Equipment needed

Lamp (containing bulb of wattage above 100 W)

A4 sheet of black paper

Metre stick

Protractor

Thermometer

Graph paper

 Safety
- Be careful not to shine the lamp in another student's eyes or touch the lamp when it is on.

Conducting the activity

1. Shine the lamp, from a height of 5 cm, at various angles on the sheet of black paper. Here are some angles that you might want to try:

   - 73° – represents 21 June (first day of summer) in Ireland
   - 90°– represents the Sun over the equator in summer in Ireland
   - 26° – represents 21 December (winter solstice) in Ireland.

2. Measure the angle by placing the metre stick at the end of the lamp and vertical (straight) to the ground. Use the protractor to measure the angle between the lamp and the metre stick and record this in the table in your Student Activity Book.

3. Ensure that you shine the lamp from the same distance each time. All you are changing is the angle at which the light is shining.

4. Using the thermometer, measure the temperature where the light strikes the black sheet of paper. Record this in your table.

5. Repeat the procedure, using the same angles, now shining the lamp on a sheet of graph paper.

6. Draw a line around the outline of the light on the paper.

7. Calculate the area the light covers on the graph paper, by counting the number of full and half squares.

⑦ Question

38.6 **For each of our seasons identify the position of the Sun in the sky at midday and the resulting weather conditions.**

What are eclipses?

Earth, the Sun and the Moon are all bodies in space. As we know, the Earth and the Moon move around the Sun. But what happens when one of them gets in the way of the Sun's rays of light? When this takes place, we call the event an **eclipse**.

There are two types of eclipse: a lunar eclipse and a solar eclipse.

Lunar eclipse

A lunar eclipse happens when Earth passes between the Sun and the Moon.

This results in Earth blocking the Sun's light from reaching the Moon. A lunar eclipse is not the same as a phase of the moon.

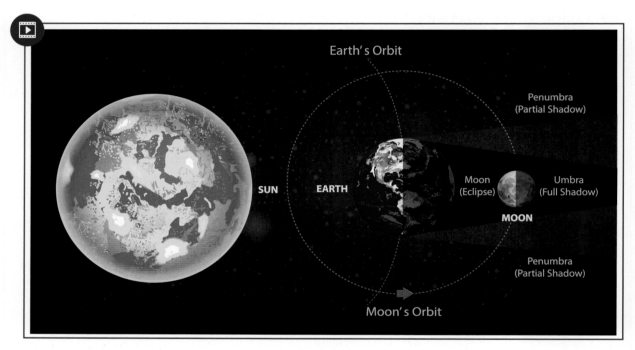

▲ Figure 38.9 *Total lunar eclipse*

Solar eclipse

A solar eclipse happens when the Moon passes between the Sun and Earth so that the Moon's shadow falls on parts of Earth.

▲ Figure 38.10 *Solar eclipse from space – note the black spot/circle*

▲ Figure 38.11 *A solar eclipse taking place*

38.7 Why is an eclipse different from a phase of the Moon?

38.8 Why do we need eye protection to view a solar eclipse but it is not necessary for viewing a lunar eclipse?

Did you know?

When a solar eclipse occurs, darkness falls in the middle of the day. Stars can be seen, temperature falls and birds might stop singing.

Each type of eclipse results in shadows being cast either onto the Moon or onto Earth.

If the Moon or Earth is in a dark shadow, this shadow is termed the umbra. When the umbra shadow completely covers another body, we call this **totality**. This means the area is in total shadow.

If the Moon or Earth is in a partial or less darkened shadow, this shadow is termed the penumbra. The penumbra is a shadow that we see at the first and final stages of an eclipse.

▲ Figure 38.12 *Eye protection for a solar eclipse*

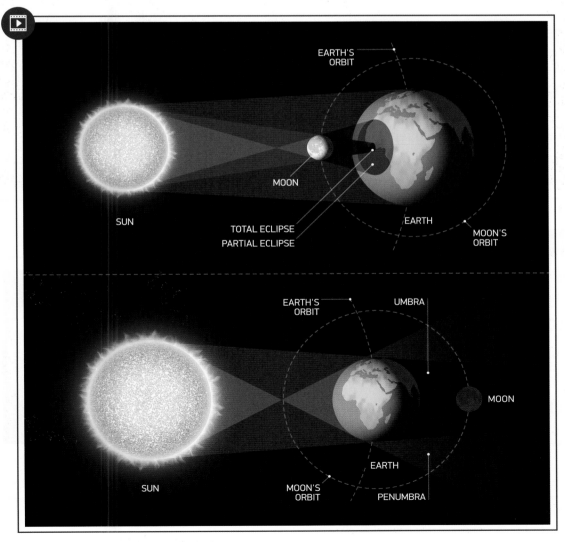

▲ Figure 38.13 *Umbra and penumbra for a solar eclipse (top image) and lunar eclipse (bottom image)*

✏ Activity 38.4 How does a lunar eclipse occur?

🧪 Equipment needed

Torch

White sheet or white board

Data logger with a light sensor

⚠ Safety
• Take care not to shine the torch directly into another student's eyes.

Working in groups of four, three people in the group will represent a particular object in the lunar eclipse, and one person will be noting the results:

You can use your Earth-Sun-Moon model here also, to demonstrate the eclipses.

● Person 1, shining the torch = the Sun

● Person 2, standing in the middle = Earth

● Person 3, holding the white sheet = the Moon

● Person 4, with the data logger, will measure and record the light levels on the white sheet

➡ Conducting the activity

1. Persons 1, 2 and 3 stand one behind each other 1 metre apart, with person 1 facing person 2.

2. Person 1 shines the torch directly at person 2's body (not near the eyes!). Person 3 holds the card directly behind person 2.

3. Person 4 observes the shadow falling on the white sheet/board and records the intensity of the light falling onto the sheet/board using the data logger.

4. Change your positions to represent a solar eclipse and repeat the investigation.

5. Person 1 shines the torch directly onto the sheet. Measure the light intensity on the card.

6. Record your findings in the space provided in your Student Activity Book.

❓ Questions

38.9 Figure 38.14 shows a blood red moon. Investigate why the Moon appears to be this colour.

38.10 Discuss with a partner whether a lunar eclipse can be observed from all parts of Earth at the same time. Give reason(s) for your answer.

38.11 Name the phases of the lunar cycle.

38.12 Explain how a lunar eclipse and solar eclipse take place.

▲ Figure 38.14 *A blood red moon during a lunar eclipse*

Summary questions

- 38.13 Explain the term 'phase of a moon'.
- 38.14 List the positions of the Earth, Sun and Moon for **(a)** a solar eclipse and **(b)** a lunar eclipse.
- 38.15 Explain the term eclipse?
- 38.16 Describe the words 'gibbous', 'waning' and 'waxing'.
- 38.17 Explain, in terms of the Sun, Earth and Moon, why we cannot see a new moon.
- 38.18 Explain, in terms of the Sun, Moon and Earth, why we can see a full moon.
- 38.19 How do seasons on Earth occur?
- 38.20 Explain why temperatures are greater in the summer in terms of the Sun's light rays.
- 38.21 Describe what the words 'umbra' and 'totality' mean in terms of eclipses?
- 38.22 Outline in terms of the Earth's rotation how seasons take place.

Assessment questions

38.23 **(a)** Draw fully labelled diagrams, showing the positions of the Earth, Sun and Moon, of:
- **(i)** A solar eclipse   **(ii)** A lunar eclipse.   **(15 marks)**

(b) Explain the following terms:
- **(i)** Umbra   **(ii)** Totality.

(c) Outline the reasons why humans need to wear sunglasses to view a solar eclipse.

38.24 **(a)** Explain, in detail, the position of Ireland, in terms of the Sun, when we experience: **(30 marks)**
- **(i)** Winter   **(ii)** Summer.

(b) Describe the weather conditions Ireland experiences during those seasons.

(c) **(i)** Identify and describe the weather conditions in the Southern Hemisphere, when the Northern Hemisphere is experiencing summer.
- **(ii)** Explain, in terms of the revolution of the Earth, why these weather conditions that you have identified, have taken place.

(d) Fully describe, in terms of the angle at which the Sun's light rays strike the Earth's surface in the summer: the heat energy, resulting temperature and area of light coverage at the following locations:
- **(i)** The equator   **(ii)** Greenland   **(iii)** The north pole.

38.25 **(a)** Explain the difference between a lunar eclipse and a phase of the lunar cycle.   **(45 marks)**

(b) Describe:
- **(i)** Why a lunar eclipse can be observed from certain parts of Earth
- **(ii)** Why, when a solar eclipse is taking place, the umbra of a solar eclipse moves from one location to another
- **(iii)** The reasons why a lunar eclipse occurs more frequently in the Northern Hemisphere than a solar eclipse
- **(iv)** Using your knowledge of the model of the Earth-Sun-Moon system, justify any changes that may take place in terms of the lunar phases and eclipses, if the Moon moves from its relative position in relation to Earth.

38.26 **Question from SEC Junior Cycle Science sample paper** (30 marks)

Solar eclipses can happen a few times each year.

(a) The diagram below shows a simple model of a solar eclipse (an eclipse of the Sun). In a copy of the diagram, write the letter **X** for Earth, **Y** for Moon and **Z** for Sun.

▲ **Figure 38.15**

(b) Two weeks before or after a solar eclipse sometimes there is a lunar eclipse (an eclipse of the Moon). Draw a labelled diagram to show a model of a lunar eclipse.

A solar eclipse in March 2015 affected the solar electrical power produced in the German electricity grid.

The graph below shows the solar electrical power produced from Monday to Friday during the week of the solar eclipse.

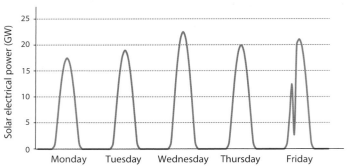

▲ **Figure 38.16**

(c) On which day of the week did the solar eclipse occur? Justify your answer.

(d) Which was the brightest day of the week? Justify your answer.

(e) The Sun can also provide power for modern spacecraft. The Juno mission to Jupiter uses solar energy to produce electricity.

Previous long-distance space missions used nuclear power to produce electricity.

State one advantage of using solar energy rather than nuclear energy during space exploration.

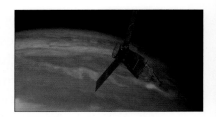

▲ **Figure 38.17**

(f) JunoCam, a camera on the Juno probe, is powered by Juno's solar panels.

Calculate the electrical power (P) generated by JunoCam when it uses a current of 0.5 A flowing across a potential difference (voltage) of 12 V.

▲ **Figure 38.18**

38.27 **Question from Junior Cycle Science exam paper** (15 marks)

Answer questions **(a)** and **(b)** by picking one of the options given.

(a) A star and all of the objects that orbit it is called a

Moon   Solar system   Galaxy

(b) A system of billions of stars is called a

Moon   Solar system   Galaxy

(c) The image below shows a planet passing in front of a star. This partial eclipse is called a transit. The brightness of the light detected from the star decreases as the planet transits the star and blocks its light.

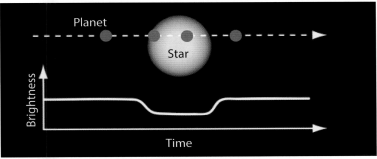

▲ **Figure 38.19**

The graphs below show how the brightness of a star changed over time as two planets, **A** and **B**, transited the same star.

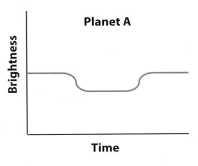
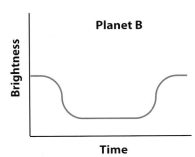

▲ **Figure 38.20**

Which planet, **A** or **B**, took the shortest time to transit the star?

Which planet, **A** or **B**, is the largest? Give a reason for your answer.

 Log on to **www.edcolearning.ie** for Additional Assessment Questions

EARTH AND SPACE

PowerPoint summary   Weblinks

Learning intentions

At the end of this chapter you will be able to:

✓ Describe the cycling of matter, including that of carbon dioxide and water, associating it with biological and atmospheric phenomena

✓ Explain the importance of nutrient cycling in the environment

✓ Describe the carbon cycle in terms of biological and atmospheric changes

✓ Describe the water cycle

✓ Examine the importance of water to all living organisms.

Keywords

- cycling
- evaporation
- condensation
- precipitation
- transpiration
- organic
- photosynthesis
- decompose
- respiration
- carbon sink
- carbon source

Does nature recycle?

For many households and businesses it is a daily routine to recycle materials such as plastic, aluminium, paper and glass. We do this in order to conserve and protect important resources in our environment.

But what about recycling in nature? How does nature recycle material and nutrients (chemicals that organisms need in order to live)?

▲ Figure 39.1 *Our daily recycling*

Scientists do not use the term 'recycling' in terms of nature. Instead they use the term **cycling** or cycles. **Nature excels at cycling vital resources.**

Matter is anything that occupies space and has a mass.

Earth has a fixed amount of matter.

Therefore, nature is continually cycling matter to ensure that it can be used time and time again.

▶ Figure 39.2 *Cycling in nature*

Two of the key resources that nature cycles are **water** and **carbon**. We will be looking at both of these areas in nature and their importance to us and our planet.

What is the water cycle?

Humans cannot live without water, nor can a vast range of organisms in the environment.

Water can exist in all three states of matter: solid (ice), liquid (water) or gas (water vapour).

Did you know?

When you get a glass of water from your tap you probably don't think of the age of the water. The amazing thing is, although the water in your glass may have fallen as rain last week, that same water has been around since Earth was formed!

▲ **Figure 39.3** *Water can exist in solid (ice), liquid (water) or gas (water vapour) form*

Water in nature is always in constant motion.

The water cycle is the movement of water from the oceans to the atmosphere and back to the oceans.

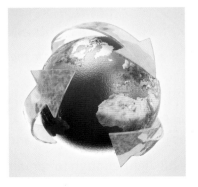

◄ **Figure 39.4** *Water is constantly cycling itself on Earth*

What are the stages of the water cycle?

Within the water cycle there are six key stages:

- Stage 1 – evaporation
- Stage 2 – condensation
- Stage 3 – precipitation (rainfall)
- Stage 4 – infiltration (soaking)
- Stage 5 – run-off/collection
- Stage 6 – transpiration.

We will look at each stage individually.

▲ **Figure 39.5** *The water cycle*

Stage 1 – evaporation

Evaporation is the changing of water in the form of a liquid to water in the form of a gas.

Most of the evaporation that takes place on Earth comes from the oceans. Only a small amount of evaporation takes place from inland water (rivers and lakes) and plants.

Evaporation requires energy in the form of heat. It is the Sun's heat energy that drives this process, causing water to change from a liquid to a vapour/gas.

Stage 2 – condensation

Condensation takes place when a gas changes to liquid.

Think of steam from the shower hitting a mirror – what do you notice happening?

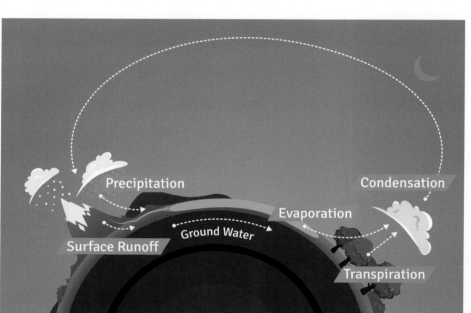

▲ **Figure 39.6** *Stages in the water cycle*

The higher up you go on Earth the colder it gets – think of snow caps on the tops of mountains. So as water vapour rises it starts to get colder and condenses.

The water droplets are still light enough to remain suspended or held in the air. The droplets come together in vast numbers and clouds are formed.

Activity 39.1 How can we demonstrate evaporation?

 Equipment needed

A piece of material about 30 cm square, cut in half

Stopwatch or timer

Zip-lock bags

Beaker

Basin

Open container

Water

Top-pan balance/weighing scales

⚠ Safety	• Ensure that water does not spill on the floor, making another student's area unsafe.

➡ Conducting the activity

1. Measure 50 cm^3 of water into a beaker.
2. Place your two pieces of material in a basin and pour the water from the beaker onto the material.
3. Leave the material to soak in the water for 5 minutes.
4. Remove the material and twist the pieces once for 10 seconds.
5. Place one piece of material on a top-pan balance/weighing scales and record the mass of the material soaked with water. Do the same with the second piece.
6. Place one piece of material into a zip-lock bag, and seal the bag.
7. Place the second piece of material into an open container.
8. Leave both the bag and the container in an open, airy place for 2–3 days.
9. After the 2–3 days record the mass of each piece of material and note the 'dryness' of the material. There is space in your Student Activity Book for you to note your observations.

Stage 3 – precipitation/rainfall

As the water droplets held within the clouds continue to rise they carry on getting colder.

When the water droplets that are held within clouds become too heavy to be held in the cloud, the water falls back to Earth as rain, sleet or snow. This is called precipitation.

Stage 4 – infiltration

Infiltration occurs when the rain hits the ground and infiltrates or soaks through the soil and the rocks. This water then collects and forms ground water.

▲ **Figure 39.7** *Rain falls when water droplets become too heavy to be held in the cloud*

Ground water is water that is held in the ground and supplies wells and springs.

⑦ Question

39.5 **When might the level of the ground water increase or decrease?**

Did you know?

Water can spend thousands of years locked up in ground water or frozen within the polar ice caps. Yet it can remain within the atmosphere only for a few days.

Stage 5 – run-off/collection

Run-off is the draining away of water from an area of land.

The water eventually runs off the land or out of the soil and collects into the rivers and lakes.

Stage 6 – transpiration

Plants are constantly taking up water from the soil through their roots. To continue this uptake of water from the soil, the plants must lose water into the air from their leaves in the form of water vapour. **This loss of water from plants is called transpiration.**

The water has now completed its full cycle.

What is the carbon cycle?

Scientists know that carbon is the basis of all life. Carbon is the second most abundant element in living things.

Any substance that contains carbon is called an **organic** substance.

We all need carbon for survival. **Earth has only a certain amount of carbon and so it is very important that nature continues to cycle it to maintain its supplies.**

However, a fine balance must be kept between too much carbon and too little carbon in the atmosphere. We will be looking at this delicate balance in chapter 41.

▲ Figure 39.8 *Ground water runs off the land into rivers and lakes*

? Question

39.6 What element is found in the greatest quantities in living things?

? Question

39.7 Carbon is the fourth most abundant element in the entire universe. What do you think are the top three elements in our universe?

What are the stages of the carbon cycle?

Carbon, like water, is constantly moving in nature from one process to the next. It is this constantly moving carbon that results in the carbon cycle. This is shown in Figure 39.9.

Within the carbon cycle there are six key stages. In these stages carbon moves from:

1. The atmosphere to plants
2. Plants to animals
3. Plants and animals to the ground

4. Living things into the atmosphere
5. Fossil fuels back into the atmosphere
6. The atmosphere into the oceans.

We will look at each stage.

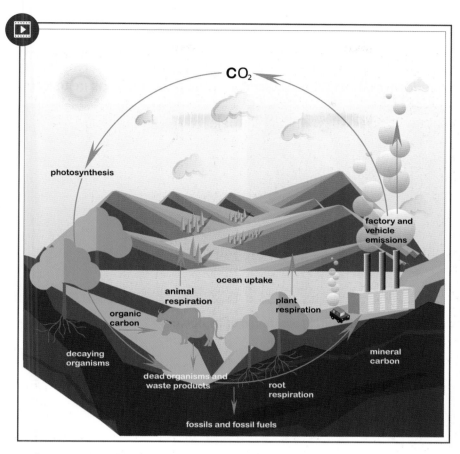

▲ Figure 39.9 *The carbon cycle*

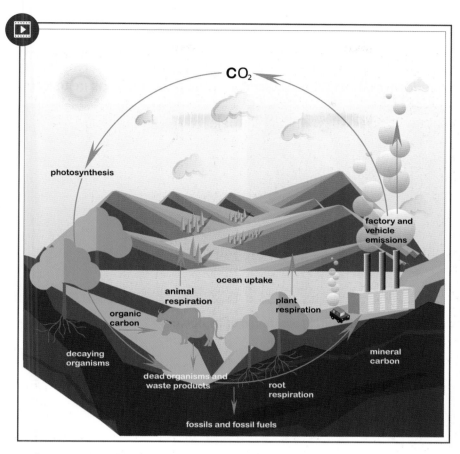

? Question

39.8 Carbon appears in many forms, such as coal, diamonds and graphite in pencils. Research these three forms of the same element, carbon, and clearly distinguish between them in terms of:

   (a) Appearance   **(b)** How they are formed   **(c)** What they can be used for.

Carbon moves from the atmosphere to plants

Carbon, in the form of carbon dioxide gas, is taken from the atmosphere by plants and is converted into food containing carbon. **This process, which allows plants to uptake carbon dioxide and make food, is called photosynthesis** (see chapter 10).

Carbon moves from plants to animals

Animals eat plants and other animals in order to get their supply of carbon.

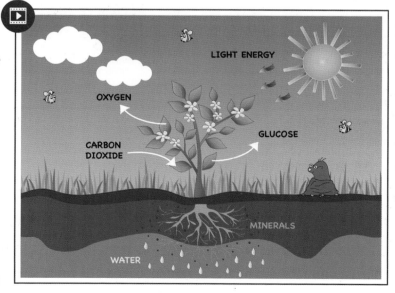

▲ Figure 39.10 *The process of photosynthesis*

THE WATER AND CARBON CYCLES   **437**

Carbon moves from plants and animals to the ground

When plants, animals and micro-organisms such as bacteria and fungi die the remains of their structures **decompose** (break down into smaller parts) into the ground. Over millions of years the decomposed/broken-down matter is compressed by Earth's heat and pressure to form fossil fuels.

▲ Figure 39.11 *Animals get carbon by eating plants and other animals*

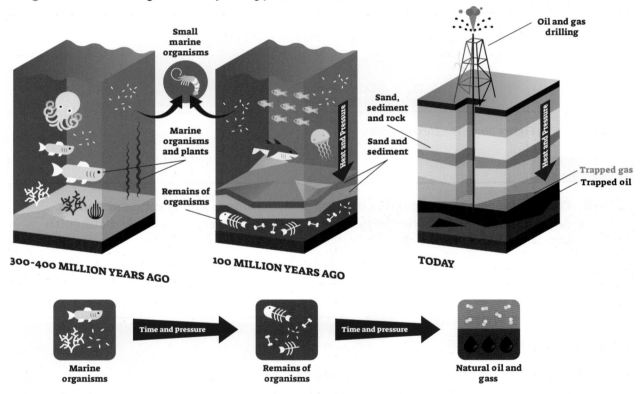

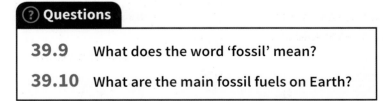

▲ Figure 39.12 *Formation of fossil fuels*

> ⓘ **Questions**
>
> **39.9** What does the word 'fossil' mean?
>
> **39.10** What are the main fossil fuels on Earth?

Carbon moves from living things into the atmosphere

Plants, animals and micro-organisms break down food containing carbon in a process called respiration (see chapter 10). **This process releases energy to the organism but produces both water and carbon dioxide as waste products.** The carbon dioxide is released into the atmosphere.

Carbon moves from fossil fuels back into the atmosphere

Fossil fuels contain carbon and hydrogen. Substances that contain both carbon and hydrogen are called hydrocarbons.

When we burn fossil fuels they release carbon dioxide and water vapour into the atmosphere.

▲ **Figure 39.13** *Burning fossil fuels releases carbon dioxide and water vapour into the atmosphere*

> ? **Question**
>
> **39.11** Identify four ways in which humans burn fossil fuels.

Carbon moves from the atmosphere into the oceans

Most of the carbon that is removed from the atmosphere is absorbed by the oceans. Carbon is involved in many processes that take place in the oceans.

> **Did you know?**
>
> The amount of carbon in the oceans is 50 times greater than the amount contained in the atmosphere.

▲ **Figure 39.14** *Organisms in the oceans use carbon*

What are carbon sinks and sources?

- **In nature, places that store carbon are called carbon sinks or reservoirs.** An example of a carbon sink is a forest full of trees.

- **Places where carbon is given off or released in great quantities are called carbon sources.** An example of a carbon source is a volcano.

▲ **Figure 39.15** *A forest is a carbon sink*

> ? **Question**
>
> **39.12** What structures within the trees contain carbon?

► **Figure 39.16** *A volcano is a carbon source – carbon is released when it erupts*

Summary questions

● **39.13** List the six main events in the carbon cycle.

● **39.14** List three examples of a carbon sink.

● **39.15** List three examples of a carbon reservoir.

● **39.16** Explain the term 'water cycle'.

● **39.17** Describe the following processes, in terms of the water cycle:

    (a) Evaporation   **(d)** Infiltration

    (b) Condensation   **(e)** Runoff

    (c) Precipitation   **(f)** Transpiration

● **39.18** Explain the terms 'photosynthesis' and 'respiration'.

● **39.19** Outline what a carbon sink and a carbon source are.

Assessment questions

39.20 The left-hand boxes contain descriptions that relate to a term in the right-hand boxes. Currently they do not match up. Match the correct description to the correct term, by matching the description to the correct number. **(15 marks)**

(a)	Carbon is given off or released by these.	1	Heat and pressure
(b)	Plants, animals and micro-organisms break down food containing carbon to release energy in this process.	2	Hydrocarbons
(c)	These are fuels containing carbon and hydrogen.	3	Photosynthesis
(d)	Fossil fuels are formed as a result of these conditions.	4	Carbon dioxide and water
(e)	Plants take in carbon in this form.	5	Carbon sources
(f)	Plants use carbon from the atmosphere in this process to make food.	6	Carbon sinks
(g)	These are places that store carbon.	7	Carbon dioxide
(h)	When burned, fossil fuels release this.	8	Oceans
(i)	Most of the carbon is absorbed by these.	9	Decomposing plant and animals
(j)	Fossil fuels are formed from these.	10	Respiration

39.21 Read the article below on Ireland's heatwave in the summer of 2018. Answer the questions that follow related to this article. **(30 marks)**

> The heatwave this summer saw Met Éireann record the highest June temperature in Ireland in more than 40 years, at Shannon Airport weather station, Co Clare.
>
> In a monthly weather report, the national forecaster said the recent period of warm and dry weather set several records.

On June 28th the forecaster recorded a temperature of 32 degrees at Shannon Airport station, the highest temperature recorded in June since 1976.

On June 29th, 1976, a weather station in Boora, Co Offaly, recorded a temperature of 32.5 degrees. The next closest recording had been a report of 31.1 degrees in Athy, Co Kildare, on June 29th, 1995.

The reading of 32 degrees at Shannon Airport was also the highest for any month since July 2006, when 32.2 degrees was recorded at Elphin, Co Roscommon.

Malin Head, Co Donegal, got the most sunshine in a single day for June this year, with 16½ hours on June 28th, Met Éireann said.

Ireland has had one of its mildest winters in recorded history.

Knock Airport station recorded 16 hours of sunshine on July 3rd, the highest amount recorded since the station opened in 1997.

All stations across the country had above average levels of daily sunshine for the month of June.

Johnstown Castle, Co Wexford, got the most sun, reporting 244 hours of sunshine over the entire month of June. The weather station also topped the chart in July, with 240 total hours of sunshine.

Oak Park weather station in Co Carlow notched up an 11-day heatwave in late June, the longest heatwave in the last 20 years.

Met Éireann defines a heatwave as when there are five consecutive days of temperatures in excess of 25 degrees. Official heatwaves were recorded at 15 weather stations this June. Prior to this summer, Met Éireann had only recorded six heatwaves at stations since 2000.

The longest heatwave in the last half-century was recorded at Birr station, Co Offaly, in August 1976. It lasted 14 days.

Met Éireann said that last month half as much rain fell in the east of the country as was normal for the region in July. Gurteen, Co Tipperary, only had 35 per cent of normal rainfall levels in July.

Phoenix Park in Dublin recorded its lowest rainfall total for the months of June and July since records began in 1850, at 34.5 mm combined.

Rainfall in the west of the country was 80 per cent of normal levels in July.

Source: *The Irish Times*

(a) What was the highest recorded temperature and at what Met Éireann station was this temperature recorded?

(b) Describe how Met Éireann defines a 'heatwave'.

(c) Identify the date in Ireland's history of the last lowest recorded rainfall level.

(d) Using your knowledge of the water cycle, describe the negative impact of a heatwave on the processes that take place within the water cycle.

(e) Describe three impacts that a heatwave and low water levels would have on a heavily populated area.

39.22 Figure 39.17 shows the water cycle above a graph outlining the historical increase in global temperatures. Comparing both images, answer the following questions:

(45 marks)

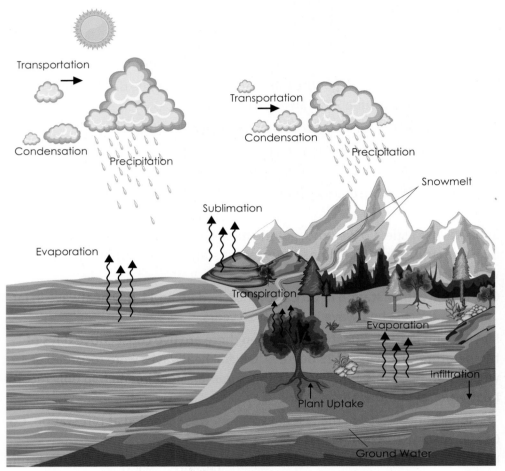

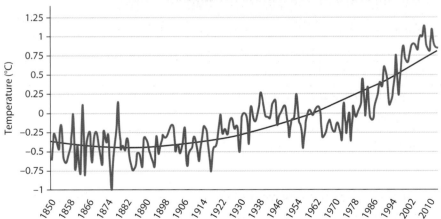

▲ **Figure 39.17**

(a) Outline three possible changes that may take place in the water cycle due to increased global temperatures.

(b) One of the effects of increased global temperatures is the higher levels of temperatures in the oceans. Explain two effects of increased ocean temperatures on the water cycle.

(c) From your knowledge of the carbon cycle, which process(es) within that cycle are having a direct impact on global temperatures?

(d) Increased global temperatures are causing changes within our climate, especially in terms of rising sea levels and increased storm activity. How will this impact on the water cycle?

39.23 Question from Junior Cycle Science exam paper (15 marks)

The diagram below illustrates the water cycle.

Some of the key stages of the water cycle are labelled **1**, **2**, **3** and **4**.

▲ **Figure 39.18**

(a) Write the numbers **1**, **2**, **3** or **4** in order to match each of the labelled processes shown in the diagram with the correct description.

Process	1, 2, 3 or 4?
Air currents cause clouds to move onshore	
Water falls to the Earth as precipitation	
Heat from the Sun converts liquid water into water vapour	
Plants lose water through the process of transpiration	

(b) In 2018 Ireland experienced low rainfall throughout the year. This led to water shortages and restrictions on water use.

Describe one way in which water usage in a home could be reduced.

39.24 **Question from SEC Junior Cycle Science sample paper** **(15 marks)**

The diagram below shows some of the processes involved in the carbon cycle.

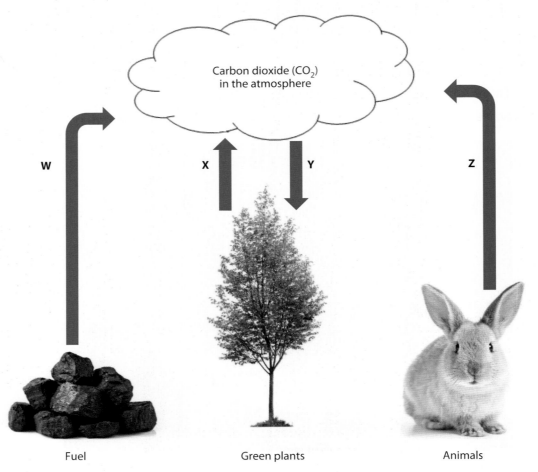

▲ **Figure 39.19**

Each of the blue arrows **W**, **X**, **Y** and **Z** represents one of the following three processes:

Respiration **Photosynthesis** **Combustion**

Write down which process is occurring at each of W, X, Y and Z.

(Note that one process appears twice.)

 Log on to **www.edcolearning.ie** for Additional Assessment Questions

PowerPoint summary Weblinks

ENERGY – OUR USE AND OUR NEED

LO: ES6

Learning intentions

At the end of this chapter you will be able to:

✓ Describe different examples of renewable and non-renewable sources of energy

✓ Consider our future needs in terms of energy

✓ Research different energy sources and formulate and communicate an informed view of ways that current and future needs on Earth can be met.

Keywords

- non-renewable
- renewable
- fossil fuel
- biomass
- geothermal
- solar
- nuclear power

How do we use energy and where does it come from?

What are the forms of energy we use in our homes?

Where does that energy come from?

We usually flick a light switch without any thought as to what source of energy produces the electricity in the light.

In order to supply homes with energy, some source of fuel or resource must be changed or transformed to electrical energy.

There are two forms of resources available to us: **non-renewable** and **renewable**.

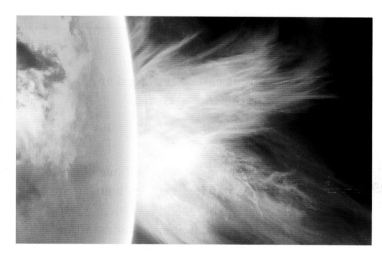

▲ Figure 40.1 *Radiation from the Sun*

? Question

40.1 List all the forms of energy that you can identify that are used in your home.

Non-renewable resources

Non-renewable resources are limited resources that will run out and that we will be unable to replace. In common terms we call these **fossil fuels**.

What are fossil fuels?

Fossil fuels are the remains of animals and plants from millions of years ago. The remains were compressed (squashed) in the earth over a long period of time, producing the fossil fuels. The formation of fossil fuels is part of the carbon cycle (see chapter 39).

The main fossil fuels are:

● Coal   ● Gas   ● Oil   ● Peat

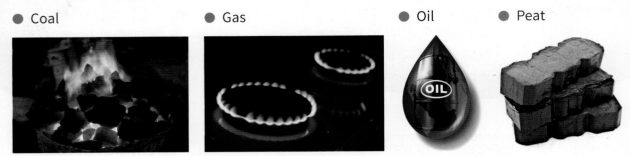

▲ **Figure 40.2** *Different forms of fossil fuel*

Fossil fuels have held energy in the earth for millions of years. Coal can be mined and broken into nuggets of a suitable size for our fires.

We are using fossil fuels at a much greater rate than they can actually be produced. More than three-quarters of Earth's energy needs are met by the burning of fossil fuels.

⑦ Question

40.2 In pairs or groups explore:

(a) The advantages and disadvantages of the combustion (burning) of fossil fuels

(b) The advantages and disadvantages of the use of nuclear energy.

Renewable resources

Renewable resources can be replaced and will not run out in the short term.

Some examples of renewable resources and their uses are:

● **Wind power** – Turbines/windmills have blades that turn and rotate in the wind, converting the kinetic energy of the blades to electrical energy. Many countries have vast areas of land and/or sea containing wind turbines.

▲ **Figure 40.3** *Wind turbines convert wind energy to electrical energy*

● **Water** – This is using the energy within moving or falling water and changing it to electrical energy, for example in hydroelectric stations.

▶ **Figure 40.4** *Energy from falling water is converted to electrical energy*

- **Biomass** – This is the burning of fuel that comes from living things, such as wood from trees. It is renewable only if the trees that are cut down are then replaced.

- **Geothermal** – This requires us to use the heat that is beneath the ground. Water is pumped underground and warmed from the heat in the rocks. This heat energy is generated and stored in the earth.

- **Solar panels/tubes** – Solar panels heat water that runs through them. The energy source that supplies the heat is the light from the Sun.

- **Solar cells** – These cells are found in devices that transform light energy to electrical energy. An example is a solar-powered calculator.

> **Did you know?**
>
> The fastest-growing source of energy in the world is the wind turbine. One wind turbine, of sufficient size, can supply enough energy to provide all the energy needs to over 300 homes.

▲ **Figure 40.5** *Biomass can be converted to electrical energy*

▲ **Figure 40.6** *Geothermal plant*

▲ **Figure 40.7** *Solar panels harness light energy from the Sun*

▲ **Figure 40.8** *Some solar panels are small, like the one on this calculator. These smaller panels are called 'solar cells'*

Did you know?

Enough energy from the Sun falls on Earth every hour that could power the entire Earth for a full year – if only we could work out how to trap or use it!

? Question

40.3 Research the following areas and determine the effect, be it positive or negative, on the energy output of the following renewable sources of energy. Present your findings in your copy.

Solar panels

(a) Can the presence of clouds or solid particles impact the energy output from the panels?

(b) Is the angle and direction in which a solar cell or panel is facing important? Explain your answer.

Wind turbines

(c) Does the number of blades or the length of the blades on a wind turbine affect the amount of energy being produced from that turbine?

(d) Does the direction the wind turbine is facing affect its efficiency?

(e) What are the main advantages and disadvantages in using solar panels and wind turbines?

Following on from your research design a poster showing the positives and negatives of solar power and wind turbines.

What are our current and future energy requirements?

We have become an energy-hungry society. This means, per individual on Earth, we have a very high demand and requirement for energy.

Evidence of this is in a satellite image of Earth – look at all the light that can be seen from space coming from cities and people's homes in Figure 40.9.

Most of our current energy needs are met by:

- Burning fossil fuels
- Nuclear energy.

These two energy sources supply 93% of the world's energy requirement. The remaining 7% comes from renewable energy sources.

▲ **Figure 40.9** *A satellite image of Europe shows up electric light from cities and towns*

Table 40.1 shows how much fossil fuel is used just to supply the world's electrical demands.

Changing energy demands

As economies and countries become more developed, the demand for energy increases dramatically.

A simple example of this is the number of cars that are currently on the world's roads. From a study done in 2014, there are now over one billion cars on the road, with the United States having the highest number of cars and China having the second highest.

In addition, the world's population is also expanding – and it is expected to reach about ten billion people in the next 50 years – and so our energy demands will also increase.

Energy experts expect that by the time we reach 2030 the world energy demand will have increased by 55% compared to today.

Changing energy use targets

Not only will we have to use renewable energy in greater and greater amounts, we will need to be more efficient about how we use our energy. Energy efficiency is essential, as scientists believe that within the next 50 to 100 years our fossil fuels will run out.

The European Union (EU) has set targets for all member states to help the environment.

The European Union's goal is to reduce greenhouse gas emissions by 80–95% by 2050, and Ireland must try to reach these target percentages.

Table 40.1 OECD data on the percentage of types of fuel used to supply the world's electrical demands

Energy type	% of world electrical supply
Combustible (fossil) fuels	58.7
Nuclear	17.6
Hydro	13.9
Geothermal, wind, solar and other	9.8

▲ Figure 40.10 *Traffic on a road in the United States*

Did you know?

On average 15% of electricity used in the home is used by devices and equipment that are on standby.

? Question

40.4 In pairs or groups, investigate all renewable energy forms that are being used in Ireland. How efficient are they?

▶ Figure 40.11 *Renewable energy in the form of solar garden lights*

▲ Figure 40.12 *Wind farm energy*

ENERGY – OUR USE AND OUR NEED   449

We can no longer continue with our current dependency on fossil fuels. Nor can we continue to ignore how important it is for us to begin to use renewable energy in greater amounts.

Our future, in terms of energy, depends on what we do now and how we begin to plan for our future energy needs.

Did you know?

Scientists believe that it would take only 1% of Earth's land area covered in solar panels to supply all of the world's present electrical needs!

Many governments, along with trying to reach targets using renewable energy resources, are also looking to other forms of energy. One of those energy sources is the use of **nuclear power**. Why has nuclear power become one of the go-to fuels for many countries?

Nuclear power

Nuclear power has many advantages:

- High energy output
- Very little greenhouse gas emissions
- Reduces our dependence on fossil fuels
- Very efficient in the production of energy.

These advantages are significant and important when countries are looking to produce vast quantities of energy from lower quantities of fuel.

However, many people have serious concerns about the use of nuclear power. The word 'nuclear' causes worry in many people's minds, mainly due to the disadvantages of using this form of power:

- Safety issues
- Problems in storing used fuel and its disposal
- Mining and refining of uranium, the fuel used in nuclear power stations, which can cause vast environmental and health issues
- The limited life span of a nuclear reactor, which is approximately 60 years.

▲ Figure 40.13 *A nuclear power plant*

What countries do next in terms of energy use, and especially in the area of selecting and utilising certain forms of energy, may determine the survival of our planet.

✏ Activity 40.1 How can we outline the environmental impact(s) of nuclear energy disasters?

Research the following nuclear disasters: (a) the Three Mile Island disaster in the United States; (b) the Chernobyl disaster in the Ukraine; (c) the Fukushima Daiichi disaster in Japan. Identify the causes of each accident and the immediate and ongoing safety issues following the disaster.

Using this information, have a class discussion about the development of a nuclear power plant in your own local area. Discuss in terms of (a) the advantages and disadvantages of generating nuclear power; (b) the ethical considerations; (c) the environmental concerns; (d) the economical benefits for the area. After the discussion, have a class vote on whether you would support or oppose an application to build a nuclear power station in your locality.

Summary questions

● 40.5 List three fossil fuels.

● 40.6 Identify four examples of renewable resources.

● 40.7 Name the fuel that is currently providing the highest percentage of our electrical supply.

● 40.8 Explain the terms 'renewable' and 'non-renewable' in terms of energy resources.

● 40.9 List four advantages and four disadvantages for the use of nuclear power.

● 40.10 Outline the main advantages and disadvantages of using wind turbines to produce power.

Assessment questions

40.11 Figure 40.14 shows different forms of energy. **(15 marks)**

 (a) Name the fossil fuels in the image.

 (b) Nuclear power is used to generate large volumes of power. List two advantages and two disadvantages of nuclear power.

 (c) Explain how fossil fuels are formed.

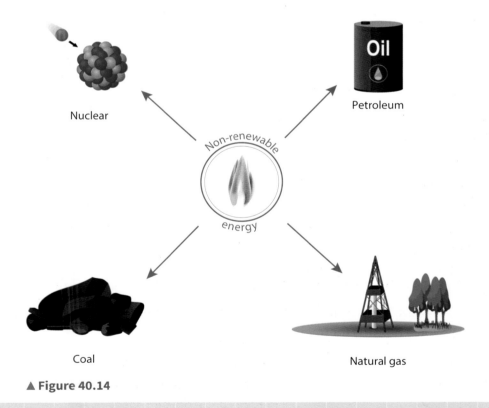

Nuclear

Petroleum

Non-renewable energy

Coal

Natural gas

▲ **Figure 40.14**

40.12 The graph in Figure 40.15 shows the renewable energy use of countries **(30 marks)** in 2005 and targets that were set, by the European Union, for the year 2010. Study the graph and answer the question below.

RENEWABLE ELECTRICITY USAGE IN 2005
Share of renewable electricity in EU (%)

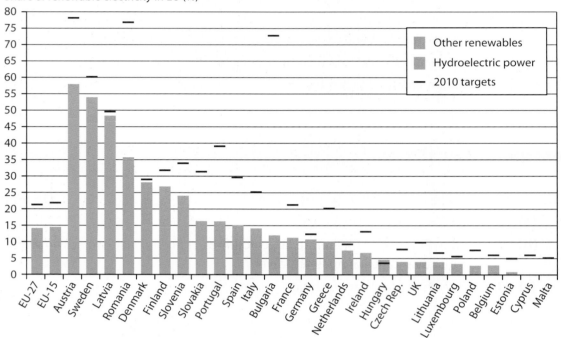

SOURCE: European Environment Agency

▲ **Figure 40.15**

(a) Identify two countries who were the closet to the target set by the EU.

(b) List three countries that used the most hydroelectric power.

(c) Suggest why the countries in the answer to part (a) are more successful in attaining their targets in terms of renewable sources of energy.

(d) Hydroelectric power is the use of water to generate power. Explain three forms of hydroelectric power.

(e) France uses nuclear power to generate power. Outline two advantages and two disadvantages of nuclear power.

(f) If a nuclear power station was to be built in the middle of Ireland, suggest why this could:

 (i) Be successful in terms of power output for the country, and

(ii) Involve hazards for Ireland as a whole.

PowerPoint summary   Weblinks

CLIMATE CHANGE

LO: ES7

What is the difference between global warming and climate change?

▲ Figure 41.1 *The burning of fossil fuel is impacting on Earth*

▲ Figure 41.2 *The effects of global warming*

From chapter 40 we know that we are burning fossil fuels to an extent that it has now begun to have an impact on the processes that take place on Earth.

You may be more aware of the term **global warming** than the term **climate change**. So what is the difference between the two terms?

Climate change is any long-term change, usually in terms of decades, to Earth's climate.
Climate means weather over a long period. This means climate change causes weather changes.

Global warming is the increase in Earth's average surface temperature due to the effect of greenhouse gases. Greenhouse gases are discussed on page 455.

It is the current global warming taking place on Earth that is causing our climate to change. Globally, temperatures have risen by approximately 0.8°C over the last 100 years. Europe is warming faster than many parts of the world – by 1.3°C in the twentieth century, according to EU research.

These increases in temperature may appear small, but they are potentially serious and dangerous to the balance of nature.

▲ Figure 41.3 *Rising global temperatures*

▲ Figure 41.4 *Animals such as the polar bear are losing their habitats because of global warming*

Activity 41.1 How can we demonstrate global warming?

As we know, carbon dioxide gas is one of the main greenhouse gases that has added to global warming. In this activity we will use effervescent tablets to demonstrate the release of carbon dioxide gas. The 'effervescence', or bubble release, represents the release of carbon dioxide.

🔬 Equipment needed

Two large, clear plastic drinks bottles with lids

Effervescent tablets, or similar

Beaker with water

Metre stick

One heating lamp or heating element

Two thermometers, or digital equipment to monitor temperature change

A marker that can write on a plastic bottle

 Safety
- Take care when setting up the equipment.
- Be careful around the heated lamp.
- Avoid any water spills.

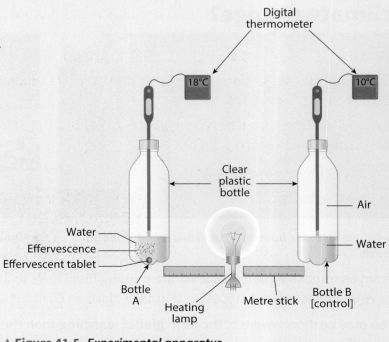

▲ Figure 41.5 *Experimental apparatus*

> ## → Conducting the activity
>
> 1. Make a hole in the lids of the two bottles so that the temperature probe fits through. Then set up the equipment as shown in Figure 41.5. Label one bottle A and one bottle B.
> 2. Record the initial temperature of the water in both plastic bottles.
> 3. Place a metre stick in between both bottles and ensure that each bottle is an equal distance away from the lamp.
> 4. Open up bottle A quickly and carefully and add in one effervescent tablet.
> 5. Close the bottle immediately.
> 6. Turn on the lamp. This needs to be done at the same time as when the tablet is added.
> 7. Record the temperature change, each minute, over a 5-minute period. You can complete this activity over a longer period of time if you choose. Record your results in the table in your Student Activity Book.
> 8. Record in your table what you observe happening to the tablet and to the temperature.
> 9. Are there any changes in bottle B?
> 10. Note your new hypothesis.
>
> ## Extension
> Do you think you would get the same result by adding additional tablets?
>
> - Repeat the same activity, adding two tablets this time.
> - Observe if there are any changes in comparison to your original recordings.
> - Explore what any differences mean in terms of carbon dioxide being released and global warming.
> - Outline, with your lab partner, what this activity demonstrates to you in terms of global warming.

What are the factors that are causing our planet to warm up? What are the impacts on our environment? And how can we, as individuals and as countries, make a difference?

What is the greenhouse effect?

The greenhouse effect occurs when gases in Earth's atmosphere prevent some of the heat from escaping into space.

These gases, which trap the heat in the atmosphere and as a result make Earth much warmer, are called greenhouse gases.

The main greenhouse gases are:

- Carbon dioxide (CO_2)
- Methane (CH_4)
- Nitrous oxide (N_2O)
- Water vapour (H_2O).

Did you know?

The snows on Mount Kilimanjaro have melted more than 80% since 2012.

In describing the greenhouse effect we will look at the most commonly known greenhouse gas, carbon dioxide.

We looked at the carbon cycle in chapter 39, and at how carbon is cycled through nature.

▲ Figure 41.6 *Earth is getting too hot*

▲ Figure 41.7 *Heat trapped by greenhouse gases resulting in an increase in atmosphere temperature*

Earth is surrounded by the atmosphere. This acts like a blanket, trapping heat energy from the Sun. As a result, Earth has a surface temperature that allows life to exist. Increasing levels of carbon dioxide in Earth's atmosphere trap more of this heat energy. This results in our atmosphere warming up above previous normal levels.

Carbon dioxide concentration

Carbon dioxide is released by many means:

Human activities

- Burning fossil fuels
- Production of lime to make cement
- Extraction (removal), processing, transport and distribution of fossil fuels
- Disposal of all household waste
- Addition of fertiliser onto the soil
- Agriculture

Natural activities

- Animal and plant respiration
- Volcanic eruptions

▲ Figure 41.8 *Burning fossil fuels releases increased volumes of carbon dioxide into the atmosphere*

- Carbon dioxide exchange between the oceans and the atmosphere.

There is a balance of carbon dioxide within the atmosphere:

- Too little and Earth is too cold to sustain life
- Too much and Earth warms up, and even small temperature rises begin to affect how our planet functions.

However, due to the increased burning of fossil fuels, this balance of carbon dioxide has been dramatically affected. It is this increased level of CO_2 that has resulted in global warming and the resulting changes to our climate.

> **? Question**
>
> **41.1** Explain what events took place during and since the Industrial Revolution that you think have resulted in the 40% increase in the level of carbon dioxide.

According to NASA scientists, there has been a 40% increase in the level of carbon dioxide concentration in the atmosphere since the Industrial Revolution in the late 1700s.

It is the 'warming up' due to excess carbon dioxide that is causing the worldwide climate to change.

So how is Earth coping? Many factors are causing the planet to struggle. We will look at three:

- Oceans
- How our surfaces reflect light
- A process called 'global dimming'.

 Question

41.2 Identify some of the uses for burning fossil fuels.

How do the oceans affect climate?

The oceans are very important to Earth's climate. Oceans trap heat energy from the Sun, which warms the water. This warm water is then distributed around Earth by the oceans' currents. As the warm water passes by land it warms that land.

Therefore our oceans are crucial in maintaining the heat transfer around Earth.

The changing acidic nature of Earth's oceans

A key factor for Earth's climate is that the oceans absorb carbon dioxide. Currently the oceans are absorbing approximately 40% of all the carbon dioxide that is being released into the atmosphere. Oceans absorb CO_2 directly from the atmosphere or in the form of acid rain (rain in which CO_2 is dissolved within the raindrops). CO_2 is an acidic gas, which means that when it is dissolved in water it makes that water more acidic.

This affects how animals and plants live within the oceans.

Oceans are also absorbing 90% of all the excess heat that is being generated due to the increased amounts of the greenhouse gases.

Colder water absorbs carbon dioxide much more easily than warmer water. So as the oceans warm up they will be unable to absorb as much CO_2.

The heat will then be returned to the atmosphere. This in turn will cause more heat to stay in the atmosphere, causing the planet to warm up even more.

▲ **Figure 41.9** *The oceans affect Earth's climate*

Did you know?

Earth's oceans have absorbed 20 times more of this increased amount of heat over the last 50 years.

This increased warming of Earth's oceans is not something that may happen in the future – it is happening right now. Scientists have been studying the levels of carbon dioxide in the North Atlantic Ocean for the last 30 years. They have found that there are large sections of the North

Atlantic that are currently unable to absorb as much CO_2 as they used to. This has also been observed in the Sea of Japan.

As some scientists have stated, our oceans are doing 'a service to humans'. It is important that we protect them more than we are currently protecting them.

Surface reflectivity

When sunlight reaches Earth it will either be absorbed or **reflected**.

The lighter colour an object is – for example, snow, ice, clouds – the more the heat energy is reflected back into space. This helps Earth to remain cool.

The darker colour an object is – for example, oceans, forests and soil – the more of the heat from the Sun is absorbed to warm up Earth.

Earth usually absorbs around 70% of the sunlight and reflects the remaining 30%. It is this balance that allows

▲ **Figure 41.10** *Deforestation contributes to global warming*

Earth to remain warm but avoids it warming up too much. But what happens if the balance changes? What if, due to global warming, the reflectors such as ice and snow begin to melt into the oceans?

What happens when the world's **glaciers** begin melting and retreating?

? Question

41.3 Research the following issues.

(a) The evidence that scientists have gathered to show that global warming and climate change is actually taking place

(b) The melting of the polar ice caps is resulting in more fresh water going into Earth's oceans; outline the effect this is currently having, and what effects it may cause in the future

(c) As well as CO_2, water vapour and methane gas are major contributing greenhouse gases; describe the effects of each of these three gases in terms of climate change, and outline why more and more of these gases are being released into the atmosphere.

Global dimming

When we burn fossil fuels, not only are we releasing greenhouse gases into the atmosphere, we are releasing particles, such as soot and ash, into the air.

These particles allow water vapour to gather on them to create larger clouds.

The more fossil fuels we burn, the more particles there will be in the atmosphere and the greater the amount of water within the clouds.

In simple terms, polluted clouds contain more water than unpolluted clouds.

This means that these clouds act like mirrors, reflecting more sunlight back into space. This is global dimming. The result of global dimming is that water in the northern hemisphere has become colder due to the reflection of solar energy back into space. This has led to evaporation taking place at slower rates and has caused rainfall in certain parts of the world to be significantly lower, resulting in drought.

What are the effects of climate change?

Some of the effects of climate change are:

- Rising sea levels
- Shrinking glaciers
- Storms and floods
- Heatwaves
- Drought.

Rising sea levels

The melting of glaciers, polar ice sheets and sea ice occurs when the temperature increases cause the ice to change its state of matter to water. More water flows to the oceans, increasing the levels of Earth's waters. The ocean waters then warm and expand.

This has played a large role in the increase of the sea level between 10 to 20 cm in the last 100 years, according to the Intergovernmental Panel on Climate Change (IPCC), which has resulted in flooding taking place more frequently.

▲ Figure 41.11 *Flooding is becoming more frequent – Bangkok airport*

Shrinking glaciers

A glacier is a river of ice. Glaciers are formed when snow does not completely melt away in the summer. With each winter extra snow gets laid down, compressing the layers of snow beneath it. Eventually, over thousands of years, the accumulation of these now solid layers forms a glacier.

Did you know?

If the ice sheet in the country of Greenland melts, the world's sea level will rise by 5 to 7 metres.

Glaciers move and flow through the landscape. People who live near glaciers depend on glaciers for their fresh water. This fresh water comes from meltwater from the glaciers.

▲ Figure 41.12 *Glaciers are shrinking*

▲ Figure 41.13 *The retreating glacier in the Himalayan Mountains*

Glaciers are very sensitive to changes in temperature. Climate change is causing many of the world's glaciers to retreat, or go backwards. Many of these glaciers are retreating so rapidly that they may completely disappear within decades.

Did you know?

The glaciers in the Himalayas are shrinking and getting shorter by 37 metres every year and could possibly disappear by 2035.

Storms and floods

Warmer waters in our oceans give strength to storms, making them more powerful. Local flooding results when these storms reach land.

▲ **Figure 41.14** *Storms are becoming more regular in some parts of the world*

▲ **Figure 41.15** *Storms and rising water levels are causing more flooding of homes and businesses*

? Questions

41.4 What is the name of the category 5 hurricane that hit New Orleans in August 2005?

41.5 Describe any of the effects from the storms that battered Ireland in 2014, 2017 and 2018.

Heatwaves

Heatwaves occur when the normal temperatures of a region are much greater than previous temperatures. According to records, nine of the ten warmest years on record have taken place since the year 2000.

Did you know?

2015, 2016 and 2017 were the warmest years on land and in oceans since records began in 1880 according to NASA.

▲ **Figure 41.16** *Rising temperatures cause heatwaves*

Drought

As heatwaves take place, drought (lack of sufficient supplies of water) may result.

The United Nations International Decade for Action: 'Water is Life', stated that with the existing climate change scenario, by 2025 1.8 billion people will be living in countries or regions with absolute water scarcity and by 2030 almost half the world's population will be living in areas of high water stress.

▲ **Figure 41.17** *Droughts kill crops, animals and people*

We are aware that climate change is taking place. It is how we now respond to it that will determine how much we can slow down the process.

Carbon footprint

A carbon footprint is a measure of the amount of carbon that is produced from the activities carried out by humans. It can then be a measure of the impact that we have on the environment.

For example, the electricity required to power a video game, or the fossil fuel required by the car, train or bus that brought you to school, each has a carbon footprint. Carbon footprints can be measured for individuals, businesses, councils and so on.

Having a small carbon footprint is much better than having a large carbon footprint. Reducing the amount of energy you use will lower the carbon footprint that you have.

▲ Figure 41.18 *Our carbon footprint*

? Question

41.6 Many initiatives have been undertaken across the world to reduce the effects of climate change.

In groups or pairs research the following.

(a) Any agreements that governments or any countries have made in order to reduce the carbon footprint on Earth. Determine, from your research, if these agreements have been successfully put in place and if they are having any effect.

(b) Outline any initiatives that have been undertaken in your local area or school to reduce the carbon footprint of that area.

(c) Make a list of daily activities that you carry out that require energy. Determine from that list if you feel you have a large or a small carbon footprint.

We can look at ourselves and what we are doing on a day-to-day basis to reduce our own carbon footprint. It is not just what governments decide that will reduce the effect of climate change: we all have a role to play.

It may be what we – each of us – do within our daily routine that may have the biggest impact.

▲ Figure 41.19 *Switching away from carbon dioxide*

ⓘ Question

41.7 Monitor the energy use in your home (or school) over the period of a week. Record your findings in the table provided in your Student Activity Book.

Decide on a particular time in the evening to complete your checks. Keep to the same time frame for the remaining days of the week.

Things that you will need to take account of, if they are applicable to your circumstances, are:

- The number of lights on in each room
- How many rooms with no person in them have a light on
- The electrical devices that are on standby each day
- The temperature at which the thermostat is set for your heating.

You will also need to make a note of:

- The type of fuel that is being used in your home to generate heat
- The number of compact fluorescent or LED light bulbs that are currently in use in your home; these are the energy-efficient light bulbs
- Whether your home is an energy-efficient building, based on your recordings
- Three ways in which energy use can be reduced in your home.

Repeat all of the tasks above if you choose to select your school building to complete your checks.

▲ **Figure 41.20** *Our planet needs protecting*

Summary questions

41.8 List three of the main greenhouse gases.

41.9 Identify four human activities that are adding to the greenhouse effect.

41.10 Distinguish between the terms 'climate change' and 'global warming'.

41.11 Describe the greenhouse effect.

41.12 Explain the role of the oceans in the uptake of carbon dioxide gas.

41.13 Explain why the oceans' ability to uptake carbon dioxide is reducing.

41.14 Outline how the oceans are becoming acidified.

41.15 Explain global dimming.

41.16 List three effects of climate change.

41.17 Explain, in detail, one of the effects that you have chosen in your answer to question 41.16.

41.18 Outline one initiative that governments around the world are taking to address the problem of climate change.

Assessment questions

41.19 Question from Junior Cycle Science exam paper   (15 marks)

Global warming can cause the melting of ice sheets and glaciers, which is partly responsible for rising sea levels.

▲ Figure 41.21

(a) Name a human activity which has led to global warming.

(b) State a consequence of rising sea levels on coastal areas.

(c) Ice sheets are the natural habitat of animals such as polar bears. State one adaptation of polar bears that makes them suited to this habitat.

(d) Would you expect the population of polar bears to increase or decrease as ice sheets melt?

(e) When solid ice changes state to become liquid water, this is called melting. What name is given to the change of state when liquid water becomes solid ice?

41.20 Copy and complete the following paragraph on climate change and global warming, using the words below.   (15 marks)

greenhouse effect long increase shrinking short reducing temperature

gas liquid carbon dioxide nitrogen dioxide glaciers fossil fuels

atmosphere rising heatwaves

The _____ of Earth is increasing due to the _____ _____. Gases, for example _____ _____, have caused our _____ to warm up. Human activity, for example the burning of _____ _____ has added to an increase in greenhouse _____ emissions. This has resulted in an _____ in the Earth's average surface temperature, causing our weather to change over _____ periods of time. _____ sea levels and _____ are two of the effects of climate change.

41.21 Read the article below on 'heatwaves' from Met Eireann and answer the questions that follow.   (30 marks)

What causes a heatwave?

A heatwave occurs when a high pressure system moves into an area. This results in air from the upper levels of the atmosphere being pushed to the ground, where it becomes compressed and increases in temperature. The high atmospheric pressure makes it hard for other weather systems to move in, blocking them. Therefore heatwaves normally last for several days.

Three broad types of heatwave events may be identified as:

1. Dry heatwaves, associated with a continental or Mediterranean climate, and stable periods of weather with clear skies and large amounts of solar radiation.

2. Moist heatwaves are very warm with humid conditions throughout the day and night, often with night-time cloud cover, which prevents the escape of day's accumulated heat and therefore little relief at night-time.

3. Either of the above plus the Heat Island Effect. Large urban areas experience heatwaves with more intensity as the Sun's heat is stored efficiently in road tarmac and buildings. This heat only escapes during the night-time if conditions allow.

Following June 2019, now the warmest June on record globally, the World Meteorological Organisation (WMO) reports that for the second time in less than a month, 'Europe is experiencing a widespread and intense heatwave, with many new maximum and minimum temperature records, disruption to transport and infrastructure and stress on people's health and the environment'.

- Meteo France reported 43.1°C in Saint-Maur-des-Fossés.
- DWD in Germany reported 42.6°C in Lingen, its highest temperature on record.
- Netherland reached 40.7°C at Gilze-Rijen, its highest temperature on record.
- The Belgium record of 39.9°C at Kleine Brogel was broken at Beitem with 40.7°C.
- The UK Met Office stated today that the highest daily *maximum* air temperature recorded yesterday was 38.7°C at Cambridge, this value is provisional. It may become the highest temperature ever recorded in the UK once quality control checks are complete. They also have a new Scottish highest *minimum* temperature of 20.9°C at Achnagart.

Temperature changes in Ireland will more or less mirror global changes, that is an increase in 1.5°C to 4°C by end of the century. Following from this, we will have less days with frost/ice and more days with temperatures above 25°C. Consequently milder winters and warmer, drier summers with more heatwaves are likely during summer. There is also likely to be a seasonal change in that Ireland will get more rainfall in winter, and more heavy-rainfall-days, and less rainfall in the summer months with an increase in dry periods.

Source: Met Eireann, https://www.met.ie/temperatures-extremes-and-heatwaves-during-july-2019

(a) Describe how Met Eireann defines a 'heatwave'.

(b) Explain, in your own words using information from the article regarding the three forms of heatwave, why a town in central Europe, surrounded by land, may experience a different form of heatwave to a town on the coast of Ireland.

(c) Using your knowledge of the water cycle, select two processes within the cycle and describe one negative impact, of a heatwave, on those named processes which you have chosen.

(d) With an increasing global temperature, identify and explain – using information from the article – the seasonal changes that may take place resulting from increasing global temperatures.

(e) Explain one impact that low water levels would have on a heavily populated area.

 Log on to www.edcolearning.ie for Additional Assessment Questions

 **PowerPoint summary** | **Weblinks**

SPACE EXPLORATION – 'TO INFINITY AND BEYOND!'

CHAPTER 42

LO: ES8

Learning intentions

At the end of this chapter you will be able to:

- ✓ Describe the benefits of space exploration
- ✓ Explain the dangers of space travel
- ✓ Outline the future of space exploration for humans
- ✓ Examine some of the current hazards and benefits of space exploration and discuss the future role and implications of space exploration in society.

Keywords

- 🔑 exploration
- 🔑 astronauts
- 🔑 technology
- 🔑 hazards
- 🔑 density

What is out there?

Since the time of the first explorers, such as Christopher Columbus, humankind has been fascinated by the unknown worlds that lie beyond our horizon.

One of our greatest wonders lies in the worlds beyond our planet and what possibly may exist there.

▲ **Figure 42.1** *What wonders lie beyond our world?*

▲ **Figure 42.2** *A probe in space, looking at worlds beyond our own*

Our history tells us that it was during the Cold War – a period of time, beginning in the late 1940s, when the United States and Russia had a very difficult political relationship – that some of our greatest achievements in space **exploration** took place.

The desire to explore space was called the 'Race to the Moon'. Both Russia and the United States wanted to be the first country to land **astronauts** on the Moon.

It was during this time, in 1958, that the National Aeronautics and Space Administration (NASA) was started. Its main mission was to ensure that an American astronaut was the first human to set foot on the Moon.

Even though a Russian, Yuri Gagarin, was the first human to orbit Earth in 1961, the United States won the 'race' for a human to walk on the Moon eight years later. On 20 July 1969, the American astronauts Neil Armstrong and Buzz Aldrin stepped on to the Moon, announcing to the world 'That's one small step for man, one giant leap for mankind'.

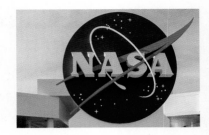

▲ Figure 42.3 *The American organisation NASA was set up to send astronauts to the Moon*

It is this 'giant leap' – the leap into space exploration – that we will be focusing on in this chapter. We will be looking at what we have learned from our journeys into space.

▲ Figure 42.4 *In 1961 Yuri Gagarin was the first human to orbit Earth*

▲ Figure 42.5 *Neil Armstrong, the first human on the Moon, on Apollo 11*

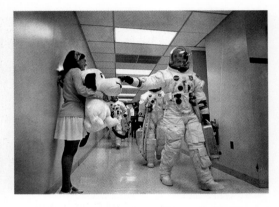

▲ Figure 42.6 *In 1969 Apollo 10 astronauts 'snooped around' the Moon's surface to find a landing site for Apollo 11. The crew called the lunar module 'Snoopy' and the command module 'Charlie Brown'. Snoopy has been their mascot ever since*

✍ Activity 42.1 How can we learn about space exploration from previous exploration events in our history?

The Space Race was a time during the 1950s, 1960s and 1970s, when the United States and Russia vied to be the first nation to put a human into space and to land on the Moon. From this time in our history, and to the modern day, many great moments in humankind's journey into space have taken place.

In groups of three to four people, research the following titles, using the internet and the school library, and present your findings to the class, as a slide presentation. Include in your presentation the time sequence, using the year in which the space exploration took place and a brief explanation of the major events.

(a) The Race to the Moon, between the United States and Russia

(b) Apollo 11 landing on the Moon

(c) The Space Shuttle missions, starting with the Space Shuttle Columbia mission in 1981

(d) The development of the International Space Station

(e) Space disasters, or any other disaster that took place on a piloted mission to space

(f) The current missions to Mars

What are the benefits of space exploration?

In developing rockets and shuttles that could be launched into space, scientists were driven to make computers and digital **technology** that was small enough and light enough to fit into spacecraft.

Spin-offs of the research into technology for the space programme have benefits for the rest of us on a day-to-day basis.

Table 42.1 gives a list of just some of the technologies that we all now make use of, which came about because of research and development for the space programme.

Did you know?

A modern smartphone has many millions more computing power compared to the Apollo 11 spacecraft.
Apollo – 145 000 lines of code
Facebook – 62 000 000 lines of code
Google – 2 000 000 000 lines of code

▲ **Figure 42.7** *The Apollo 11 Moon landing*

Table 42.1 Technologies developed by the space programme that are now available to everyone

Nutrition	
Food in space must have a long shelf life. Food needs to be nutritious and stay edible for long periods of time. This need led to the development of long-life foods, which we now find on our supermarket shelves. *Example*: powdered food such as soup.	 ▲ **Figure 42.8** *Long-life foods used in spacecraft*
Industry	
In spacecraft all piping has to be lightweight but extremely strong, and this had to be developed specifically. This form of piping is used now in industry. *Example*: Heat pipes are now used in computer systems. Along with piping, cordless tools that were developed for space shuttle use are now also widely found in ordinary households. The use of robotic technology, which was developed for spacecraft, is now also used in industry.	  ▲ **Figure 42.9** *Cordless tools* ▲ **Figure 42.10** *Robotic arm used in manufacturing*

Medicine

Heart monitors were developed to observe the heart rates of the astronauts on missions to space. They are now used in all hospitals.

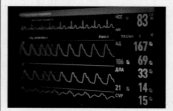

▲ Figure 42.11 *Heart monitor*

Materials

The safety of astronauts was an essential part of all development. Materials that astronauts wore needed to be fireproof. Firefighters now wear protective suits made from material used in space suits.

Spacecraft have to endure some harsh conditions. Materials used in spacecraft to withstand extreme changes in temperature are now used as fire-resistant materials in new homes.

▲ Figure 42.12 *Heat shield for lunar module re-entry to Earth*

Mobile phone cameras

The cameras on our mobile phones are a result of technological developments of cameras in spacecraft.

▲ Figure 42.13 *Camera on a mobile phone*

Computers

To ensure spacecraft were light enough to be launched into space, all computers on board needed to be very lightweight. This lightweight technology has been applied to all computers that we now use.

▲ Figure 42.14 *Computers in industry*

---

⑦ Question

42.1 The first satellite in space was launched by the Russians on 4 October 1957. The satellite's name was Sputnik.

Since that date, there have been major developments in the use of satellites and their role. Using the internet and the school library, prepare a slide presentation on:

(a) Satellite development

(b) The role of satellites in space exploration

(c) Use of satellites in current everyday technology.

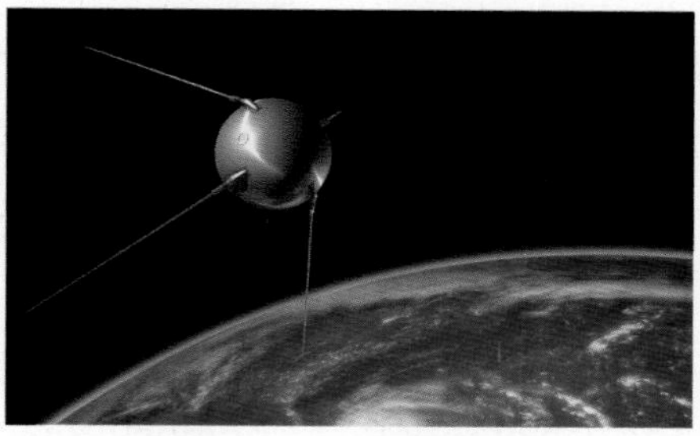

▲ Figure 42.15 *Sputnik satellite orbiting Earth*

Apart from all the amazing technology that has been and continues to be developed, it was the excitement that came from our interest in space exploration that attracted people to study and take up careers in science, technology, engineering and maths – or STEM, as it is sometimes called.

Space exploration has also enabled us to use technologies to look into space and to look from space to monitor what is taking place on Earth and outside our planet.

A range of benefits has resulted from space exploration. But what are the dangers of space travel?

Did you know?

Astronauts wear orange spacesuits for launch and re-entry (re-entry is when the spacecraft returns to Earth's atmosphere). Orange is easily seen if there is an emergency. Astronauts wear white space suits during space walks.

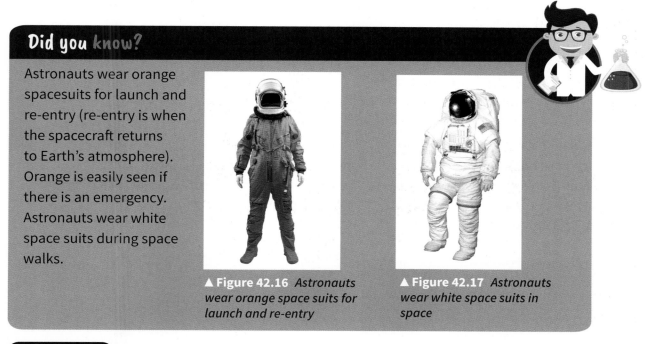

▲ **Figure 42.16** *Astronauts wear orange space suits for launch and re-entry*

▲ **Figure 42.17** *Astronauts wear white space suits in space*

? Question

42.2 Why do astronauts wear white space suits when on a spacewalk?

What are the hazards of space exploration?

There are **hazards** in space exploration. Throughout the history of all space travel there have been many disasters.

Disasters in space

The most famous and most unfortunate disasters resulted in not only a loss of the spacecraft but sometimes the loss of the crew.

Apollo 1 in 1967 All three astronauts were killed in a fire in the cockpit during pre-launch tests.

Apollo 13 in 1970 An oxygen gas tank exploded on the command module part of the spacecraft. This meant that the astronauts could not land on the Moon, as had been planned. The crew suffered great hardships because of the problems, but they all returned home safely.

▲ **Figure 42.18** *Apollo 13 was badly damaged*

Challenger space shuttle in 1986 Just 73 seconds into lift-off the shuttle exploded, killing all seven crew members.

Columbia space shuttle in 2003 The shuttle broke apart on re-entry to Earth, after a two-week mission. All seven crew were killed.

Health risks

Astronauts risk their lives, but there can also be a risk to the condition of their bodies after a mission to space.

Our bodies are designed to work on Earth in response to gravity. When we lift anything our muscles need to apply strength to pull an object against the effect of gravity. This makes our muscles and bones strong. But in space there is a lower effect from gravity.

According to scientists, 'space is not an environment we are evolved to survive in'. Scientists have spent years studying the effect of being in space and the reduced gravity, experienced within spacecraft, on the human body.

▲ Figure 42.19 *The Challenger space shuttle exploded within 2 minutes of take-off*

▲ Figure 42.20 *The effect of micro gravity*

▲ Figure 42.21 *This is what happens when an astronaut combs her hair in space*

▲ Figure 42.22 *Astronauts floating in micro gravity*

Did you know?

You may have heard the term 'zero gravity'. This does not mean there is no gravity, but that it is not the same as on Earth. In spacecraft humans experience 'zero' or 'micro' gravity. 'Micro' means small, so humans experience a much smaller effect from gravity in space. The effect of gravity gets smaller and smaller as a body moves away from another body in space; for example, as a spacecraft moves away from Earth.

Effects of reduced gravity on the body

Bone

When astronauts are floating around in a spacecraft they are not using their bones in the same way as they use their bones on Earth. As a result, **astronauts will suffer from bone loss in space as their bones are no longer experiencing the resistance, or pull, from Earth's gravity and so they have to exercise carefully**.

Loss of bone **density** will begin to occur after only one week in space. Bone loss occurs when the rate at which bone is absorbed into the body is greater than the rate at which bone is being produced. As a result, the bone becomes weaker.

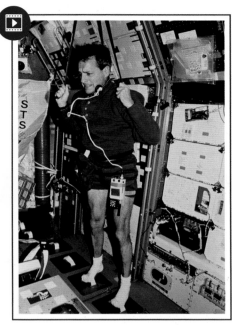

▲ **Figure 42.23** *Astronauts have to exercise while in space to prevent bone loss*

> **? Questions**
>
> **42.3** What is the term that describes the loss of bone density?
>
> **42.4** Describe any effects to the body that may result from the loss of bone density.

Did you know?

NASA estimates that a return trip to Mars would result in the same bone loss that you would experience in your whole lifetime on Earth.

Muscle

The muscles in the body shrink in space, leaving the body weaker when the astronaut returns to Earth.

Immune system

Long missions to space cause the immune system to be less effective at fighting off infections.

Circulatory system

NASA says that being in space is 'like standing on your head'. Blood collects in the upper part of the body, resulting in increases in blood pressure.

Heart

The heart does not have to work as hard in space as it does on Earth. This may sound like an advantage, but it is very dangerous as the heart may become weaker if it is not worked hard enough.

Sleep patterns

There is constant noise and light on a spacecraft, which makes it very difficult to sleep.

Radiation

Astronauts are exposed to one of the greatest dangers in space: radiation. Astronauts have experienced flashes of light inside their eyelids. This comes from the increase in cosmic rays that are actually passing through them at great speed.

⑦ Question

42.5 **Looking at the list of difficulties that the body experiences in space, investigate how scientists have developed technology and information for astronauts to overcome the effect of zero gravity.**

✎ Activity 42.2 How does being in space affect bone loss?

🧪 Equipment needed

Puffed cereal (around 150 g)

Book

5 zip-lock bags

Metre stick

Markers

Dust pan for cleaning up!

> **Safety**
> - Be careful when dropping the book on to the bag of cereal.
> - Wear goggles to prevent any cereal getting into your eyes.

➡ Conducting the activity

1. Bag 1 – fill the bag with the puffed cereal, leaving very little air in the bag. This bag now represents normal bone density and is equal to 100%.
2. Count how many pieces of cereal you have placed into the bag.
3. Close the bag tightly, removing as much air as possible from it without squashing the cereal.
4. Fill the remaining four bags with less cereal to represent bone density loss:

   Bag 2 – fill to 90% = 10% bone loss

   Bag 3 – fill to 80% = 20% bone loss

   Bag 4 – fill to 70% = 30% bone loss

   Bag 5 – fill to 60% = 40% bone loss.
5. Calculate the percentage bone loss using the total amount you have in Bag 1 and removing the puffed cereal to make up the 10%, 20%, 30% and 40% bone loss.
6. Place Bag 1 on the desk.
7. Drop the book onto the bag from a height of 50 cm, measured using the metre stick.
8. Record what happens in the table provided in your Student Activity Book.
9. Count how many puffed cereal pieces remain unbroken and record this in your table.
10. Repeat the procedure for each bag and record the results.

The International Space Station

The International Space Station (ISS) was first launched in November 1998 and took 13 years to build. It is a habitable low-orbit satellite that has been continuously occupied by astronauts since 2000.

The ISS is a joint project involving five space agencies: NASA (United States), Roscosmos (Russia), JAXA (Japan), CSA (Canada) and the European Space Agency (ESA). The ISS has been visited by astronauts from 14 different countries. By November 2014, the ISS had taken part in 100 Russian launches and 37 space shuttle launches.

The ISS allows us to have a constant human presence in space. It allows crew members to conduct experiments while also allowing scientists to see the long-term effects of micro gravity on the human body.

Did you know?

From as early as 2020, you may be able to purchase a seat for a private 30-day astronaut mission to the International Space Station. The cost is estimated to be $52 million per person.

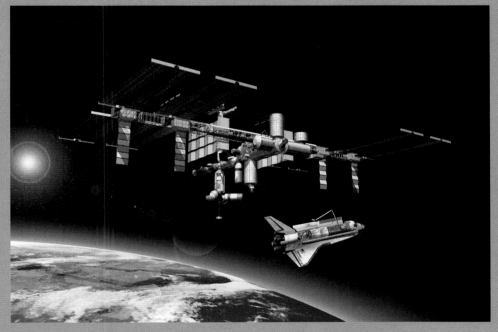

▲ **Figure 42.24** *The International Space Station and the space shuttle above Earth*

? Question

42.6 The European Space Agency (ESA) was formed in 1975.

In pairs or groups complete the following activity using the internet and your school library to find information.

(a) Name the countries that sit on the ESA's governing council.

(b) Identify any major developments and/or missions that the ESA has been involved in. Outline the main outcomes/results of the topic you have chosen.

(c) Draw a poster showing future missions/projects that the ESA will be involved in.

What is the future of space exploration?

Where do we go from here? What are the next destinations that we are looking to explore?

Mars

The planet Mars is the next big destination. Recently NASA sent probes successfully to the planet. NASA launched their Insight Mars Lander on May 5th 2018. The probe is stationary and is studying the composition of Mars.

You may wonder why Mars is the next planet scientists want to look at closely.

Apart from Earth, Mars is the other planet in the solar system that could possibly support humans living on it. It is a planet rich in the elements carbon, nitrogen, oxygen and hydrogen – all of which we need to survive.

▲ **Figure 42.25** *Probes on Mars*

▲ **Figure 42.26** *Mars – the next planet to explore*

▲ **Figure 42.27** *A future space station on Mars*

Also Mars has one key element that makes it a possible planet for exploration: it has water. Although the water is frozen, as ice, the key fact for scientists is that it has water.

The journey to Mars takes approximately six months. Astronauts would need to remain on Mars for 30 days or 300 days. These might seem like odd lengths of time, but the orbit of Mars around the Sun does not exactly match that of Earth. So there would be a window of opportunity for astronauts to return to Earth at 30 days. If this was missed the astronauts would have to wait for another 270 days for Mars to have completed its orbit around the Sun and be in the correct position again to exit Mars and return to Earth.

Scientists are very aware that long stays in space badly affect our bodies. Overcoming this problem could be one of our greatest difficulties for prolonged space travel.

> **? Question**
>
> **42.7** **Discuss with a partner how a mission might remain in space for a long period of time in terms of fuel use, food and water supplies.**
>
> **Explain, in your answer, how you think astronauts could access the required extra oxygen and water that they would need.**

Minerals

Another area of space exploration that scientists are looking at is minerals.

There will come a time in Earth's future when our mineral resources will run out. We need to begin to explore new areas and possibly new worlds that have high quantities of minerals.

Research on meteorite collisions with Earth have shown that these asteroid rocks from space are rich in minerals.

NASA has developed a programme called the Asteroid Redirect Mission. It is NASA's intention to move an asteroid close to the Moon and allow astronauts to explore it. This mission they hope to have launched by the early 2020s.

▲ Figure 42.28 *Asteroids are rich in minerals*

? Question

42.8 Space exploration has always been enormously expensive for countries that have space agencies and space programmes.

Discuss within groups, whether you would:

(a) Discontinue a space exploration programme, if you were in charge, due to its high financial cost

(b) Maintain the programme.

If you decide to maintain the programme you must give your reasons for your decision.

Summary

Humans are curious about what exists beyond our planet. We have questioned, explored and discovered vast amounts of knowledge because of this thirst for information.

Yet we still crave and desire to know more. We keep looking outwards towards space and the infinite possibilities that exist there. It is humans' drive to seek out the unknown and it is this that maintains our constant search into the worlds and galaxies beyond our own planet.

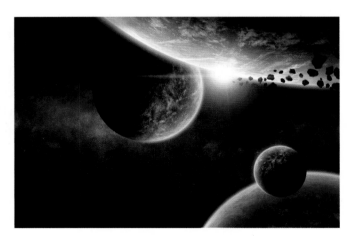

▲ Figure 42.29 *We have a huge interest in and curiosity about space*

Our relationship with space can be summed up by a quote from the famous *Star Trek* TV series:

'To explore strange new worlds, to seek out new life and new civilisations, to boldly go where no man has gone before.'

Summary questions

- 42.9 Name the two countries involved in the race to the Moon.
- 42.10 Name the first human to orbit Earth.
- 42.11 Name the first human to land on the Moon.
- 42.12 Name two disasters that took place on people-carrying missions to space.
- 42.13 List three technologies developed by the space programme that we now use in everyday living.
- 42.14 Explain why astronauts wear two different coloured space suits – white and orange.
- 42.15 List four health risks to humans in space.
- 42.16 Describe the effect of micro-gravity in space on the bones of humans.
- 42.17 Identify three reasons why space missions are going to Mars.
- 42.18 Outline two reasons why **(a)** space exploration should continue *and* **(b)** why space exploration should stop.

Assessment questions

42.19 **(a)** Space exploration can be very dangerous for humans. Using your **(15 marks)** knowledge of life in space and the risks to humans, explain how astronauts may be able to overcome the problems of:

   (i) Micro-gravity

   (ii) Poor sleep patterns.

(b) Astronauts in the International Space Station have oxygen tanks in their space suits for space walks outside the station. Explain why they require the oxygen when outside in space.

▲ **Figure 42.30** *Space shuttle Challenger exploding after take-off*

(c) The colour of the suit for space walks is white. Explain why this colour was selected for the astronauts' space-walk suits.

42.20 NASA scientists have successfully grown plants, for example lettuce, in **(30 marks)** the micro-gravity of the International Space Station. NASA hopes that this will provide data/information for missions to space that have prolonged journeys. The main purpose of this experiment was to optimise the growth of the plants whilst observing any growth of micro-organisms – bacteria and fungi – and learning how to minimise it.

Answer the following questions in relation to the information above.

(a) Outline three reasons why scientists would need to grow vegetables on board for prolonged space travel.

(b) Explain why the scientists are monitoring very carefully the growth of micro-organisms on any plants they grow.

(c) Future manned flights to Mars may take up to six months to arrive at the planet. Scientists are looking at various forms of energy to maintain a flight for this duration.

Describe two possible ways in which a mission to Mars may utilise other forms of fuel/energy for this prolonged journey.

42.21

(45 marks)

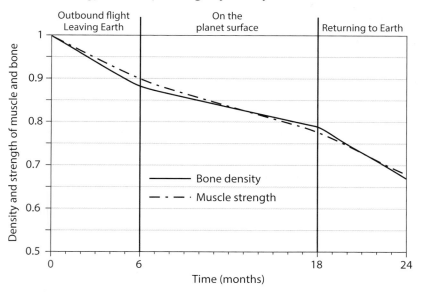

▲ **Figure 42.31**

The graph in Figure 42.31 shows the change in muscle and bone strength during a complete mission – leaving Earth, landing on a planet and returning to Earth.

(a) Outline the following, using the graph as a source of reference:

  (i) The change in muscle strength and bone density on the outbound flight and the return flight

  (ii) The change in muscle strength and bone density when on the planet.

(b) Explain the reasons behind both the muscle and bone losing strength and density at the same rate.

(c) Describe two activities that astronauts can undertake to maintain muscle strength and bone density when on a space flight.

(d) Explain the following in terms of the astronauts' return to Earth:

  (i) Identify the force that will stimulate muscle and bone development back on Earth.

  (ii) Two activities different to your answer in part (c), that will stimulate muscle and bone development on Earth.

GLOSSARY OF TERMS

A

acid rain Rainwater with a pH of less than 5.5

area The amount of surface that covers an object

asteroid A small, rocky body that orbits a sun

astronaut A person who is trained to travel in a spacecraft in space and to carry out investigations in space

astronomer A person who studies astronomy

astronomy The study of space and the universe

atom The smallest part of an element that still has the properties of that element

axis An imaginary line around which a body rotates

C

carbon footprint The amount of carbon dioxide released that results from the activities of a person, persons or community

carbon sink Part of Earth that can absorb carbon dioxide from the atmosphere

celestial Something that belongs to space

chemical change A change (reaction) in which a new substance is formed

climate change A change in the climate patterns of Earth over time

comet A celestial body with a nucleus of ice and dust and that has tails

compounds Made up of two or more different types of atom chemically combined

condensation Where cooling a gas causes it to change into a liquid

convection The transfer of heat through liquids and gases by the mass movement of particles

crescent Curved shape of a waning or waxing moon

D

density The mass of each cubic metre of a material

E

eclipse When a body in space obscures another body in space

electric current The movement of charge through a material

electrical energy Energy caused by moving charges

elements Substances made up of only one type of atom

evaporation The changing of a liquid to a gas

exploration Investigations that are undertaken in an unfamiliar area

F

force The idea used to describe the cause of motion or a change in the motion of a body

fossil The remains of something that was once living long ago

fossil fuel A natural fuel – coal, oil, peat and gas – that was formed over millions of years from the remains of dead plants and animals

fuel A substance that burns in oxygen and produces heat

G

galaxies Systems of millions or billions of stars, together with gas and dust, held together by gravity

geothermal energy Energy that comes from the heat in the earth beneath the planet's surface

gibbous When more than half of the Moon is illuminated

glacier A slow moving river of ice

global warming An increase in the temperature in Earth's atmosphere due to the greenhouse effect

gravity Force in space that causes gases to condense, get smaller and come together

greenhouse effect When the heat energy of the Sun is trapped within Earth's atmosphere

H

halogens The elements of Group 7 of the periodic table, e.g. chlorine

heat A form of energy that is transferred from warmer bodies to colder ones

K

kinetic energy Energy stored in a body that is moving

L

length The straight-line distance between two points

lunar Of the Moon

M

magnetic field The space around a magnet in which a magnetic force can be detected

mass The amount of matter in an object. This amount never changes

mass number The number of protons *and* neutrons in an atom of that element

matter Anything that occupies space and has mass

meteor A small body in space that enters Earth's atmosphere

meteoroid A small body found in the solar system. Can also be called an asteroid

micro-organism A small living thing

Moon A satellite of Earth that reflects light from the Sun

N

nebulae A cloud of gas and dust in space

neutron An uncharged subatomic particle found in the nucleus of an atom

noble gases The elements of Group 8 of the periodic table, e.g. helium

non-renewable Sources of energy that cannot be replaced once they are used

nuclear energy Energy from making and breaking nuclear bonds

nuclear fusion Atoms that fuse together releasing energy in the form of heat and light

nucleus The central part of an atom that is made up of protons and neutrons. It also controls the cell's activities

O

orbit A regular, repeated course that an object in space completes around a star or planet

organism A living thing

P

penumbra A partial shadow cast by Earth or the Moon during an eclipse

phase of the Moon Different ways that the Moon appears from Earth during its 28-day cycle

photosynthesis The way in which green plants make food

planet A structure that orbits a star

planetoid A small structure that is considered too small to be called a planet

power The amount of work done in a unit of time. It is measured in watts

precipitation Rain, hail, sleet or snow that falls to the ground

pressure The amount of force acting on a unit of area

R

radiation The transfer of heat by means of waves that can travel through a vacuum

recycle Find other uses for as much of what we do not need as possible

reduce Decrease the amount of materials that we buy

reflect When a body throws back heat and light and does not absorb it

renewable A source of energy that can be reused

revolve To move in a circular motion

rotate To move in a circle around a central object

S

satellite A body that orbits earth or another planet

singularity Very small, very hot, dense area which was the origin of the Big Bang

solar Energy that comes from the Sun

solar system A collection of eight planets and their moons that orbit a sun and other smaller bodies such as comets and asteroids

sound Produced when objects vibrate

speed The distance travelled by an object in one unit of time

star A fixed luminous object in space that releases heat and light energy

surface area The measure of how much surface of reactants is exposed

T

telescope An instrument designed to allow us to see far away objects

temperature A measure of how hot or cold an object is

terrestrial Relating to the earth

time It is measured by a basic unit called the second (symbol s)

totality When an area is in total shadow as a result of an eclipse

transpiration The loss of water vapour from a plant

U

umbra A full shadow cast by Earth or the Moon during an eclipse

universe All the matter and space that works together

V

volume A measure of the space taken up by an object

W

waning When less of the Moon is being illuminated

water cycle The natural circulation of water on the planet

waxing When more of the Moon is being illuminated

INDEX

CLASSROOM-BASED ASSESSMENTS IN SCIENCE

Classroom-Based Assessments give students a chance to show what they have learned. There are two Classroom-Based Assessments in Science.

Extended Experimental Investigation (EEI)

EEI takes place over a three-week period towards the end of second year. Students can choose from eight topic areas for their investigation. Students can collaborate with classmates. Each student keeps a record of their research. Together students will develop their research question and plan and develop their investigation. Students individually consider the results of their investigation. Then, they might jointly reflect on their work. They then develop their individual reports. A report may be presented in a wide range of formats.

Watch these videos of students talking about their EEI CBAs:

Science in Society Investigation (SSI)

Students research an issue pertaining to science in society. This CBA takes place around Christmas time in third year over a three-week period. Students can choose a topic that relates to one of these areas.

- A technological application of science
- Or an application of science that has an effect on
  - Human health
  - The environment
  - Society

The topic must provide a strong basis for scientific research and a good research question needs to be developed. This CBA is carried out individually but students can discuss in small groups various aspects of their investigation. Students should keep research records throughout the three weeks of the CBA.

ACKNOWLEDGEMENTS

The authors and publishers would like to thank the following for permission to reproduce photos and other material: P1 Juice Images/Getty; p2 National Institutes of Health/NIAID/Science Photo Library, Martyn F Chillmaid/Science Photo Library, Science Photo Library, European Space Agency/Science Photo Library; p4 Philippe Psaila/Science Photo Library; p5 Matej Kastelic/Shutterstock; p6 jianbing Lee/Shutterstock; p12 Lisa F. Young/Shutterstock, Corbin O'Grady Studio/Science Photo Library; p15 science photo/Shutterstock, p17 Giovanni Cancemi/Shutterstock, Pixel-Shot/Shutterstock, Alfira/Shutterstock, Baishev/Shutterstock, Camptoloma/Shutterstock, givaga, OtmarW, Ruslan Ivantsov, Imageman, Odua Images, Yuri Samsonov, stockphoto-graf, Bertold Werkmann, irin-k, Pineapple studio and CWIS, all Shutterstock; p19 Erik Lam, Ozkan Serin, Chros, cellistka, Mirek Kijewski, yevgeniy11, irin-k, Khoroshunova Olga, all Shutterstock; p21 Dr Robert Calentine/Visuals Unlimited/Science Photo Library, Dr David Furness, Keele University/Science Photo Library, D. Kucharski K. Kucharska; p22 SpeedKingz/Shutterstock; p24 Steve Gschmeissner/Science Photo Library; p25 Kevin & Betty Collins, Visuals Unlimited/Science Photo Library, Francis Leroy, Biocosmos/Science Photo Library; p30 Ozgur Coskun/Shutterstock; p32 Science Photo Library, PR. G Gimenez-Martin/Science Photo Library; p33 Kotin/Shutterstock; p39 Sinclair Stammers/Science Photo Library; p40 The Print Collector/Heritage Images/Science Photo Library; p41 Yok_onepiece/Shutterstock, Natural History Museum, London/Science Photo Library, Chris Mattison/Nature Picture Library/Science Photo Library; p42 Natural History Museum, London, Science Photo Library; p43 Science Photo Library; p51 Sebastian Kaulitzki/Shutterstock; p55 Springer Medizin/Science Photo Library, Sebastian Kaulitzki/Shutterstock, MDGRPHCS/Shutterstock; p56 Klaus Guldbrandsen/Science Photo Library, Sashkin/Shutterstock; p62 Bangkoker/Shutterstock; p66 Sebastian Kaulitzki/Science Photo Library; p68 Science Photo Library; p69 MDGRPHCS/Shutterstock; p77 huafeng207/Shutterstock, sittitap/Shutterstock, ESB Professional/Shutterstock, liza54500/Shutterstock; p78 Nick Beer/Shutterstock; p79 Jerry Mason/Science Photo Library, Andrew Lambert Photography/Science Photo Library, Science Photo Library; p80 all photos Shutterstock; p83 Nigel Cattlin/Alamy, Nigel Cattlin/Alamy; p84 The Photolibrary Wales/Alamy; p86 Claude Nuridsany and marie Perennou/Science Photo Library, Darren Baker/Shutterstock; p87 JÃ?Â¡nos NÃ?Â©meth/Shutterstock, Bob Gibbons/Science Photo Library; p88 Dieter Hawlan/Shutterstock, Mark Medcalf/Shutterstock, WILDLIFE GmbH/Alamy, ShaunWilkinson/Shutterstock; p89 Shutterstock, Eric Isselee/Shutterstock, Eric Isselee/Shutterstock, Shutterstock, Zerbor/Shutterstock, photomaster/Shutterstock, Shutterstock; p94 Pim Leijen/Shutterstock; p95 altafulla/Shutterstock; p96 Mauro Fermariello/Science Photo Library; p97 Dr Stanley Flegler, Visuals Unlimited/Science Photo Library, Denis Kuvaev/Shutterstock; p98 Natalia Lisovskaya/Shutterstock; p100 SafeFood; p103 Science Photo Library; p104 Africa Studio/Science Photo Library; p105 Nobeastsofierce/Science Photo Library; p106 Andrii Vodolazhskyi/Shutterstock, Power and Syred/Science Photo Library; p107 Dr P. Marazzi/Science Photo Library, REDPIXEL.PL/Shutterstock; p108 anyaivanova/Shutterstock; p114 Jacob Lund/Shutterstock, bbernard/Shutterstock; p115 Dziurek/Shutterstock; p120 John Durham/Science Photo Library; p125 MicheleB/Shutterstock; p126 Dennis Kunkel Microscopy/Science Photo Library; p128 Eye of Science/ Science Photo Library; p131 Dr Yorgos Nikas/Science Photo Library; p132 Sebastian Kaulitzki/Science Photo Library; p133 James Stevenson/Science Photo Library; p134 Keither/Custom Medical Stock Photo/Science Photo Library; p136 Tefi/Shutterstock; p137 istock photo; p138 Steve Gschmeissner/Science Photo Library, Sam Ogden/Science Photo Library; p141 Simon Booth/Steve Gschmeissner/Science Photo Library, Olga Vasilek/Shutterstock; p143 Nicolas Raymond/Shutterstock; p144 Richard McManus/Getty Images, Vadim Petrakov/Shutterstock; p146 Ken Schulze/Shutterstock, OPgrapher/Shutterstock; p147 Evan Lorne/Shutterstock, marcobir/Shutterstock, Public Health England/Science Photo Library, Huguette Roe/Shutterstock; p148 mervas/Shutterstock, Anton Kossmann/Shutterstock, Imfoto/Shutterstock; p151 TTstudio/Shutterstock, Matteis/Look at Sciences/Science Photo Library, Sylvan Van Wittwer/Visuals Unlimited/Science Photo Library; p152 deadlyphoto.com/Alamy, Jean-Bernard Nadeau/Look at Sciences/Science Photo Library; p154 Keith Naylor/Shutterstock; p155 Yakobchuk Viacheslav/Shutterstock; p156 Hiko Photography/Shutterstock; p157 Ivan Feoktistov/Shutterstock, Rahul D'silva/Shutterstock; p158 Belinda Gallacher/Shutterstock, bunyarit/Shutterstock, OlegDoroshin/Shutterstock; p165 Ollyy/Shutterstock, Anteromite/Shutterstock, David Crockett/Shutterstock, FFoFF/Shutterstock, Robyn Mackenzie/Shutterstock, Piyawat Nandeenopparit/Shutterstock, Victor Moussa/Shutterstock; p166 Science Photo Library, Fer Gregory/Shutterstock, antoniodiaz/Shutterstock, katjen/Shutterstock; p180 Melica/Shutterstock; p183 Mr.Suchat/Shutterstock, Gill Couto/Shutterstock; p184 Peter Hermes Furian/Shutterstock; p185 Andrew Lambert/Science Photo Library, Ventin/Shutterstock, Fablok/Shutterstock, Albert Russ/Shutterstock, Mara Fribus/Shutterstock, Astrid & Hanns-Frieder Michler/Science Photo Library; p187 Leigh Prather/Shutterstock; p189 Oleg Golovnev/Shutterstock, Everett Historical/Shutterstock; p193 Everett Historical/Shutterstock; p194 Science Photo Library; p195 Andrew Lambert Photography/Science Photo Library, Andrew Lambert Photography/Science Photo Library, Aleksei Semykin/Shutterstock; p200 LoopAll, Shutterstock, LoopAll/Shutterstock, concept w/Shutterstock; p204 burnel1/Shutterstock; p205 RCB Shooter/Shutterstock; p206 grey_and/Shutterstock, Jiri Hera/Shutterstock, peterschreiber.media/Shutterstock, Oleksandr_Delyk/Shutterstock, Baishev/Shutterstock, giedre vaitekune/Shutterstock, yongyut rukkachatsuwa/Shutterstock, Mikhail Grachikov/Shutterstock, rozbyshaka/Shutterstock; p208 Shutterstock; p211 Krakenimages.com/Shutterstock.com; p213 dolphfyn/Shutterstock; p214 Science Photo Library; p215 Daxiao Productions/Shutterstock, AlexZaitsev/Shutterstock; p217 Kuraev/Shutterstock, Patrick Landmann/Science Photo Library, Sputnik/Science Photo Library; p218 Maridav/Shutterstock, Caftor/Shutterstock; p219 Science Photo Library, Deyan Georgiev/Shutterstock, Serg64/Shutterstock, ekipaj/Shutterstock; p220 Ruslan Ivantsov/Shutterstock, ekipaj/Shutterstock; p221 anaken2012/Shutterstock, Voronin76/Shutterstock, design56/Shutterstock, NarisaFotoSS/Shutterstock, urbanbuzz/Shutterstock, Anest/Shutterstock, Foto2rich/Shutterstock, YuryKo/Shutterstock, Science Photo Library; p222 dcurzon/Shutterstock, Noppharat689/Shutterstock, Cher_Nika/Shutterstock, Chris Harvey/Shutterstock, Sebastian Kaulitzki/Shutterstock, Science Photo Library; p223 benjamas154/Shutterstock; p226 Nik Merkulov/Shutterstock, Romolo Tavani/Shutterstock; Victor Moussa/Shutterstock; p231 Mickael Guyot/Shutterstock; p234 koosen/Shutterstock, Settawat Udom/Shutterstock, Dan70/Shutterstock; p236 Bekshon/Shutterstock, Anna Nikonorova/Shutterstock, brulove/Shutterstock, Jr images/Shutterstock; p237 carballo/Shutterstock, Africa Studio/Shutterstock, antoniodiaz/Shutterstock; p239 gresei/Shutterstock, Edler von Rabenstein/Shutterstock, Africa Studio/Shutterstock, Ivaschenko Roman/Shutterstock, Joshua Resnick/Shutterstock, Shutterstock, photong/Shutterstock; p243 Martyn F Chillmaid/Science Photo Library, Martyn F Chillmaid/Science Photo Library; p250 Anton Chernov/Shutterstock, nd3000/Shutterstock; p251 Science Photo Library; p256 bluesnote/Shutterstock; p258 Siberian Art/Shutterstock; p260 Shutterstock; p261 Christian Koch, Microchemicals/Science Photo Library; p262 Luciano Mortula - LGM/Shutterstock; p263 Mark Agnor/Shutterstock, Milos Muller/Shutterstock, Gayvoronskaya_Yana/Shutterstock, Huguette Roe/Shutterstock; p265 SGr/Shutterstock, Evan Lorne/Shutterstock; p267 Peter Menzel/Science Photo Library, Jim West/Science Photo Library, Science Photo Library, Jim West/Science Photo Library; p268 Philippe Psaila/Science Photo Library, Shutterstock, Sputnik/Science Photo Library; p269 Dream79/Shutterstock, priia studio/Shutterstock; P273 l i g h t p o e t/Shutterstock; p274 jirasaki/Shutterstock; p275 E_Vector/Shutterstock; p276 Shutterstock, Cordelia Molloy/Science Photo Library; p277 Science Photo Library; p278 kurhan/Shutterstock; p281 Shutterstock; p284 Trevor Clifford Photography/Science Photo Library; p285 Shutterstock; p286 Designua/Shutterstock; p289 Nik Merkulov/Shutterstock, Valentyn Volkov/Shutterstock, Art_rich/Shutterstock, Bborriss.67/Shutterstock, VERSUSstudio/Shutterstock; p290 StefanK/Shutterstock; p291 Pat_Hastings/Shutterstock; p292 Avigator Fortuner/Shutterstock; p295 ilove/Shutterstock, Sailorr/Shutterstock; p300 Mauricio Graiki/Shutterstock; p306 Georgios Kollidas/Shutterstock; p307 takasu/Shutterstock, supergenijalac/Shutterstock; p309 Science Photo Library; p311 Christian Kieffer/Shutterstock; p312 Robert Kneschke/Shutterstock; p314 Dmitry Kalinovsky/Shutterstock; p315 Alis Photo/Shutterstock; p316 Matryoha/Shutterstock; p317 1000 Words/Shutterstock, naKornCreate/Shutterstock; p318 The Print Collector/Heritage Images/Science Photo Library; p322 Monkey Business Images/Shutterstock; p323 Pressmaster/Shutterstock; p324 DJ Srki/Shutterstock, Efired/Shutterstock, All kind of people/Shutterstock, Tatiana Popova/Shutterstock, J. Lekavicius/Shutterstock, Daniel Prudek/Shutterstock; p325 Anna Kucherova/Shutterstock, Andrea Danti/Shutterstock, LuisPortugal/Shutterstock; p326 Tatiana Popova/Shutterstock, xpixel/Shutterstock; p327 wavebreakmedia/Shutterstock; p328 Serjio74/Shutterstock; p330 Jim West/Science Photo Library; p332 Scott Mattock/Shutterstock; p333 Aynur_sib/Shutterstock, Rattiya Thongdumhyu/Shutterstock; p337 Luciano Mortula - LGM/Shutterstock, WDG Photo/Shutterstock, Andriy Blokhin/Shutterstock; p338 Petr Malyshev/Shutterstock; p339 Lindsay Helms/Shutterstock; p345 Andrei Nekrassov/Shutterstock, Science Stock Photography/Science Photo Library, Science Photo Library; p349 Oxford Science Archive/Heritage Images/Science Photo Library; p355 Fouad A. Saad/Shutterstock, Afiq Sam/Shutterstock, Martyn F. Chillmain/Science Photo Library; p356 Mavrick/Shutterstock, p360 HomeArt/Shutterstock; p361 mama_mia/Shutterstock; p366 Shutterstock; p367 Andrew Lambert Photography/Science Photo Library; p370 Martyn F Chillmain/Science Photo Library; p375 Neal Grundy/Science Photo Library; p376 alphaspirit/Shutterstock, Cordelia Molloy/Science Photo Library, Wladimir Bulgar/Science Photo Library; p377 Silvere Teutsch/Eurelios/Science Photo Library, Shutterstock; p379 AndreasG/Shutterstock, Aitormmfoto/Shutterstock, Ellagrin/Shutterstock; p383 Andrey Armyagov/Shutterstock; p384 Twocoms/Shutterstock; p385 FlashMovie/Shutterstock, istockphoto; p386 Emilio Segre/Segre Visual Archives/American Institute of Physics/Science Photo Library, Juergen Faelchle/Shutterstock, Albert Barr/Shutterstock; p387 banderlog/Shutterstock; p388 Mullard Radio Astronomy Laboratory/Science Photo Library; p389 Designua/Shutterstock; p391 Science Photo Library; p392 silver tiger/Shutterstock, Liliya Butenko/Shutterstock, Martin Capek/Shutterstock, xfox01/Shutterstock; p393 sciencepics/Shutterstock, Kirschner/Shutterstock; p394 silver tiger/Shutterstock, njaj/Shutterstock, Siberian Art/Shutterstock; p395 Dima Zel/Shutterstock; p396 Aaron Rutten/Shutterstock, sashabinuy/Shutterstock, Vadim Sadovski/Shutterstock; p397 bluecrayola/Shutterstock, NASA/Science Photo Library Y, Tristan3D/Shutterstock, MichaelTaylor/Shutterstock, Naeblys/Shutterstock; p398 VectorPot/Shutterstock; p402 Detlev van Ravenswaay/Science Photo Library, Johan Swanepoel/Shutterstock, Claus Lunau/Science Photo Library, Marko Aliaksandr/Shutterstock, John Sanford/Science Photo Library; p404 Rev. Ronald Royer/Science Photo Library, Science Photo Library, Elenarts/Shutterstock; p405 Esteban De Armas/Shutterstock, solarseven/Shutterstock; p406 Dotted Yeti/Shutterstock; p407 Marc Ward/Shutterstock, Walter Myers/Science Photo Library, Chris Butler/Science Photo Library, Chris Butler/Science Photo Library; p409 Sputnik/Science Photo Library; p411 ravl/Shutterstock, photovideostock/Getty Images; p412 Vadim Sadovski/Shutterstock, NASA/Science Photo Library, HelenField/Shutterstock, Vadim Sadovski/Shutterstock; p413 Dotted Yeti, Shutterstock, p414 narvikk/Getty Images, NASA/Getty Images, Russell Croman/Science Photo Library; p415 BlueRingMedia/Shutterstock, annalisa e marina durante/Shutterstock; p416 NASA/Science Photo Library, NASA/Science Photo Library, Tristan3D/Shutterstock; p417 Elenarts/Shutterstock, Mopic/Shutterstock; p420 Gary Hincks/Science Photo Library; p422 Myotis/Shutterstock, AndrewSproule/Shutterstock, NoPainNoGain/Shutterstock; p423 LilKar/Shutterstock; p424 Designua/Shutterstock, Siberian Art/Shutterstock, Science Photo Library; p415 Natee Jitthammachai/Shutterstock, Mark Garlick/Science Photo Library, muratart/Shutterstock; p427 Suzanne Tucker/Shutterstock, Alhovik/Shutterstock; p428 ChameleonsEye/Shutterstock; p432 Andrea Danti/Shutterstock, boonyarak voranimmanont/Shutterstock; p433 Valentyn Volkov/Shutterstock, somchaij/Shutterstock, Africa Studio/Shutterstock, Mopic/Shutterstock; p434 stockshoppe/Shutterstock, Beatriz Gascon J/Shutterstock; p435 Shutterstock; p436 Lauren Hamilton/Shutterstock; p437 danylyukk1/Shutterstock, Milena Moiola/Shutterstock; p438 Fiona Ayerst/Shutterstock, Dudarev Mikhail/Shutterstock, VectorMine/Shutterstock; p439 huyangshu/Shutterstock, Glöck/Shutterstock, irabel8/Shutterstock, vovan/Shutterstock, Catmando/Shutterstock; p442 Vecton/Shutterstock; p445 IgorZh/Shutterstock; p446 huyangshu/Shutterstock, Maxal Tamor/Shutterstock, Lightspring/Shutterstock, trevorb/Shutterstock, zhu difeng/Shutterstock, Andrew Zarivny/Shutterstock; p447 Arztsamui/Shutterstock, N.Minton/Shutterstock, Smileus/Shutterstock, 3Dalia/Shutterstock; p448 Anton Balazh/Shutterstock; p449 Shutterstock, Vector_creator/Shutterstock, Shutterstock; p450 TTstudio/Shutterstock; p451 Designua/Shutterstock; p453 Norma Cornes/Shutterstock, kwest/Shutterstock; p454 Andrea Danti/Shutterstock, Shutterstock; p456 Leena Damle/Shutterstock, artiomp/Shutterstock, Ungnoi Lookjeab/Shutterstock; p457 Shutterstock; p458 guentermanaus/Shutterstock; p459 Kamonrat/Shutterstock, Curioso/Shutterstock, Belozorova Elena/Shutterstock; p460 Shutterstock, Lisa-S/Shutterstock, Misterfullframe/Shutterstock, janniwet/Shutterstock; p461 HuHu/Shutterstock, www.3drenderedlogos com/Shutterstock; p465 Shutterstock, Vadim Sadovski/Shutterstock; p466 Alexanderphoto7/Shutterstock, Sputnik/ Science Photo Library, NASA/Science Photo Library, C1M8HY alamy; p467 NASA/Science Photo Library, NASA/Science Photo Library, Yanas/Shutterstock, wellphoto/Shutterstock; p468 sfam_photo/Shutterstock, David Ducros/ Science Photo Library, Golubovy/Shutterstock, Edwin Verin/Shutterstock, Graphic Compressor/Shutterstock; p469 Dmitry Zimin/Shutterstock, Castleski/Shutterstock, NASA/Science Photo Library; p470 Everett Historical/Shutterstock, ArchMan/Shutterstock, NASA/Science Photo Library, NASA/Science Photo Library; p471 NASA/Science Photo Library; p473 Leonello Calvetti/Science Photo Library; p474 Henning Dalhoff/Science Photo Library, Tristan3D/Shutterstock, Julian Baum/Science Photo Library; p475 Dabarti CGI/Shutterstock, sdecoret/Shutterstock; p476 Shutterstock.

All illustrations and drawings by Michael Philips and Compuscript.